GW00656579

FORENSIC
FABLES

United Kingdom	Butterworth & Co (Publishers) Ltd, 88 Kingsway, LONDON WC2B 6AB and 61A North Castle Street, EDINBURGH EH2 3LJ
Australia	Butterworths Pty Ltd, SYDNEY, MELBOURNE, BRISBANE, ADELAIDE, PERTH, CANBERRA and HOBART
Canada	Butterworth & Co (Canada) Ltd, TORONTO and VANCOUVER
New Zealand	Butterworths of New Zealand Ltd, WELLINGTON and AUCKLAND
Singapore	Butterworth & Co (Asia) Pte Ltd, SINGAPORE
South Africa	Butterworth Publishers (Pty) Ltd, DURBAN and PRETORIA
USA	Butterworth Legal Publishers, ST. PAUL, Minnesota, SEATTLE, Washington, BOSTON, Massachusetts, AUSTIN, Texas and D & S Publishers, CLEARWATER, Florida

with love
william orpen

"O" *by Orpen*

FORENSIC
FABLES

by

O

A REPRINT OF THE
COMPLETE EDITION 1961
with additional contributions by
Francis Cowper & Hubert Picarda

LONDON
BUTTERWORTHS
1961

Forensic Fables	.	.	.	.	1926
Further Forensic Fables	.	.		.	1928
Final Forensic Fables	.		.	.	1929
Final Forensic Fables (Second Series)			.		1932
Fifty Forensic Fables (a Selection)	.		.		1949
Forensic Fables (Complete Edition)			.		1961
(Reprinted)	.	.			1982
(Reprinted)	.	.			1983
(Reprinted)	.	.			1985

Printed and bound in Great Britain by
Biddles Ltd, Guildford and King's Lynn

FOREWORD

By *Lord Birkett, P.C.*

ᔄ

It is to me a very special pleasure to welcome this complete
edition of the *Forensic Fables* which were originally published in
four separate Volumes so long ago as 1926–32. I have long
urged that a collection such as this should be made for the
delight of the present generation of readers, and to preserve the
memory, not only of a learned lawyer, but of a great English
humorist. For I regard the *Fables* as notable literary posses-
sions. They have style and humour of a rare and splendid
kind, and they deal with almost every phase of legal life with
great insight and understanding. Above all, they present the
life of the law with a kindly sympathy for all the frailties of
human nature, whether they are exhibited by famous judges and
counsel, or by more ordinary folk, who find their way into
the courts. English humour at its best is always kindly and the
Fables are in the great tradition. My four volumes of the
Fables were inscribed by the author and they now stand on my
shelves by the side of *Pie Powder* by J. A. Foote, *As I went on my
Way* by A. J. Ashton and *Memorials of His Time* by Lord
Cockburn. When Dickens published his *Christmas Carol*, scores
of people wrote to him to say that they had placed the book on a
little shelf by itself to show their pride and affection for it. I
quite understand the feeling, but I have placed the Fables in the
very highest legal company to mark my pride and pleasure.
Theo. Mathew was a dear friend and colleague of mine, and he
loved the Temple and the Courts. He has captured the atmosphere of that wonderful world and set it down on the printed
page for the delight of his own and succeeding generations.
All these Fables are my favourites, but some make a special
appeal such as *The Double First and the Old Hand*, because the
drawing of the Old Hand brings an old opponent to life, and
recalls the excitements of early days at the Bar. *The Witty
Judge and the Bronchial Usher* is a very delightful satire on the
judicial humorist of the day; and this great gallery of characters

in the law is presented with truth and charm that gives perpetual delight. Izaac Walton said when he published his masterpiece that those who did not like his discourse would like the pictures. Readers of this collection will like both stories and pictures, for they blend perfectly together; and although the dresses of the "pretty young things" have gone out of fashion, the *Fables* defy the passage of Time. The Publishers are to be congratulated on their enterprise, and the present generation of readers on the opportunity to make the acquaintance of a great figure in the law and in literature. I commend the book with all my heart.

STICK TO A STUFF-GOWN*

By *Hubert Picarda, Barrister*

ONE day perhaps, and may it be soon, while there are still enough eye-witnesses about, someone should write a history of the Bar between the Wars. In its coverage of the Junior Bar pride of place would go to the most popular junior of that period—Theobald Mathew, known to all in his day (and to posterity) as "Theo", whose wonderful *Forensic Fables* are here republished.

What sort of a man was he? The bare outlines of his life have been drawn many times by obituarists. He was born on December 6, 1866 and died on June 20, 1939 in the city of his birth, London. His great uncle (the Apostle of Temperance in Ireland) was Father Theo Mathew, a name that sounds down through successive generations of the family. His father was Mathew L. J. who was also "father" of the Commercial Court.

After education at the Oratory and Trinity College, Oxford, as befitted a son of admirers of Cardinal Newman, Theo was called to the Bar by Lincoln's Inn in 1890. In his early days he joined the South Eastern Circuit and also interested himself in the Commercial Court on whose practice he wrote a book. At one stage he sat in many commercial arbitrations as an arbitrator, and Lord Denning remembers well appearing before him in those days. But Theo really came into his own in the chambers of Lord Robert Cecil at 4 Paper Buildings, first as a frequently briefed counsel on Canadian appeals to the Privy Council with Sir Malcolm Macnaghten, and latterly more and more as a junior in prominent libel cases. He was much sought after as a pupil master, and in his time had as pupils reading with him: Mr. Clement Attlee, Mr. Stafford Cripps, Mr. Quintin Hogg, Mr. Kenneth Diplock and Mr. Peter Thorneycroft.

His biographer in the Dictionary of National Biography conveys an impression of a junior—for so he remained all his life—who controlled his work flow and was never over burdened. The recollection of his clerk Sydney Aylett, in *Under the*

vii

Wigs (1978), was different and his pupils and contemporaries corroborate the clerk's eye view.

Lord Diplock, in an interview in late 1982 with the writer, recalled his former pupil master with obvious affection more than 43 years after his death. "I was a pupil in 1931-1932 and stayed on to devil for him for about six months afterwards. He had a very large junior practice and was very much the old fashioned junior. By that time he had no commercial work at all and had a large number of pupils. These were lodged in the dog hole (as we called it) in 1 King's Bench Walk. He was a great specialist in libel. His main work was in interlocutory matters before the Masters and he was in the Bear Garden at least three times a week. He almost never went into court without a silk and was led time and again by Pat Hastings and Norman Birkett."

"Master-pleader" was the description of another celebrated pupil, the present Lord Chancellor, in an evocative poem "Legal Ghosts" to be found in *Verses from Lincoln's Inn*. The description was one in which Lord Diplock fully concurred. Yet he remembered wryly that "Pat Hastings had at one consultation with Theo the impertinence to say 'This case has been ruined by the incompetence of the pleadings' ". The charge was absurd. Hastings won the case. But Theo always took the precaution thereafter when they were jointly instructed of seeing Hastings *before* drafting a pleading. For him it was a Forensic Fable with a Moral!

While he was no great advocate (albeit a superb after-dinner speaker) he was a lawyer of great distinction in a distinguished generation of learned lawyers. There are many nuances in *Forensic Fables* which reflect this. And he was a notably cunning forensic technician. As an admirer of Gladstone (as well of Dr. Johnson and Dickens) he achieved a notable triumph in *Wright v Gladstone* (1927) *The Times*, February 4, where Captain Peter Wright had defamed Lord Gladstone's dead father, and was manoeuvred by Theo's stratagems into suing Lord Gladstone for libel, giving the latter the means of avenging his dead father. Mr. Norman Birkett, as the biography by H. M. Montgomery Hyde shows, stole the thunder but the true coup was that of his junior.

Theo Mathew was, and remains still, the finest cartoonist the Bar has known. But his greatest claim to fame was and is his wit. It is the fate of most witty men that their wit dissolves in the

viii

ether. In this generation those who had the joy of hearing Mr Philip Hope Wallace in flood get scant comfort from reading reprints of his reviews. In the case of Theo Mathew posterity is luckier. For *Forensic Fables* (the pun Foibles would have sounded in his ear) and *For Lawyers and Others* give a fair measure of the style of a man who was giftedly *"spirituel"*. "He was a most entertaining man" Lord Denning remembers. To Sir Patrick Hastings "he was a man with a mind that saw humour in everything". Lord Diplock elaborates still further: "He was the wittiest man I have ever met: he bubbled over with it. And another characteristic, he did not save it for the occasion. I would call on him perhaps once a week and we would go to a tea shop in the vicinity which we called 'The Ladies' because it was run by two gentlefolk. He had no other audience than myself, but that made no difference. His wit was like champagne, nice at the time but evanescent."

There are, of course, many Theo stories. Lord Diplock recalls hearing a well vouched for story of a meeting of the Newman Society where there was a discussion about the desirability of the Pope taking a more active line in social problems of the day. He poured an appropriate jug of cold water on the idea by his jesting observation "You know, if you are infallible you have to be awfully careful what you say."

Three other characteristics stand out from the memories, written and unwritten of his friends.

First, he had a great love and mastery of language. His writing, as Richard Ludlow rightly observed in the *Law Journal* of July 1, 1939, "like his speech was pointed, and in style approached perfection: he never wasted or misused a word; and it was said of his writing that a phrase could not be altered without spoiling it". Nor was this love of precision confined to the English language. The writer's father, a French advocate and Middle Templer, remembered Theo cross-examining him on the different words in French, through the ages, for false teeth: he luxuriated in the nineteenth century "ratelier" and on being asked in later years how he was, he would assume a mock Racine tragedy style and say in his deep solemn voice: "L'ange de la Mort me frôle de son aile". Now a subsequent generation of readers can judge for itself his unerring aptness of phrase.

Next, he was obviously the kindest of men. A pious Catholic, his acts of charity and "comfortable words" were naturally private; but not unremarked. The man who could dissolve in merriment over "Frothy Bob" Fortune putting out a fire "with a few well chosen words" would link arms with high and humble alike. Lord Diplock, remembering Theo's Requiem Mass at Brompton Oratory, adds an illuminating gloss to the obituary notice by Richard Ludlow. The turn out of senior members of the judiciary and of the front row was remarkable for a Thursday in term time; in fact the sittings of the High Court were postponed until 11 a.m. But, he adds "there was also the largest assembly of bores ever seen, because Theo was so patient with them".

Thirdly, his love of his profession and his Inns of Court shines through his writings with a peculiar incandescence. Although he was a Bencher of Lincoln's Inn, of which he would have been Treasurer had he lived another year, he lunched often in the Middle Temple where he belonged *ad eundem*. There, in Hall, he would start at his table of old men (as they seemed to youngsters in the Thirties) and then at the end of his luncheon, munching a Cox's orange pippin, he would circulate from table to table. His conviviality spilled out of his Inns and into the Garrick Club of which he was, naturally, also a member.

Lord Hailsham who also kindly allowed himself to be quizzed about his former pupil master underlined the point of Theo's love of his profession. In a conversation with the writer, a conversation suffused with the mellow affection felt by all Theo's pupils, he summed up: "Theo was the quintessence of the English Bar and Forensic Fables I consider to be the best book about the Bar there is. I used to recommend all my pupils to read it for that very reason."

Though some have wondered why a man with all his obvious qualities never became a judge "one of those unsolved mysteries of the Law or the Lord Chancellor's office" as the *Law Journal* obituarist suggested, there is perhaps no mystery. He would, from time to time, ruefully declare that solicitors were chary of briefing him because of his books. But the facts belied this. And as a Recorder and arbitrator he avoided levity like the pestilence. His father was a junior, an Irishman and a Catholic. None of those factors was a bar to his preferment in his day. But by the 1920's, the period in Theo's life when he was most eligible, there had been one disastrous appointment from the junior bar to the High Court Bench and, Treasury devils apart, a convention was

x

congealing. He was, in fact, in the words of Lord Diplock "a stuff-gownsman *par excellence*". And none the lesser for that. No junior has been remembered with such affection by such a roll call of legal talents. His two favourite pupils, and his two most frequent leaders, Sir Patrick Hastings and Lord Birkett have all recorded their pride in their association with him.

He was assuredly "The Established Junior who had nothing to complain of" (*Forensic Fables*, p 255). And for those who knew him personally, and for those who, like the writer, were too young to know him, his pleasant voices, his nightingales live on.

*NEW LAW JOURNAL   December 23, 1982

TABLE OF CONTENTS

PAGE

FOREWORD v

"STICK TO A STUFF GOWN" vii

TABLE OF STATUTES xix

TABLE OF CASES CITED xxi

FORENSIC FABLES

1. The Common Law Leader and The Promising
   Equity Junior 1

2. The Inexperienced Advocate and The Holder in
   Due Course 3

3. The Youthful Barrister and The Exceedingly Painful
   Case 7

4. The Circuiteer and The Nice Old Buffer . . 9

5. The Tactful Magistrate and The Much-Respected
   Colleague 13

6. The Double-First and The Old Hand . . . 15

7. The Two Aged Conveyancers and The Good Story 19

8. The Zealous Clerk who Overdid it . . . 21

9. The Judge who Closed his Eyes 23

10. The Elderly Junior and The Lady Pupil . . 27

11. The Enthusiastic Beginner who Thought Better of it 31

12. The Witty Judge and The Bronchial Usher . . 35

13. Irene, her Young Man and The Necklace . . 39

14. The Defeated Litigant and The Rash Attendant . 43

15. The Society Suit and The Unexpected Settlement . 45

16. The Traveller who Suffered From Shock and The
    Railway Company's Physician 49

17. Adolphus Brown, Mr. Justice Grump and The Interesting Case 51

18. Mr. Blowhard, K.C. and Mr. Footle, K.C. . . 55

19. The Blushing Beginner and The Bearded Juryman 57

20. The Utter Barrister and The Important Treatise . 61

21. The Common Law Junior and The Originating Summons 65

22. The Sarcastic Counsel and Mr. MacIntosh, the Moneylender 69

23. The Ambitious Youth who Wanted Eligible Chambers 73

24. The White-Haired Trustee and The Highly-Placed Official 75

25. The Real Property Lawyer and The Surly Game-keeper 79

26. The Industrious Youth and The Stout Stranger . 83

27. Mr. Whitewig and The Rash Question . . 87

28. The K.C., M.P. and The Bill for the Suppression of Night Clubs 91

29. Mr. Justice Cattemall and Mr. Justice Dearlove . 95

30. The Sound Lawyer who Made a Good Resolution 97

31. The Kindly Judge and The Lady Barrister . . 101

32. The Experienced Advocate and The Half-Year's Rent 105

33. The Old Stager and The Exchequer Suit on the In-formation of the Attorney-General issuing out of the Petty Bag 109

34. The Prudent Counsel, The New Client and The Strident Person 113

35. The Tearful Performer and The Plaintiff with a Past 115

36. Mr. Slasher, Mr. Justice Foozle and The Halved Seventeenth 119

37. The Mature Junior and The Diligent Pupil . . 123

38. The Junior who Lunched at the Club, The Bald Old
     Gentleman and The Heavy Brief . . . 127

39. Beefy Thomas and Anæmic Henry . . . 131

40. Young Mr. Tittlebat, The Leading Solicitor and
     The Unexpected Victory 135

41. The Australian Plutocrat, The Millionaire's Nephew
     and The Old Bailey Practitioner . . . 139

42. The Judge of Assize and The Old School Friend . 143

43. The Emeritus Professor of International Law and
     The Police Court Brief 147

44. Mr. Fledgling and The Application for Particulars
     of the Statement of Claim 151

45. The Proud Parent who Did his Best for Alfred . 155

46. The Idle Apprentice and The Industrious Ditto . 157

47. The Young Solicitor and The Sagacious Old Buffer 159

48. The Judge whose Appearance Terrified the Public 163

49. Mr. Buffle, The Young Person and The Seedy
     Individual 167

50. The Two Templars and The Long Vacation . 171

51. The Cautious Solicitor and The Chinese Witness . 173

52. The Habitual Criminal and The First Offender . 177

53. The Enthusiastic Tourists and The Capable Guide 181

54. The Careful Junior and The Leading Question . 183

55. The Athletic Templars who Climbed the Dent du
     Chien 185

56. The Prudent Judge and the Stout Usher . . 189

57. The Three Elderly Jurists who Met after Many Years 193

58. The Nervous Youth who Did his Best in the Circum-
     stances 197

59. The Aged Judge who Remembered the Past and
     Changed his Mind 201

60. The Litigants in Person who Compared Notes . 205

61. Mr. Titmouse, Mrs. Titmouse and the Claim for Goods Sold and Delivered 209

62. The Deaf Reporter, the Diligent Young Counsel, and the Glorious Win 213

63. The Distinguished Architect and the Palace of Justice 217

64. The Languid Leader and the Ducal Action . . 221

65. The Wise Old Bird who Retired 225

66. The Great Lawyer who Told his Audience how to Do it 227

67. The Experienced Judge, the Running Down Case and the Law Relating to Contributory Negligence 231

68. The Man of Affairs, the Intelligent Solicitor and the Promising Son 235

69. Mable Gudgeon, the Dressmaker's Bill, Uncle Peter and the Articled Clerk 237

70. Mr. Sharp, Mr. Bright and the Award Stated in the Form of a Special Case 241

71. The Disgruntled Practitioner who Thought Poorly of Everybody 245

72. The Barony of De Montazure and Front-de-Bœuf, the Committee for Privileges and the Sweet Young Lady 247

73. Mr. Justice Heavyside and the Faithful Clerk . 251

74. The Established Junior who had Nothing to Complain of 255

75. The Domestic Tyrant, the Crushed Worm and the Bibulous Butler 259

76. The Youth who Resolved Always to Make a Careful Note of the Facts 263

77. The Beginner who Thought He Would Do It Himself 267

78. The Callow Youth, the Brief in the Divorce Court
and the Weeping Lady 271

79. The Careful Lawyer who could not Make up his
Mind 275

80. The Silk who Knew How to Make a Good Show 279

81. Miss Snaffleton (Infant) and The Old-Fashioned
Judge 283

82. Mrs. Sarah Stout, The Last Will of Mr. Buffin and
The Draft Affidavit 287

83. The Kindly Judge and Little Effie . . . 291

84. Mr. Bobby Chump, The Successful Defence and its
Singular Consequences 295

85. The Profound Lawyer who Received a Subpoena
Ad Testificandum 297

86. The High Sheriff's Chaplain and The Assize Sermon
which Gave Universal Satisfaction . . . 301

87. The Brilliant Person, The Vulgar Individual with a
Cockney Accent and The Two Malefactors . 305

88. Lord Pushleigh of Runnymede and his Coat-of-
Arms 309

89. The Judicial Personage who Disapproved of Cinemas
and Sensational Literature 313

90. The Fierce Advocate who Really Had a Soft Heart 317

91. The Brilliant Orator who Won Fame as a Defender 321

92. Diehard and Stickit, JJ. 325

93. Mr. Bluebag, Mr. Bert Baumstein and "The Old
Judge" 327

94. Mr. Pottle's Nasty Accident, The Sagacious Cook
and The Action at Law 331

95. The Chancery Judge who Observed that The
Intellect of His Common-Law Brother was Failing 335

PAGE

96. The Husbands who Met in The Elysian Fields .   337

97. The Erudite Judge and The Question of Doubtful
Admissibility   341

98. Boodle, Cash & Co. and The Big Job .   .   345

99. The Learned Youth, Uncle Robert and The Consultation   347

100. Mr. Tompkyns, Corinne Bozieu and The Close-up   349

101. The Voluble Plaintiff and The Laconic Interpreter   353

102. The King of the Upper and Lower Cannibal Islands
and The Regius Professor   .   .   .   355

103. Mr. Pumpkin, K.C., M.P., The Portrait and The
Wedding Bells   359

104. Mr. Splasher, K.C. and The Brief which was Suitably Marked   361

105. Beefy and Brawn   363

106. The Two Clerks who Exchanged Experiences   .   365

107. Mr. Justice Snappy and Jane   .   .   .   367

108. Young Mr. Simple and The Venerable Solicitor   .   369

109. Mr. Justice Lien and Mr. Justice Drop   .   .   371

110. The Old Buffer who Lived in the Temple   .   .   373

APPENDIX 1: The Distinguished Bencher and the Lost Fable   375

APPENDIX 2: Some Characters Revealed   .   .   379

INDEX   389

TABLE OF STATUTES

PAGE

43 Ed. 3, c. 6 (*De Vacca Detinenda*) Ruff. Stat. . . 247

1 & 2 Ric. 2, c. 4 110

27 Hen. 8, c. 10 (Statute of Uses) 335

18 Eliz. 1. c. 14 110

36 & 37 Vict. c. 66 (Judicature Act, 1873) . . . 110

38 & 39 Vict. c. 77 (Judicature Act, 1875) . . . 110

54 & 55 Vict. c. 51 (Slander of Women Act, 1891) . 45

1 & 2 Geo. 5, c. 57 (Maritime Conventions Act, 1911) . 232

TABLE OF CASES CITED

PAGE

Dublin, Wicklow & Wexford Railway Co. *v.* Slattery,
3 App. Cas. 1155 232

In re Puffington's Settlement (unreported) . . . 66

Lickbarrow *v.* Mason, 5 T.R. 683 52

MacIntosh *v.* FitzCholmondely (unreported) . . 69

Potte *v.* Kettle (unreported) 45, 46

R. *v.* Shakespeare (unreported) 35

Radley *v.* L. & N.W. Railway Co., 1 App. Cas. 759 . 232

The Bernina, 12 P.D. 36 232

The "Parlement Belge", 4 P.D. 129; 5 P.D. 197 . . 149

The Overseers of the Parish of Criggleswick *v.* The Mudbank-super-Mare Docks and Harbour Board Trustees
and Others (unreported). 23, 24

The Volute, [1922] 1 A. C. 129 232

Whitelocke *v.* Baker, 13 Ves. 514 342

THE COMMON LAW LEADER AND THE
PROMISING EQUITY JUNIOR

THE COMMON LAW LEADER
AND
THE PROMISING EQUITY JUNIOR

ᨌ

A PROMISING Equity Junior, who had been a Senior Classic in the Sixties, once Found himself Briefed with an Eminent Common Law Leader. It was a Witness Action. During the Luncheon Interval the Eminent Leader Discovered that he had a More Important Case to Attend to Elsewhere. So he Told his Junior Quite Distinctly What Questions he must Put to the Witnesses in Cross-Examination and What Cases he must Cite to the Judge. Owing to Increasing Deafness the Promising Junior was Unable (Despite his Ear-Trumpet) to Hear What the Eminent Common Law Leader was Talking About; but he Wisely Pretended that the Fact was Otherwise. He was an Intelligent Old Bird.

Was the Promising Equity Junior's Performance a Failure? Not at all. He did not Cross-Examine Anybody or Call the Attention of the Judge to the Relevant Authorities; but, when the Plaintiff's Evidence was Concluded, Submitted Successfully that there was No Case for the Defendant to Answer.

Moral.—*The Unexpected Often Happens.*

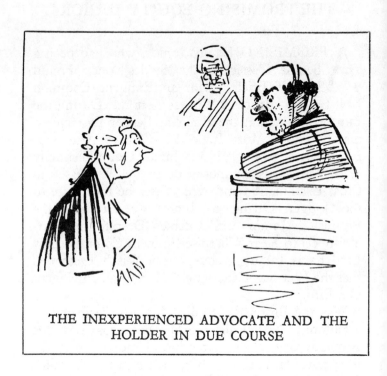

THE INEXPERIENCED ADVOCATE AND THE
HOLDER IN DUE COURSE

THE INEXPERIENCED ADVOCATE
AND
THE HOLDER IN DUE COURSE

༈

AN Inexperienced Advocate was once Requested by a Learned Friend to "Devil" a Short Cause. As he had Never Raised his Voice in Court (except to Apply for a Case to Stand Out of the List till next Sittings, Keeping its Place) the Inexperienced Advocate was Rather Alarmed at the Prospect. But, being Ambitious, he Agreed to Do his Best. He Gathered that he was to Appear for the Defendant, and that the Plaintiff was the Holder in Due Course of a Bill of Exchange. Also that he was to Knock the Plaintiff About a Bit in Cross-Examination. Pulling himself Together he Went into Court and the Case was Soon Called on. The Plaintiff had a slightly Red Nose and his Linen was not Unimpeachable, but he gave his Evidence Clearly and in a Firm Voice. When he Rose to Cross-Examine the Plaintiff, the Inexperienced Advocate Shook Very Much, Particularly at the Knees, and the Court seemed to be Spinning Round and Round. The Judge and the Plaintiff Completely Disappeared from his Vision and were Replaced by Strangely-Coloured Sparks and Chaos. His Jaw Dropped and his Eye was Glazed. He Became Unconscious of his Surroundings. The Plaintiff was so Horrified by the Inexperienced Advocate's Appearance that he

Completely Lost his Nerve. Asking in Faltering Tones what he was Looking at him like That for, the Plaintiff Added that he had been a Respectable Man Ever Since————. Here he Paused. But the Judge Took up the Running, and Before the Inexperienced Advocate had Recovered his Senses, the Plaintiff had Admitted that he had been Convicted of Fraud on Divers Occasions, and the Judge had Given Judgment (with Costs) for the Defendant. The Defendant's Solicitor was so Delighted with what he Regarded as a Splendid Histrionic Display that he thereafter Showered Briefs upon the Inexperienced Advocate.

Moral.—*Silence is Golden.*

THE YOUTHFUL BARRISTER AND THE
EXCEEDINGLY PAINFUL CASE

THE YOUTHFUL BARRISTER
AND
THE EXCEEDINGLY PAINFUL CASE

❧

A YOUTHFUL Barrister was Briefed at The Assizes to Appear for the Prisoner in an Exceedingly Painful Case. He did not Know Much about That Sort of Thing, and was Naturally Rather Anxious. In Particular he Dreaded the Necessary Interview with the Accused. He felt it was Pretty Certain that she would be Overwhelmed with Misery and Shame, and Too Much Distressed to Tell her Sad Story. And he was Sure that she would Look Just Like *Effie Deans* or *Hetty Sorrel*.

The Youthful Barrister had a Very Pleasant Surprise. When he Went Down to the Cells he was Confronted by a Smart Young Person who Appeared to be in the Best of Health and Spirits. She Wore a Fur-trimmed Coat and Sun-Burn Stockings, and Carried both a "Chubby" and a Vanity Bag. Her Nose was Powdered. It was Clear that she did not Feel her Position Acutely, or View the Forthcoming Trial with Any Great Degree of Apprehension. And her Confidence was not Misplaced. For, although the Youthful Barrister's Speech was Long and Incoherent, the Jury Acquitted the Young Person without Leaving the Box.

Moral.—*Keep Smiling.*

7

THE CIRCUITEER AND THE NICE OLD BUFFER

THE CIRCUITEER
AND
THE NICE OLD BUFFER

∽

A CIRCUITEER, Recently Elected to the Bar Mess, Determined to Try his Luck at the Assizes. Arriving at the Railway Terminus Rather Late, he Just had Time to Fling himself into a Carriage as the Train Steamed Out. It was Occupied by an Elderly Party, whom the Circuiteer Diagnosed as a Nice Old Buffer. He had a Rug over his Knees and he Wore a Top Hat. He was Smoking an Excellent Cigar. The Nice Old Buffer Appeared to be Rather Surprised at the Circuiteer's Intrusion; but the Latter, being of a Chatty and Affable Disposition, Soon Put him at his Ease. Before Long the Nice Old Buffer had Offered the Circuiteer a Cigar and they were Getting on Like a House on Fire. The Circuiteer Told him about his University Career, his Uncle Thomas, the Man he had Read With in Chambers, and a Lot of Other Things. Turning to the Object of his Travels, he Mentioned to the Nice Old Buffer that he was Going to the Assizes; that Mr. Justice Stuffin was the Presiding Judge; but that the Profession did not Think Much of him. Stuffin said the Circuiteer, would Never have got a Judgeship on his Merits; but he had Married a Woman with a good Deal of Money and had a Safe Tory Seat. He was just Going to Tell the Nice Old Buffer what

9

the Court of Appeal had Said the Other Day about One of Stuffin's Judgments when the Train Arrived at its Destination. There were Javelin-Men and Trumpeters on the Platform, together with the High Sheriff of the County and his Chaplain. They had Come to Meet the Judge. Sick with Horror, the Circuiteer became Aware from the Demeanour towards his Travelling Companion that the Nice Old Buffer was Stuffin, J. He Made up his Mind Then and There that he had Better Adopt Some Other Profession, and Caught the First Train Back to London. He is Now a Stockbroker, and Doing Very Well Indeed in the Industrial Market.

Moral.—*Take Care.*

THE TACTFUL MAGISTRATE AND THE MUCH-
RESPECTED COLLEAGUE

THE TACTFUL MAGISTRATE AND
THE MUCH-RESPECTED COLLEAGUE

∽

A TACTFUL Magistrate who had Dined Very Comfortably the Night Before with a Much-Respected Colleague (to Meet Several Old Friends) Took his Seat Punctually at Ten-Thirty to Deal with the Business of the Day. The First of the Drunk-and-Disorderlies to Meet his Astonished Gaze was his Host of Last Night. It Seemed that, After Taking Leave of his Guests, the Much-Respected Colleague had Continued his Merry-Making Elsewhere into the Small Hours of the Morning. His Contact with the Police had Occurred in the Neighbourhood of Vine Street at Three O'clock A.M. It likewise Appeared that in a Burst of Mistaken Confidence he had Given his Real Name and Address to the Officer in Charge. The Situation was Distinctly Awkward. The Tactful Magistrate did not Lose his Head. Sternly Addressing the Culprit as John Marmaduke Bundlepump (a Name which Occurred to him on the Spur of the Moment), he Told the Much-Respected Colleague that his Attempt to Conceal his Identity, Based as it was upon a Superficial Facial Resemblance to a Public Servant of Unblemished Reputation, was as Mean as it was Dishonest; and that in All the Circumstances he Could not Inflict a Smaller Penalty than a Fine of Ten Pounds. The Defendant must also Pay the Doctor's Fee. He Hoped it would be a Warning. It was.

Moral.—*Be Prepared for Everything.*

THE DOUBLE-FIRST AND THE OLD HAND

THE DOUBLE-FIRST AND
THE OLD HAND

∽

ADOUBLE-FIRST, whose Epigrams were Quoted in Every Common-Room of the University, became Weary of Tuition and went to the Bar. His Friends were Satisfied that he was Bound to become in the Near Future either Prime Minister or Lord Chancellor. They Doubted, however, whether Either of these Jobs Afforded Sufficient Scope for his Splendid Abilities. Shortly after his Call, a Near Relative Provided him with a Brief. He was to Appear for a Public Authority which Owned a Tram-Car. The Plaintiff was a Young Lady who had Sustained Injuries while being Carried Thereon from her Place of Residence to her Place of Business. Her Story, as Set Forth in the Statement of Claim, was that the Conductor, without Any or Alternatively Sufficient Warning, had Rung the Bell whilst she was Stepping off the Vehicle, and that by Reason of his Said Negligence she had Fallen Heavily in the Road, Abraded her Shin-Bone, and Suffered from Shock and Other Discomforts. Her Claim (including Extra Nourishment and Various Items of Special Damage) Totalled 583*l.* 4*s.* 9*d.* The Double-First had Little Doubt that the Claim was Grossly Exaggerated, if not Actually Dishonest. He was Confident of Victory. When he Got into Court the Double-First found himself Opposed by an Old Hand of Unrivalled

Experience in that Class of Action. He Looked Harmless Enough, and the Double-First Felt no Alarm. But Strange Things Soon Happened. The Old Hand Conducted the Case for the Plaintiff in a Manner which Shocked the Double-First Exceedingly. After the Jury had been Sworn he Informed his Solicitor-Client in a Whisper which could be Heard in the Central Hall that he would not Settle for Less than Five Hundred, and he Asked the Double-First in Stentorian Tones, with Reference to the Plan, whether he would Agree (1) the Exact Spot where the Pool of Blood was Found, and (2) the Precise Locality where the Conductor had Admitted to the Policeman that he had Done the Same Thing on Another Occasion. When the Double-First Cross-Examined the Plaintiff, the Old Hand Asked the Judge to Protect his Client from Insult; and when he Addressed the Jury the Old Hand Repeatedly Begged that he would not Deliberately Misrepresent the Evidence. The Double-First Struggled against these Tactics in Vain. In his Final Speech, the Old Hand Reminded the Jury of the Possibility that Tetanus or Paralysis might Hereafter Supervene, and the Certainty that a Disfigured Tibia would Seriously Impair the Plaintiff's Matrimonial Prospects. Apart from his Successful Application for a Stay of Execution on the Ground that the Damages (1,000*l.*) were Excessive, the Double-First had a Disastrous Day.

Moral.—*Despise not Your Enemy.*

THE TWO AGED CONVEYANCERS AND
THE GOOD STORY

THE TWO AGED CONVEYANCERS
AND THE GOOD STORY

꙼

TWO Aged Conveyancers (who were also Equity Draftsmen) Lunched Together at the Megatherium Club to Celebrate the Sixtieth Anniversary of Their Call to the Bar. One was Eighty-Two and the other was Eighty-Three.

They did themselves Very Well. After a Second Old Brandy Both Felt Mellow and Comfortable and Ready for Frivolous Conversation. So They Told each other Merry Stories of the Good Old Days. Eighty-Two reminded Eighty-Three of the Humorous Observation Made by Old Buffle when the Originating Summons was Called On in the Vice-Chancellor's Court Out of Its Turn; Eighty-Three (not to be Outdone) Recalled the Pun Made by Snorter in the Debenture-Holders' Action; and Eighty-Two Retaliated with the Anecdote of the Solicitor's Clerk who Mixed Up the Draft Affidavits of the Spinster Executrix and the *Feme Coverte*.

Then they Turned to Modern Times, and Eighty-Three Opined that on the Whole the Funniest Thing he Remembered was his Pupil's Opinion in the Ejectment Action. Shaking with Laughter, he told Eighty-Two that the Pupil had Advised that the Trustees of the Marriage Settlement should be Joined as Defendants in the Alternative. Eighty-Two's Appreciation of the Story was so Noisy that Several Members Woke Up and Looked at Both of Them Angrily. And so a Happy Afternoon Came to an End.

Moral.—*A Joke's a Joke.*

THE ZEALOUS CLERK WHO OVERDID IT

THE ZEALOUS CLERK WHO
OVERDID IT

〜

A SILK, whose Professional Activities were not as Extensive as they had been, was Sitting in his Chambers Contemplating Some Venerable Papers which Represented Struggles of the Past. He was Immensely Cheered when his Zealous Clerk Informed him that an Old Client had Turned Up with a Brief. The Zealous Clerk Confided to the Silk that he Thought he could get it Marked Up to Twenty-Five. The Silk Directed that the Old Client should be Shown In At Once. The Old Client Said he was Afraid it was a Small Affair, but he would be Greatly Obliged if the Silk would Give it his Personal Attention. It was a Common Jury, Fixed for Next Monday. The Silk, Winking Slightly at his Zealous Clerk, Asked him to Look at the Book and See what his Engagements were for that Day. The Zealous Clerk Produced a Large Diary, Scanned it with Attention, and Found that Monday was Free, Except for the Privy Council Case, which would Probably not be Reached, a Special Jury, which he was Sure Sir John would Agree to Adjourn, and the Part-Heard before the War Compensation Court, in which they had a Capable Junior. These Causes and Matters Existed Only in the Imagination of the Zealous Clerk; but he Hoped they would Create a Favourable Impression on the Mind of the Old Client. Unfortunately the Old Client was so Startled to Hear of the Many Calls upon the Time of the Silk that he Took the Brief Away and Delivered it to Somebody Else.

Moral.—*Draw It Mild.*

THE JUDGE WHO CLOSED HIS EYES

THE JUDGE WHO CLOSED HIS EYES

∽

A JUDGE of Considerable Experience was Trying
on a Summer's Day a Case of Unexampled
Dullness. Counsel for the Plaintiff was Opening. He Continued to Cite to the Judge a Multitude
of Authorities, including the Well-known Decision of
the House of Lords in *The Overseers of the Parish of
Criggleswick* v. *The Mudbank-super-Mare Docks and
Harbour Board Trustees and Others,* and the Judge was
Satisfied that he had Never been So Bored in the
Whole Course of his Professional Life. At about
Three-Thirty P.M. the Judge Allowed his Attention
to Wander Slightly, as he Felt Sure that Counsel for
the Plaintiff would not have Finished his Opening at
the Rising of the Court. Five minutes Later he Fell
into a Gentle Doze Which Soon Developed into a
Profound Sleep. He was Aroused at Four O'clock
by the Sudden Cessation of Counsel's Droning and
the Cries of " Silence " with which the Usher Preluded
the Coming Judgment. The Case was Over, and the
Judge had no Notion what Counsel for the Defendants had been Talking about. Was the Judge
Dismayed? Not at all. He Assumed a Look of
Lively Intelligence and Said that, as he had Formed
a Clear Opinion, no Useful Purpose would be Served
by his Reserving his Judgment. He Admitted that
During the Course of the Excellent Arguments which
had been Addressed to him his Opinion had Wavered.

But, After All, the Broad Question was whether the Principle so Clearly Stated in the House of Lords in *The Overseers of the Parish of Criggleswick* v. *The Mudbank-super-Mare Docks and Harbour Board Trustees and Others* Applied to the Facts of the Present Case. On the Whole, despite the Forceful Observations Made on Behalf of the Defendants, to which he had Paid the Closest Attention, he Thought it Did. It was Therefore Unnecessary that he should Discuss a Variety of Topics which, in the View he Took, Became Irrelevant. There would, accordingly, be Judgment for the Plaintiffs, with Costs; but, as the Matter was One of Great Public Interest, there would be a Stay of Execution on the Usual Terms. The Judgment, which was Appealed Against in Due Course, was Affirmed both in the Court of Appeal and the House of Lords; the Lord Chancellor Commenting, in the Latter Tribunal, on the Admirably Succinct Manner in which the Experienced Judge had Dealt with a Complicated and Difficult Problem.

Moral.—*Stick to the Point.*

THE ELDERLY JUNIOR AND THE
LADY PUPIL

THE ELDERLY JUNIOR AND
THE LADY PUPIL

∽

AN Elderly Junior with a Substantial and In-
creasing Practice was Surprised One Afternoon
to be Told that a Lady Wished to See him.
Her Visiting-Card Supplied the Information that her
Name was Miss Jones, and that she had an Impressive
Address in the Neighbourhood of Hyde Park. The
Elderly Junior had no Notion What she Wanted, but
Requested the Clerk to Show her In. On Entering
the Elderly Junior's Room, Miss Jones Smiled Very
Pleasantly at him and Asked Whether he Could
Possibly Manage to Take a Lady Pupil. She Added
that it Would be Sweet of him to Say Yes.

Her Appearance and Manner Appealed Strangely to
the Elderly Junior. In fact, they Captivated him.
He did not Care about Lady Pupils, but he Felt Sure
that he had Never Seen so Attractive an Individual as
Miss Jones. Her Figure was Elegant and her Eyes
were Exceedingly Nice. Particularly so when she
Held her Head Down and Looked through her Eye-
lashes in an Upward Direction. He was a Single
Man.

The Elderly Junior Begged Miss Jones to be Seated.
They Soon were in the Thick of a Delightful Con-
versation, and the Elderly Junior was Overjoyed when
Miss Jones said she would Like a Cup of Tea Very
Much Indeed. The Elderly Junior said he was Sorry

There were only Three Digestive Biscuits Left in the Tin, but Miss Jones Assured him that It Didn't Matter a Bit. She Took a Second Cup of Tea and Ate all the Digestive Biscuits, and the Elderly Junior became so Much Excited by the Whole Affair that he Quite Forgot his Five-Thirty Appointment.

As she Continued to Converse, the Elderly Junior Began to Envisage every Sort of Romantic Possibility, and Determined that he would Receive, at Any Rate, One Lady Pupil. When the Interview had Lasted Almost an Hour Miss Jones said she was Afraid she Must be Going Now, and did he Think he Could Give her a Favourable Answer? The Elderly Junior, by this Time in a Complete Twitter, Replied Gallantly that he Could not Refuse Any Request which Miss Jones might Make, and Enquired When she would Like to Come. "The Sooner," he Added, "the Better"; Slightly Pressing (as he Said these Words) Miss Jones' Well-Shaped Hand. Miss Jones Laughed Merrily, and Said she was Afraid she had been Awfully Silly. She Ought to have Explained that she was Only a Messenger on Behalf of her Aunt Jane, who had Recently been Appointed a Female Sanitary Inspector and Desired to be Called to the Bar. But, of Course, that would not Make any Difference, would it? The Elderly Junior Answered in a Weak Voice that it would Not, and Off Tripped Miss Jones.

Aunt Jane Presented herself the Following Monday and the Worst Fears of the Elderly Junior were Realised.

He is Still Single.

Moral.—*Be Circumspect.*

28

THE ENTHUSIASTIC BEGINNER WHO
THOUGHT BETTER OF IT

THE ENTHUSIASTIC BEGINNER WHO
THOUGHT BETTER OF IT

∽

AN Enthusiastic Beginner was Overjoyed to Receive a Brief in a Privy Council Case. The Appeal had to do with a Right of Way, a Second Mortgage, an Emphyteutic Lease and the Doctrine of the Lost Grant. It Bristled with Points of Interest and Difficulty. There had been Great Difference of Opinion in the Lower Courts. It was the Chance of a Lifetime. The Enthusiastic Beginner Quickly Set to Work to Master the Instructions and Make a Careful Note of the Facts and the Authorities. It Became Quite Clear to him that if the Argument were Properly Presented the Appellant was Bound to Succeed. He Bitterly Regretted that the Etiquette of the Profession Prevented him from Opening the Appeal, but Remembered that, however Feeble the Performance of his Leader might be, he could Put Everything Right by Adding a Few Trenchant and Luminous Words on his Own Account. First, he would Summarise the Authorities in Three Legal Propositions; Secondly he would put the Estoppel Point; Thirdly, he would Laugh the Case for the Respondent out of Court. The Appeal Came On. Five Elderly Gentlemen Seated at a Circular Table Listened to the Leader, who Addressed them in Conversational Tones. It was Obvious to the Enthusiastic Beginner that the Leader was Making a

Mess of it, and that the Elderly Gentlemen were Against him. He Longed to Drag the Leader from his Place and Show him How to Do it. During the Luncheon Interval the Leader Said he would Soon Run Down now, and he Hoped the Enthusiastic Beginner would Follow him. When they Got Back into the Council Chamber the Enthusiastic Beginner Felt Rather Uneasy. His Enthusiasm had Abated. He did not Like the Look of the Old Gentleman on the Left, and the One in Spectacles had a Nasty Way of Putting Questions which Could not Readily be Answered. The Enthusiastic Beginner Thought he would Content himself with the Three Legal Propositions, and Leave Out the Estoppel Point and the Ridicule of the Respondent's Case. A Few Minutes Later he Came to the Conclusion that the Leader had not Done it So Badly After All, and that he had Better Condense the Three Legal Propositions into One. When at Last the Leader Sat Down, the Enthusiastic Beginner Informed their Lordships, in a Weak Voice, that he had Nothing to Add.

Moral.—*Second Thoughts are Best.*

THE WITTY JUDGE AND THE
BRONCHIAL USHER

THE WITTY JUDGE AND THE
BRONCHIAL USHER

ᢍ

A WITTY Judge, while Perusing the Depositions for the Forthcoming Sessions at the Old
Bailey, Saw the Chance of a Lifetime. A
Prisoner Bearing the Name of William Shakespeare
was Charged with Obtaining Money by False Pre-
tences. It seemed that his Habit had been to Simulate
Epileptic Fits in Order to Arouse the Sympathy of
Bystanders. His Stock-in-Trade was a Piece of
Yellow Soap, which, Diligently Chewed, Produced
the Effect of Foaming at the Mouth. This Symptom,
together with Gnashing of the Teeth and Rolling of
the Eyes, had Convinced Large Numbers of Spectators
of the Genuineness of his Attacks. William Shakespeare had Consequently Enjoyed an Income which
was Amply Sufficient for his Daily Requirements.

The Witty Judge Felt that if, at the Appropriate
Moment, he were to Observe that this Seemed to be a
Case of *Poeta Gnashitur Non Fit,* his Reputation as a
Jester of the First Order would be Made for Ever.

The case of R. v. *Shakespeare* Came On. Unhappily
(as it Proved) the Usher of the Court was a Bronchial
Subject. On the Day in Question he was Afflicted
with a Severe Catarrh and a Rich and Resounding
Cough. Half Way through the Opening of the Case
for the Prosecution, which was Conducted by a
Counsel of No Importance, the Witty Judge Felt that

the Psychological Moment had Arrived. By Way of Preparing the Ground he Asked in an Innocent Manner Whether there was not Once a Poet named William Shakespeare. Counsel Replied in the Affirmative. The Witty Judge was in the Very Act of Loosing Off his Epoch-making Jest when the Bronchial Usher was Seized with a Paroxysm of Coughing which was Audible in Newgate Street. Then an Appalling Calamity Occurred. The Counsel of No Importance, Resuming his Interrupted Address, Said that his Lordship's Question Prompted the Remark that this Seemed to be a Case of *Poeta Gnashitur Non Fit*. He had Made the Witty Judge's Joke! The Court Rocked with Laughter, in which the Prisoner (who was Something of a Scholar) Joined Heartily, and the Reporters Signalled to their Messengers in Order that the Stop-Press Editions might Give to the World the Joke of the Century.

The Witty Judge was Equal to the Occasion. With Austere Dignity he Rebuked the Counsel of No Importance for his Unseemly Levity, and Begged the Press, in the Interests of Decency, not to Allude to an Incident which had Distressed him Greatly.

When the Court Rose the Witty Judge Told the Bronchial Usher Exactly what he Thought of him. He also Took Immediate Steps to have him Transferred from the Old Bailey to the Commercial Court.

Moral.—*Preparation is the Soul of Wit.*

IRENE, HER YOUNG MAN, AND THE
NECKLACE

IRENE, HER YOUNG MAN, AND
THE NECKLACE

〰

IRENE MUGG was a Young Woman of Grit and
Determination who did her Bit during the War.
The Bit was in a Munitions Factory at 7*l.* 10*s.* a
week.   When the War was over she Reluctantly Took
to Domestic Service.   Her Employers were Mr. and
Mrs. Tompkyns, of Earl's Court.   Finding her
Emoluments as House-Parlourmaid Quite Inade-
quate, Irene Determined to Supplement them.   One
Evening when Mr. and Mrs. Tompkyns were Dining
with Friends, Irene and her Young Man (who had
Come to Supper) Made a Voyage of Discovery in the
Best Bedroom.   Their Diligence was Rewarded.
As they had Taken the Precaution of Breaking the
Window, Irene's Story that Burglars had Carried off
Mrs. Tompkyns' Necklace was for the Moment
Accepted.   But a Few Days Later the Nasty and
Suspicious Demeanour of Mrs. Tompkyns Induced
Irene to Send in her Portfolio and Seek Employment
Elsewhere.   When Mrs. Jenkinson of Putney Applied
for Irene's Character, Mrs. Tompkyns Curtly
Answered that she was Unable to Recommend Irene
Mugg as a Domestic Servant.   Did Irene Take this
Lying Down?   By No Means.   She Promptly
Sought the Assistance of the Amalgamated Union of
Friendless Female Workers and Launched an Action
for Defamation against Mr. and Mrs. Tompkyns.

The Defendants Pleaded that the Occasion was Privileged. At the Hearing of the Action, Mrs. Tompkyns was Subjected to a Severe Cross-Examination. Did she Believe that Irene had Stolen the Necklace? She did. Why, then, had she not Dared to Make a Definite Charge Against Irene? Because she had no Evidence Against her. Why had she not Searched Irene's Boxes? Because she Thought Irene would Object. Had she given Irene a Chance of Proving her Innocence? She had not. The Judge Ruled (after Carefully Considering the Authorities) that the Conduct of Mrs. Tompkyns throughout the Affair, Taken in Conjunction with her Admissions in the Witness-Box, Afforded some Evidence of Malice. Filled with Righteous Indignation the Jury gave Irene 25o*l.*, adding a Rider to their Verdict to the Effect that Mrs. Tompkyns had Behaved in an Un-Womanly Manner. When the Damages and Costs had been Paid, Irene and her Young Man Disposed of the Necklace in the East End. With the Proceeds they Set up in a Licensed House in the Suburbs and are now Doing Very Nicely.

Moral.—*Have a Jury.*

THE DEFEATED LITIGANT AND THE
RASH ATTENDANT

THE DEFEATED LITIGANT AND
THE RASH ATTENDANT

∽

A DEFEATED Litigant was Leaving the Royal Courts of Justice in a State of Mind which can be Better Imagined than Described. The Case had Lasted for Thirteen Days. He had been Offensively Cross-Examined. His Expensive Leader had Left the Junior to Make the Final Speech. The Judge had Said Some Very Disagreeable Things about him in his Summing-Up. The Jury had Found Against him on Every Point. The Damages were Five Thousand Pounds. As he passed down the Central Hall the Defeated Litigant calculated that the whole Beastly Thing had Cost him Well into Five Figures. He Felt it was the Last Straw when his Solicitor (with a Watery Smile) Observed that at any rate his Case had been Patiently Heard. But it was not. As he Neared the Exit to the Strand a Rash Attendant Approached him and Respectfully Enquired whether he would Care to Take a Ticket for the Annual Concert in Aid of the Superannuation Benefit Fund of the Staff of the Royal Courts of Justice. The Defeated Litigant Gave a Scream like that of a Wounded Elephant and Let Loose a Flood of Horrid Oaths which so Startled the Rash Attendant that he Came Over Quite Queer and has Never been the Same Man Since.

Moral.—*Don't rub it in.*

43

THE SOCIETY SUIT AND THE UNEXPECTED
SETTLEMENT

THE SOCIETY SUIT AND THE
UNEXPECTED SETTLEMENT

ᔕ

THE Case of *Potte* v. *Kettle* was about to be Heard. It was a Society Suit in the Best Sense of the Term. The Countess of Potte (Married Woman) was Suing Lady Cleopatra Kettle (Spinster) for Damages for Slander under the Slander of Women Act, 1891. Lady Cleopatra Kettle (Spinster) was Counter-claiming Damages for Slander from the Countess of Potte (Married Woman) under the Slander of Women Act, 1891. If the Alleged Observations of Both Ladies were True, Neither of Them was Fit to Move in Respectable Circles. The Defence of Both Parties (Settled by Very Experienced Pleaders) was that the Words had not been Spoken and/or that the Words were Spoken on a Privileged Occasion and/or that the Words were True in Substance and in Fact. Counsel of the First Magnitude had been Briefed. Sir Nathaniel (with Another Leader and Two Juniors) was for the Plaintiff, and Sir Peregrine (with Another Leader and Two Juniors) was for the Defendant. The Representatives of the Press were Sharpening their Pencils. Fashionable Folk in the Gallery were Telling Each Other to Keep Quiet. The Judge, in a Pair of Clean Bands, was Glancing at "Fraser on Libel." The Jury was being Sworn. One of Sir Nathaniel's Juniors was Clearing his Throat Preparatory to Opening the Pleadings. The Air was

Charged with Electricity. You could have Heard a Pin Drop. When Eleven Jurors had been Sworn the Associate Whispered to the Judge that One Special Juror had not Turned Up. The Judge, who was a Scholar and an Antiquarian, Rejoiced in Archaic Terminology. "Sir Nathaniel and Sir Peregrine," he said "An event has Occurred which Makes it Necessary, if I am not Mistaken, for One or Both of You to Pray a *Tales*." Counsel Conferred. Sir Nathaniel asked Sir Peregrine Whether he Knew what on Earth the Old Boy was Talking About, and What the Blazes was the Thing he Wanted them to Pray for. Sir Peregrine Replied that he hadn't a Notion, and Didn't Sir Nathaniel Think they had Better Settle? Sir Nathaniel Cordially Agreed. And so, to the Fury of the Countess of Potte, Lady Cleopatra Kettle, and the Public, the Case of *Potte* v. *Kettle* was Settled on Terms Indorsed on Counsel's Briefs, Judge's Order if Necessary.

Moral.—*Talk English*.

THE TRAVELLER WHO SUFFERED FROM
SHOCK

THE TRAVELLER WHO SUFFERED FROM SHOCK AND THE RAILWAY COMPANY'S PHYSICIAN

༄

A TRAVELLER, who was not Such a Fool As he Looked, had the Good Fortune to Escape from a Railway Accident with Nothing Worse than a Slight Shock to his System. But Feeling that the Railway Company might Well be Encouraged to Cough Up, he Instructed his Solicitor to Write a Suitable Letter. The Railway Company Politely Suggested that their Physician should Visit the Traveller and Ascertain the Extent of his Injuries. The Railway Company's Physician Duly Waited upon the Traveller, and Found him Seated in an Invalid Chair in a Completely Paralysed Condition. He was so Horrified by the Traveller's Deplorable Appearance that he Quite Forgot to Ask him whether his Dilapidated State was the Result of the Railway Accident. It was in fact Due to the Negligence of a Nurserymaid who had Upset the Traveller's Perambulator in Kensington Gardens in 1864, when he was Twelve Months Old. But the Traveller did not See why he should Trouble the Railway Company's Physician with these Autobiographical Details. When the Railway Company Offered the Traveller 2,000*l.* in Full Settlement, he Wisely Held Out for 2,500*l.*, and Got it.

Moral.—*Sit Tight.*

ADOLPHUS BROWN, MR. JUSTICE GRUMP, AND
THE INTERESTING CASE

ADOLPHUS BROWN, MR. JUSTICE GRUMP, AND THE INTERESTING CASE

∽

ADOLPHUS BROWN was an Amiable Youth of Gentle Manners and Undistinguished Appearance. Rather to the Surprise of his Oxford Tutor, who had Anticipated that he would Fail to Satisfy the Examiners, Adolphus Secured a Third Class in the Honours School of Jurisprudence. Heartened by his Success, old Mr. Brown Insisted that Adolphus should Become a Member of the Honourable Society of the Outer Temple, with a View to being called to the Bar. Thereafter Adolphus Devoted his Time to the Reading of "Shirley's Leading Cases" and the Sampling of such Musical Entertainments as Seemed to Deserve his Support. To Tell the Truth, Adolphus Disliked the Law Exceedingly. When Adolphus was Beginning to Feel that he Couldn't Stick It Much Longer, Mr. Justice Grump (who was an Old Friend of the Family) Proposed that he should Accompany him as Marshal on his Next Circuit. Adolphus Gladly Accepted the Invitation, as it Sounded like a Soft Job. Whilst Travelling in State to the First Assize Town, he Realised that Things were Going to be Pretty Dull. His Prognostications were Well-Founded. Mr. Justice Grump, though a Jurist of the First Water, was not Exactly Chatty. Every Evening after the Court had Risen, Mr. Justice Grump Took Adolphus for a Long Walk in the Country. The One Bright Spot about these Expeditions was that he did not Expect

Adolphus to Converse. But there came an Awful Day when Grump, J., Let himself Go. He became very Talkative about a Beastly Case he was going to Try next Week, and Told Adolphus All about it. As Mr. Justice Grump's Well-Ordered Narrative Proceeded, Adolphus became More and More Confused. The Story Concerned a County Council, a Foreshore, Prescriptive Rights, a Lunatic Not so Found by Inquisition, and a Marriage between a Roman Catholic Spaniard and an Irish Protestant in Amsterdam. When Adolphus' Attention was Beginning to Wander, Mr. Justice Grump Suddenly Stopped and Asked him for his Views as to How the Case should be Decided. Adolphus, who at the Moment was Thinking how Charming Miss Popsie Dalrymple Looked in the Second Act, nearly Died of Horror. His Brain Stopped Working and his Mouth became Dry. He Tried Unsuccessfully to Remember What had been Held in *Lickbarrow* v. *Mason*.[1] He Goggled. Then Adolphus had a Brilliant Inspiration. He Cleared his Throat and Said in a Confident Voice that he would Leave the Whole Thing to the Jury. To the Unutterable Amazement of Adolphus, Mr. Justice Grump Replied that On the Whole he Agreed that it was Largely a Question of Fact. Adolphus Breathed Again. But the Affair had Given him a Nasty Jar, and he Felt Quite Shaken. So Much So that Adolphus had to have Two Stiff Whiskies and Sodas before Dinner, Two more during the Repast, and Several after Mr. Justice Grump had Retired to Rest.

Moral.—*Fortune Favours the Brave.*

[1] 5 T. R. 683.

MR. BLOWHARD, K.C. AND MR. FOOTLE, K.C.

MR. BLOWHARD, K.C. AND
MR. FOOTLE, K.C.

‿

MR. BLOWHARD, K.C., and Mr. Footle, K.C., Stood Jointly on the Top Rung of the Professional Ladder. Whether Blowhard Made more Money than Footle was a Moot Point. Whether Footle's or Blowhard's Methods of Advocacy were to be Preferred was Another. Solicitors Wondered how on Earth they would Get On when Blowhard and Footle were Gathered to their Fathers. When in Difficulties, Managing Clerks Rushed to Retain Blowhard, and if they Found that his Services had Already been Requisitioned, they Hurried to Retain Footle. And *Vice Versâ*. Blowhard was Violent, Noisy, Quarrelsome, Aggressive, and Occasionally Insolent. Footle was Gentle, Submissive, Diffident, Deprecating and Invariably Inaudible. Blowhard Lost an Immense Number of Actions by Getting Up an Unnecessary Row with the Judge. Footle Lost an Immense Number of Actions by his Rabbit-like Behaviour. Their Respective Incomes were Enormous. They Despised Judicial Honours. They Continued to Practise at the Bar long after the Decay of their Faculties had Set In; but Happily those who Briefed them never Noticed the Difference. When they Passed Away, as they Ultimately did, the Business of the Royal Courts of Justice went on just as if Nothing had Happened.

Moral.—*Acquire a reputation.*

THE BLUSHING BEGINNER AND THE
BEARDED JURYMAN

THE BLUSHING BEGINNER
AND
THE BEARDED JURYMAN

∽

A SOLICITOR Briefed a Blushing Beginner to Defend a Prisoner at the Assizes. He Assured the Blushing Beginner that there was no Cause for Anxiety as the Prisoner hadn't an Earthly. When the Jury Acquitted the Prisoner the Blushing Beginner could Hardly Believe his Ears. He felt that he had indeed been Wise to Devote so much Time to the Study of the Works of Quintilian on Oratory and the Great Speeches of Such Masters as Cicero and Demosthenes. That his Address to the Jury had Done the Trick he had Little Doubt. For he had Observed that a Juryman with a Black Beard in the Front Row had Paid Close Attention to his Best Points. Which Particular Portion of his Speech had been Most Effective the Blushing Beginner could not be Sure. He Inclined to think it was the Peroration. For when he had Come to the Bit about the Dawn Breaking and the Sun Gilding the Distant Hills the Bearded Juryman had Shewn Considerable Emotion. Thus Meditating, the Blushing Beginner Proceeded from the Court to his Lodgings in High Spirits. On his Way he Observed the Bearded Juryman just Ahead of him. Hurrying Forward, the Blushing Beginner Wished the Bearded Juryman a Good Evening and Engaged him in Conversation.

57

"Could you tell me," he said, "without Divulging any Secret of the Jury-box, what it was that Convinced you of the Prisoner's Innocence? Was it my Cross-examination of the Prosecutor? Or the Failure of the Crown to Call Robinson? Or was it, perchance, the Argument which I Put Forward in my Final Speech?" The Bearded Juryman Replied, with Some Warmth, that he didn't Know or Care what the other Mugs Thought, but for his Part he (the Bearded Juryman) didn't See why his Sister's Son should be Sent to Quod even if the Boy *had* Stole a Tenner from the Blinking Blighter who had Done him (the Bearded Juryman) over a Deal Two Years ago. The Bearded Juryman then Expectorated Fiercely and Turned into the "Blue Pig" for Further Refreshment. The Blushing Beginner Gathered from these Remarks that there were Collateral Reasons for the Opinion of the Bearded Juryman which were not Strictly Relevant to the Main Issues in the Case. But he Decided to Treat the Bearded Juryman's Disclosures as Confidential.

Moral.—*Study Quintilian on Oratory.*

THE UTTER BARRISTER AND THE
IMPORTANT TREATISE

THE UTTER BARRISTER AND THE
IMPORTANT TREATISE

ဆ

AN Utter Barrister was Sincerely Attached to a
Charming Young Person, who Reciprocated
his Regard. But as his Professional Takings
were Negligible, and the Charming Young Person's
Relatives Manifested no Desire to Provide an Income
for Two, the Utter Barrister Felt that his Engagement
was Likely to be a Long One. He was Accordingly
Somewhat Dejected. Why Solicitors should be so
Coy he did not Understand. For (though a Modest
Man) he was Compelled to Admit that he was of
Good Appearance and Marked Intellectual Ability.
Whilst Engaged in the Soothing Occupation of
Smoking Gaspers the Utter Barrister was Struck by a
Bright Idea. To Seize Pen and Paper was the Work
of a Moment. To Draft an Eloquent Advertise-
ment for Insertion in the Public Prints was the Work
of Another. Week by Week During the Ensuing
Twelve Months the World was Informed that the
Utter Barrister had in Course of Preparation a
Treatise in Nine Volumes; Three Concerning the
Laws (Statutory) of England, Scotland, Northern
Ireland, the Irish Free State and the British Dominions
Beyond the Seas; Three Devoted to Public and Private
International Law, Conflict of Laws, Jurisprudence
and the History of Legal Tribunals; and Three Con-
taining a Complete Digest (Correlated, Analysed and

61

Indexed) of all Reported Cases on Contract and Tort since the year 1685. The Price (Payable by Instalments) was to be Twelve Guineas Net; Thin Paper Edition, Fourteen Guineas Net. As the Year Advanced the Wording of the Advertisement was Slightly Altered, and the Treatise was Declared to be "In the Press," "About to be Published," and "Shortly to Appear." The Intelligent Anticipations of the Utter Barrister were Realised. Managing Clerks Flocked to his Chambers in such Gratifying Numbers that at the Beginning of the Long Vacation he was Enabled to Lead the Charming Young Person to the Hymeneal Altar with the Full Approval of her Close-Fisted Relations. Did the Nine Volumes Appear in Due Course? They did not. On his Return from the Honeymoon the Utter Barrister, with the assistance of the Press Agency, Broke to the Public the News that Owing to the Carelessness of a Domestic Servant the Manuscript of the Great Work had been Destroyed and that its Publication was Indefinitely Postponed. Filled with Sympathy for the Utter Barrister in this Appalling Misfortune, the Solicitors of the Metropolis Redoubled their Attentions, and the Utter Barrister was so Overwhelmed with Work that he was Shortly Compelled to apply for a Silk Gown.

Moral.—*Write a Book.*

THE COMMON LAW JUNIOR AND THE
ORIGINATING SUMMONS

THE COMMON LAW JUNIOR AND
THE ORIGINATING SUMMONS

ᔐ

A COMMON LAW JUNIOR was Instructed to Appear in the Chancery Division. The Proceeding was Called an Originating Summons. He was informed by his Client that he would not be Expected to Explain the Points to the Judge, as he was to Have an Experienced Chancery Leader to Assist him. This News Comforted the Common Law Junior a Good Deal, for he could not Understand what the Dickens the Case was About. In the Affidavits there were Dark Allusions to an Estate *Pur Autre Vie,* a Gift Over on a Compound Event, and a Failure by Ademption. The Only Thing he could Grasp Clearly was that an Old Woman had Made a Will and Died. When the Case was Called on, the Common Law Junior was told by a Breathless Clerk that the Experienced Chancery Leader was in the House of Lords and that he was to Carry On till the Experienced Chancery Leader could Get Back. The Common Law Junior Rose to his Feet and Told the Judge in Faltering Accents that he would Read the Affidavits. At first All went Well. The Common Law Junior Read and the Judge Followed him Attentively. When the Common Law Junior Turned Over the Judge Turned Over also. But then a Hideous Event Occurred. Towards the End of the Third Affidavit the Judge Suddenly Said to the

Common Law Junior: "But How do you Get Over *in re Puffington's Settlement*?" The Common Law Junior Fainted.

When he Came to himself he was Aware that Three Old Gentlemen with Beards were Asking for Costs out of his Estate.

Moral.—*Ask for an Adjournment.*

THE SARCASTIC COUNSEL AND
MR. MACINTOSH, THE MONEYLENDER

THE SARCASTIC COUNSEL AND
MR. MACINTOSH, THE MONEYLENDER

～

A SARCASTIC Counsel Smiled Grimly as he Perused his Brief. He was to Appear for a Borrower (Mr. Algernon FitzCholmondely) against a Moneylender (Mr. Alexander MacIntosh, of Jermyn Street, W.1). It was a Short Cause. Mr. FitzCholmondely had Borrowed a Hundred Pounds from Mr. MacIntosh, Handing to him at the same time a Promissory Note for Two Hundred Pounds, Payable by Four Monthly Instalments of Fifty. After Paying Two Instalments, Mr. FitzCholmondely had Defaulted. He had then Borrowed a Further Hundred Pounds, Accepting, at the same Time, a Bill of Exchange for Five Hundred. Thereafter a Series of Complicated Transactions had been Carried Through, with the Final Result that Mr. Fitz-Cholmondely had Borrowed One Thousand Two Hundred and Fifty Pounds, Repaid Two Thousand Five Hundred, and Still Owed Three Thousand Pounds, Eleven Shillings and Nine Pence. As the Short Cause List was to be Taken by a Judge of Scottish Extraction, the Sarcastic Counsel Felt that he would Have Some Fun. His Lordship, he Shrewdly Surmised, would not Sympathise with the Attempt of a Caledonian from Judæa to Take Advantage of a Foolish and Needy Englishman. The Case Came on and Mr. Alexander MacIntosh went into

69

the Box. To the Extreme Surprise and Annoyance of the Sarcastic Counsel, he Proved to be a Genuine Scot with a Red Beard and an Aberdonian Accent of Appalling Purity. Whereas Mr. Algernon Fitz-Cholmondely had Relunctantly to Admit in Cross-Examination that he was Born in Warsaw and that his Name was Originally Rosenbaumski. Not Only did the Judge of Scottish Extraction Enter Judgment for the Plaintiff for the Full Amount, but he Peremptorily Refused a Stay of Execution.

Moral.—*Look Out*.

THE AMBITIOUS YOUTH WHO WANTED
ELIGIBLE CHAMBERS

THE AMBITIOUS YOUTH WHO
WANTED ELIGIBLE CHAMBERS

∾

AN Ambitious Youth was Advised that if he Wished to Succeed at the Bar it was All-Important that he should Secure Eligible Chambers. He Accordingly Embarked upon this Quest Directly After his Call. The Ambitious Youth was Quite Clear as to his Requirements. He did not Wish to Confine himself to Government Work, nor to Tie himself Up in the Commercial Court, the Admiralty Court or the Old Bailey. What the Ambitious Youth Desired was a Comfortable Room in a Set of Chambers on the Ground or First Floor where there were (1) a Busy Leader (of Conservative Politics) who would Shortly become a Judge; (2) a Junior with a Heavy Mixed Practice who was in need of a "Devil" and would Soon Take Silk; and (3) an Experienced and Active Clerk. After Six Months had Elapsed he Felt that he need not Insist on the Busy Leader. When Nine Months had Gone By he Thought that the Second Floor might Do. A Year after his Call the Ambitious Youth Closed with an Offer of Half a Room, the Other Moiety of Which was Occupied by a Coloured Gentleman. The Chambers were on the Fourth Floor. The Other Tenants were a Female Journalist and an Elderly Person who was not a Teetotaller. The Clerk was an Oaf with a Squint who Smoked Cigarettes.

Moral.—*Aim High.*

THE WHITE-HAIRED TRUSTEE AND THE
HIGHLY-PLACED OFFICIAL

THE WHITE-HAIRED TRUSTEE
AND
THE HIGHLY-PLACED OFFICIAL

༄

THERE was Once a Dear Old Trustee. He had White Hair and Gold Spectacles. His Reputation for Stability and Integrity Equalled that of the Bank of England. For Many Years he had Enjoyed the Confidence and Esteem of the Various Widows and Orphans whose Affairs and Securities were in his Capable Hands. But the White-haired Trustee, having Rashly Availed himself of Certain Inside Information as to Rubber, got into a Nasty Financial Mess and Came to the Conclusion that he had Better Do a Bolt. He Felt, at the Same Time, (1) that it would be a Pity to Leave Behind Anything Belonging to his *Cestuis Que Trustent* which could be Turned into Ready Money, and (2) that Penal Servitude Should, If Possible, be Avoided. The White-haired Trustee accordingly Placed a Nice Little Lot of Bearer Bonds and Coupons in his Bag, Procured a Ticket for the Continent, and Repaired to Scotland Yard. Here his Admirable Appearance Secured for him an Interview with a Highly-Placed Official. Stating that he had been Robbed, the White-haired Trustee Handed to the Highly-Placed Official a List of the Choses in Action which his Bag Contained, and Begged to be Told where the Thieves were Likely to Endeavour to Encash them. The Highly-

Placed Official Expressed his Keen Sympathy and Courteously Supplied the Desired Information. The White-haired Trustee Thanked him Warmly, and Disposed of the Nice Little Lot in the Cities Named by the Highly-Placed Official at Very Satisfactory Prices. The White-haired Trustee has not been Heard of Since. The Highly-Placed Official has Retired on a Pension.

Moral.—*Melius Est Petere Fontes.*

THE REAL PROPERTY LAWYER AND
THE SURLY GAMEKEEPER

THE REAL PROPERTY LAWYER AND
THE SURLY GAMEKEEPER

〜

ONCE Upon a Time there was a Learned Real Property Lawyer whose Industry and Erudition were the Pride and Joy of Lincoln's Inn. He Knew All About Reversions, Easements in Gross, Registration of Title, and Ancient Lights. In Short, he was Hot Stuff. At the Same Time he was not a Mere Book-Worm. Every Sunday he Took a Long Country Walk in Order that his Physical Frame, Exhausted by the Labours of the Week, might be Recuperated and Refreshed. After a Comfortable Tea at a Wayside Inn he would Return by Train to Porchester Terrace, where a Cold Supper Awaited him. Familiar as he was with the Niceties of the Law, Notices Forbidding him to Trespass under Pain of Prosecution Caused him no Alarm. If Challenged by the Owner of the Messuage or Hereditament through which he was Minded to Pass, he would Point Out that he was Making no Claim of Right, that his Act was Tortious and not Criminal, and that he was Ready to Pay any Damages which a Civil Court might Assess. He Found that the Owner Invariably Permitted him to Proceed upon his Way. One Sunday Evening the Real Property Lawyer, Somewhat Fatigued by a Twelve-Mile Walk, Took a Short Cut through the Deer-Park Surrounding the

79

Elizabethan Mansion of Sir Moses Blumenkopf, First Baronet. By so Doing he was Making Sure of Catching the Six-Forty-Three Train to Victoria. When the Real Property Lawyer was a Few Hundred Yards from the Highway, he Encountered a Surly Gamekeeper who was Accompanied by an Ill-Looking Dog. Barring his Progress, the Surly Gamekeeper Asked him in an Angry Voice and Highly Illiterate Terms What the Blazes he Meant by Coming on to Land Where he hadn't No Business not to Be. The Real Property Lawyer Adjusted his Spectacles, and Replied that he was Well Aware that he was Committing a Civil Trespass. He Added that he was Prepared to Accept Service of a Writ of Summons, should Sir Moses See Fit to Institute Proceedings in the Chancery Division. The Real Property Lawyer then Drew from his Pocket the Sum of Sixpence and Offered it to the Surly Gamekeeper, Begging him to Note that he had Made a Tender of An Adequate Sum by way of Damages. Did the Real Property Lawyer's Entirely Correct Demeanour Pacify the Surly Gamekeeper? Far from It. Uttering Strange Oaths, he Seized the Real Property Lawyer by the Left Whisker (Causing him thereby Considerable Pain) and Intimated that if he did not Forthwith Retrace his Steps he would Jolly Well Bash his Face In. The Ill-Looking Dog meanwhile Emitted Growls of a Very Unnerving Character. Deeming it Prudent to Close the Discussion, the Real Property Lawyer Silently Limped Away in the Direction Indicated by the Surly Gamekeeper. In Consequence he Missed his Train, was Very Late for Supper, and Incurred the Grave Displeasure of his Housekeeper.

Moral.—*Good Law Makes Hard Cases.*

THE INDUSTRIOUS ·YOUTH AND THE
STOUT STRANGER

THE INDUSTRIOUS YOUTH AND
THE STOUT STRANGER

∽

ONE Evening an Industrious Youth was
Sitting in his Chambers Reading the Current
Number of the Law Reports. He was Full
of Hope, but Briefs had hitherto been Rare and of
Poor Quality. Hearing a Knock, the Industrious
Youth Opened the Door to a Stout Stranger. Seat-
ing himself in the Arm-Chair, the Stout Stranger Told
the Industrious Youth that he was Looking Out for a
Capable Junior, and that he had been Much Struck by
the Industrious Youth's Skilful Conduct of a Case in
the Whitechapel County Court. Could the In-
dustrious Youth Undertake a Heavy Job which the
Stout Stranger had On Hand? The Industrious
Youth having Intimated that a Heavy Job would Suit
him Nicely, the Stout Stranger Expressed Extreme
Satisfaction and Said that he would Send the Instruc-
tions Along the First Thing To-morrow. He Added
that he was on his Way to Give a General Retainer to
Sir John, as Money was no Object. The Industrious
Youth Applauded this Excellent Choice of a Leader.
Having Gathered up his Papers, the Stout Stranger
was Preparing to Depart when, with a Cry of Annoy-
ance, he Discovered that he had Left his Purse on the
What-Not in his Office. Did the Industrious Youth
Happen to have Five Guineas Upon him? It was
Vital that Sir John should be Retained forthwith, as

the Other Side might Snap him Up. The Industrious Youth was Afraid he had Only Got Three Pounds, but the Stout Stranger was Very Nice about it and said he Could Probably Borrow the Balance from Sir John's Clerk. The Stout Stranger then Withdrew, Leaving behind him a Fragrant Smell of Cloves. As the Expected Instructions did not Come, the Industrious Youth Caused Enquiries to be Made at Sir John's Chambers. But Sir John's Clerk had not Seen or Heard of the Stout Stranger. And as the Instructions have not Yet arrived the Industrious Youth is of Opinion that the Stout Stranger must have Met with a Serious Accident, or been Visited by a Sudden and Complete Loss of Memory.

Moral.—*Caveat Junior*.

MR. WHITEWIG AND THE RASH
QUESTION

MR. WHITEWIG AND THE RASH
QUESTION

ᔕ

MR. WHITEWIG was Greatly Gratified when the Judge of Assize Invited him to Defend a Prisoner who was Charged with Having Stolen a Pair of Boots, a Mouse-Trap, and Fifteen Packets of Gold Flakes. It was his First Case and he Meant to Make a Good Show. Mr. Whitewig Studied the Depositions Carefully and Came to the Conclusion that a Skilful Cross-Examination of the Witnesses and a Tactful Speech would Secure the Acquittal of the Accused. When the Prisoner (an Ill-Looking Person) was Placed in the Dock, Mr. Whitewig Approached that Receptacle and Informed the Prisoner that he Might, if he Wished, Give Evidence on Oath. From the Prisoner's Reply (in which he Alluded to Grandmothers and Eggs) Mr. Whitewig Gathered that he did not Propose to Avail Himself of this Privilege. The Case Began. At First All Went Well. The Prosecutor Admitted to Mr. Whitewig that he Could not be Sure that the Man he had Seen Lurking in the Neighbourhood of his Emporium was the Prisoner; and the Prosecutor's Assistant Completely Failed to Identify the Boots, the Mouse-Trap, or the Gold Flakes by Pointing to any Distinctive Peculiarities which they Exhibited. By the Time the Police Inspector Entered the Witness-Box Mr. Whitewig Felt that the Case was Won. Mr.

Whitewig Cunningly Extracted from the Inspector the Fact that the Prisoner had Joined Up in 1914, and that the Prisoner's Wife was Expecting an Addition to her Family. He was about to Sit Down when a Final Question Occurred to him. "Having Regard to this Man's Record," he Sternly Asked, "How Came You to Arrest him?" The Inspector Drew a Bundle of Blue Documents from the Recesses of his Uniform, and, Moistening his Thumb, Read therefrom. Mr. Whitewig Learned in Silent Horror that the Prisoner's Record Included Nine Previous Convictions. When the Prisoner was Asked whether he had Anything to say why Sentence should not be Passed Upon him, he Said some Very Disagreeable Things about the Mug who had Defended him.

Moral.—*Leave Well Alone.*

THE K.C., M.P., AND THE BILL FOR THE
SUPPRESSION OF NIGHT CLUBS

THE K.C., M.P., AND THE BILL FOR
THE
SUPPRESSION OF NIGHT CLUBS

〜

A DISTINGUISHED K.C., M.P., having Balloted Successfully, became Entitled to Introduce a Bill Under the Ten Minutes' Rule. He Decided in Favour of a Bill for the Suppression of Night Clubs. The K.C., M.P., was a Man of Blameless Life and Old-Fashioned Views. Of Night Clubs he had no Personal Experience, and he Felt that he Ought to See for himself the Evils which he Desired to Stamp Out. Disguised in a Curly Wig and a Moustache (which he Secured in Covent Garden) he Repaired on Monday to the "Giddy Goat." His Worst Expectations were Realised. On Tuesday he Tried the "Bubble and Squeak," where he was Greatly Surprised and Distressed. On Wednesday he Obtained Admission to the "Tiddlywinks" and Got Home at Four A.M. On Thursday he Tried the "Giddy Goat" again. On Friday he Took Some Dancing Lessons from Madame Frou-Frou in Shaftesbury Avenue. On Saturday he became a Life Member of "Pongo's." At the Latter Establishment he Found a Lady Member who Told him that he Danced Awfully Sweetly, and they Had Supper Together. The Bill (Including Eight *Crème-de-Menthes* and Two Bottles of *Veuve Monte Cristo*) Came to Nine Pounds Eleven Shillings and Nine Pence. During the Raid which Occurred in the Small Hours of the Morning the K.C., M.P., Mingled with the Orchestra and was Able to Satisfy the Police that he was a Professional Player of the Ukulele. Thinking Matters Over during the Week-End he Came to the Conclusion that the Case against Night Clubs had been Greatly Exaggerated. The K.C., M.P., therefore Scrapped his Projected Measure, and Substituted a Bill for the Further Amendment of the Law of Property Act, 1925.

Moral.—*Experientia Docet.*

MR. JUSTICE CATTEMALL AND
MR. JUSTICE DEARLOVE

MR. JUSTICE CATTEMALL AND
MR. JUSTICE DEARLOVE

MR. JUSTICE CATTEMALL and Mr. Justice Dearlove were Experienced Judges of the King's Bench Division. Their Views and Methods in Connection with the Treatment of Prisoners Differed Widely. Cattemall, J., always Looked in *Archbold's Criminal Pleading* to See How Much he could Give them, and Proceeded to Give it. If there were Three Counts in the Indictment he Ladled out Five Years on each Count, and Made them Run Consecutively. The Lamentations of the Relatives of the Accused Seemed Rather to Gratify him than Otherwise. When he Went on Circuit the Home Office Laid on an Extra Temporary Staff to Deal with the Petitions which Poured in; and the Court of Criminal Appeal Became so Busy that it had to Borrow a Judge from the Admiralty Division to Cope with the Work. Mr. Justice Dearlove was the Very Opposite of his Learned Brother. He Liked to Bind Over the Wicked to Come up for Judgment if Called Upon, and he Shed Tears when he had to Send Anyone to Prison. Towards Old Offenders he was Particularly Gentle, because they had Never had a Chance; and he Let Off all Youthful Malefactors because he did not Wish to make Criminals of them. Cattemall, J., and Dearlove, J., often Discussed the Relative Merits of their Respective Systems. Here is a Picture of them so Discussing. The Short One is Cattemall, J., and the Tall One is Dearlove, J.

Moral.—*You Never Can Tell.*

THE SOUND LAWYER WHO MADE
A GOOD RESOLUTION

THE SOUND LAWYER WHO MADE
A GOOD RESOLUTION

〜

THERE was Once a Sound Lawyer who was Firmly Resolved that if he should ever Receive Judicial Honours he would Avoid the Errors and Failings of Some of his Predecessors. In Particular he would not Indulge in Foolish Jokes, Give Vent to Irrelevant Observations about Men and Things, or Hint that the Bar had Sadly Deteriorated Since he had Ceased to Adorn its Ranks. In Due Course the Sound Lawyer (Whose Brother-in-Law was a Personage of Some Importance) was Invited by the Authorities to Accept a County Court Judgeship. By Return of Post the Sound Lawyer Intimated that he was Ready and Willing to Grapple With the Job. Grimly Determined to Adhere to his Good Resolution, he Took his Seat on the Bench. Did he Adhere to his Good Resolution? He did not. Before the Year was Out the Reporters in his Court had Recorded that a Plymouth Brother could not be Believed upon his Oath; that it was Common Knowledge that a Married Woman was either a Slave or a Tyrant; that while at the Bar the Sound Lawyer had Frequently been so Overworked that he had not been in Bed for a Week; that the Moral Standards of Artists and Literary Men were Extremely Low; that the Legislators of the County were Obviously Half-Witted; and that Anybody who Read Boccacio could

Understand why the Latin Races were so Greatly Inferior to the Inhabitants of These Islands. They had also Taken Down a Variety of Time-honoured Jests Turning upon the Thrifty Habits of Scotchmen and the Irritating Ways of Mothers-in-Law. And the Sound Lawyer had so often Cited Apposite Extracts from the Works of Cicero, Ben Jonson, Rabelais, Tennyson, and Other Authors, both Ancient and Modern, that in Order to Get them Down Correctly each of the Reporters had been Compelled to Purchase a Copy of the "Book of Quotations," in which the Sound Lawyer Discovered them.

Moral.—*Make Good Resolutions.*

THE KINDLY JUDGE AND THE
LADY BARRISTER

THE KINDLY JUDGE AND THE
LADY BARRISTER

∽

A LEARNED JUDGE, on Arriving at the
Royal Courts of Justice to Deal with the
Non-Jury List, was Told by his Clerk that one
of the Counsel in the First Case was Miss Mary
Poppleton, the Newly-Called Lady Barrister. The
Judge, who was Kindly, Large-Minded, and an
Upholder of the Cause of Woman, Determined that
he would Give Miss Mary Poppleton a Good Run.
When the Judge took his Seat he Felt that the Fragile
Creature with a Squeaky Voice and a Mild Blue Eye
who Appeared for the Plaintiff would Need all his
Help. For a Robust and Fierce-Looking Individual
was Representing the Defendant.

The Case Began. Whenever he had a Chance the
Judge gave the Mild Blue Eye a Leg-Up. And he
Made a Point of Treating the Fierce-Looking Advo-
cate on the Other Side with Some Severity. Ulti-
mately (though not without Misgiving) the Judge
Gave Judgment for the Mild Blue Eye with Costs.
The Fierce-Looking Opponent, who had Cross-
Examined with Effect and Delivered a Pointed Legal
Argument, Promptly Asked for a Stay of Execution.

When the Court Adjourned the Judge's Clerk
Expressed the View that he had been Rather Hard on
Miss Mary Poppleton. The Judge angrily Enquired
what the Clerk Meant, and Learned, Too Late, that

he had been Misled by Appearances.   It seemed that the Mild Blue Eye was a Young Man who had Steered the University Eight to Victory Three Years Ago, and that the Fierce-Looking Counsel for the Defendant was Miss Mary Poppleton.   But Happily no Harm was Done.   For Miss Mary Poppleton Promptly Went to the Court of Appeal and had an Easy Win.

Moral.—*Spot the Lady.*

THE EXPERIENCED ADVOCATE AND THE
HALF-YEAR'S RENT

THE EXPERIENCED ADVOCATE AND
THE HALF-YEAR'S RENT

༄

A N Experienced Advocate Left the Royal Courts
of Justice in a Happy Frame of Mind after a
Full and Satisfactory Day.   He had Won the
First Case by Pointing Out to the Jury that the
Principal Witness for the Enemy had Professed to
Remember Details which Must (had his Story been
True) have Passed from his Mind.   His Second Vic-
tory was Due to his Reminder of the Jury that the
Plaintiff had failed to Recall Incidents which Must
(had his Account of the Matter in Question been
Honest) have Dwelt in his Memory.   His Third
Triumph was the Result of a Successful Invitation to
the Jury to Say that a City Merchant who Pretended
that he had Forgotten to Fill Up the Counterfoil of an
Important Cheque Ought not to be—Nay, Could not
be—Believed upon his Oath.   He was Pleased with
himself.   On Returning to Chambers the Experienced Advocate Found on his Desk a Peremptory
Reminder that his Half-Year's Rent was Due and
Owing.   The Experienced Advocate was Indignant
because he Felt Sure he had Already Sent a Cheque
for the Amount.   He Distinctly Remembered Blot-
ting the Date of the Cheque and Filling up the
Counterfoil.   The Experienced Advocate, having
Examined his Pass-Book and Cheque-Book, Ascertained that during the Past Twelve Months he had not

Filled up any Counterfoils at all, and, furthermore, that he had not Sent a Cheque, whether Blotted or Otherwise, for the Half-Year's Rent. The Experienced Advocate Rejoiced More than Ever Over his Good Day's Work.

Moral.—*Circumstances Alter Cases.*

THE OLD STAGER AND THE EXCHEQUER SUIT

THE OLD STAGER AND THE EXCHEQUER
SUIT ON THE INFORMATION OF THE
ATTORNEY-GENERAL ISSUING OUT OF
THE PETTY-BAG

∽

ONE day an Agitated Solicitor Waited upon an Old Stager. The Latter was Replete with such Learning as is to be found in the Third Edition of "Bullen & Leake." The Agitated Solicitor Wanted the Old Stager to Advise him. There was a Firm of High Standing which Owed his Clients a Lot of Money. Though the Firm of High Standing had not a Leg to Stand upon, Order Fourteen was No Good, as they could Easily Put Up some Rotten Sort of Defence. His Clients must Have the Money Forthwith as they were in a Wobbly Financial Condition. What was he to Do?

The Old Stager Said it was Clearly a Case for an Exchequer Suit on the Information of the Attorney-General Issuing out of the Petty-Bag. He Promised to Prepare without Delay the Necessary Formal Documents. When the Agitated Solicitor had Withdrawn the Old Stager got to Work on the Draft. It Began with the Observation, "*Oyez, Oyez, Oyez,*" and Recited that the Right Honourable the Attorney-General had been Informed by his Trusty and Well-beloved Thomas Binks and Thomas Binks the younger (Trading as Binks and Company) that the Firm of High

Standing Owed them the Sum of 3,921*l*. 4*s*. 8*d*. It Proceeded to Warn the Firm of High Standing that by Declining to pay the said Moneys they had Rendered themselves Liable to the Pains and Penalties Made and Provided by 1 & 2 Ric. II. c. 4, 18 Eliz. c. 14, and Divers Acts Amending the Same, the Provisions whereof were Preserved and Maintained by and Incorporated in the Judicature Acts of 1873 and 1875 (36 & 37 Vict. c. 66 and 38 & 39 Vict. c. 77). It then Summoned Each and Every of the Members of the Firm of High Standing to Attend at Twelve O'Clock (Midday) on Monday (*Die Lunae*) next after the Morrow of All Souls at the Bar of the House of Lords and there Show Cause in Person why they should not be Committed to the Clock-Tower of his Majesty's Palace of Westminster or to his Majesty's Keep or Tower of London and there be Imprisoned until Further Order. In a Few Closing Sentences it Pointed Out that if they Desired to be Assoilzied, Purged, and Acquitted of the said Debt and Relieved from the Obligation of Attending at the said Bar of the said House of Lords, the Firm of High Standing must Cause the said Sum of 3,921*l*. 4*s*. 8*d*. to be Paid in Cash to the said Thomas Binks and Thomas Binks the Younger (Trading as Binks & Company) within Twenty-four Hours. At the End of the Draft the Old Stager Added the Devout Aspiration, "God Save the King." He also Penned in the Margin a Note to the Effect that this Imposing Document should be Engrossed on Parchment and Served upon the Defendants by a Mounted Policeman. The Firm of High Standing (who were Hoping for a Government

Contract in the Near Future) were so Terrified by the Old Stager's Screed that, Without Consulting Their Solicitors, they Cashed Up At Once. When the Agitated Solicitor Subsequently Enquired of the Old Stager where he had Unearthed this Most Satisfactory Procedure, the Old Stager Modestly Confessed that he had Invented it.

Moral.—*Try it on.*

THE PRUDENT COUNSEL, THE NEW CLIENT,
AND THE STRIDENT PERSON

THE PRUDENT COUNSEL, THE NEW
CLIENT, AND THE STRIDENT PERSON

∽

THERE was once a Prudent Counsel who Took no Risks. He was Briefed for the Defendant by a New Client in a Ticklish Case. After Mature Thought the Prudent Counsel Came to the Conclusion that the Best Thing would be to Sit Tight. The Prudent Counsel Found himself Opposed by a Strident Person of Violent and Aggressive Methods. The Strident Person Made an Offensive Opening Speech, Got up a Quite Unnecessary Row with the Judge, Grossly Insulted the Prudent Counsel, and Forgot to Ask the Plaintiff the Only Important Question. The Prudent Counsel Secured Judgment without Calling the Defendant. He Felt that the New Client was his for All Time. Was the New Client Surprised and Delighted by the Performance of the Prudent Counsel? He was not. The New Client Rebuked the Prudent Counsel for his Want of Go, Dwelt upon the Admirable Fight which the Strident Person had Put Up, and thereafter Transferred to the Strident Person his Affections and all his Briefs.

Moral.—*Raise Your Voice.*

THE TEARFUL PERFORMER AND THE
PLAINTIFF WITH A PAST

THE TEARFUL PERFORMER AND THE
PLAINTIFF WITH A PAST

∽

THERE was Once a Tearful Performer in the King's Bench Division. He Knew All the Tricks of the Trade, but his Real Strong Point was the Sob-Stuff. He Often Appeared for Plaintiffs. First he would Give the Jury a Simple Outline of the Facts. Then he Assured them that he had no Wish to Work upon Their Feelings. Later, in a More Cooing Tone of Voice, he Reluctantly Went into the Harrowing Details. By the Time he Got to the Blasted Reputation, the Shocking Injuries, or the Agony of Mind (as the Case might be), there was not a Dry Handkerchief in Court. So Formidable was his Advocacy that Insurance Companies and Newspapers Usually Settled Up on Hearing that the Tearful Performer had been retained. One Fine Day, when his Engagements were Many, the Tearful Performer Rushed into Court Just in Time to Make the Final Speech for the Plaintiff in an Accident Case. He had not Heard Any of the Evidence, and his Agitated Junior only had Time to Inform him that the Plaintiff had Admitted in Cross-Examination a Conviction for Perjury at the Old Bailey Some Years Ago. The Tearful Performer was Undisturbed. He Begged the Jury not to allow themselves to be Misled by any Red Herring which his Learned Friend might Seek to Draw across the Track. He Reminded them that the

Question was whether the Defendant's Driver had been Negligent, and not whether the Plaintiff's Evidence on Another and a Different Occasion had, or had not, been Accepted. The Tearful Performer then Asked the Jury what they Thought of a Case which had to be Bolstered up by Deplorable Irrelevancies, and Invited them to Say that it was a Cruel Thing to Drag Out of a Crippled Man a Story which Must have Caused the Utmost Pain and Distress to his Innocent Wife and Children. And (Praying the Conviction in Aid) the Tearful Performer Enquired what was Better Calculated to Make a Man Absolutely Accurate in the Witness-Box for All Time than a Sentence of Imprisonment for Perjury. By the Time he had Got to the Bit about Praying the Conviction in Aid, the Tearful Performer was so Choked with Emotion that he could Hardly Proceed with his Address. And as at that Moment his Clerk Told him he was Wanted in Another Court he Left the Matter there. Was the Speech of the Tearful Performer a Success? It was. The Jury Gave the Plaintiff such Enormous Damages that the Tearful Performer Advised him to Accept Half the Amount rather than Run the Risk of a New Trial being Ordered.

Moral.—*Tears bring relief.*

MR. SLASHER, MR. JUSTICE FOOZLE, AND
THE HALVED SEVENTEENTH

118

MR. SLASHER, MR. JUSTICE FOOZLE,
AND THE HALVED SEVENTEENTH

ᔓ

MR. SLASHER, of Plum Tree Court, was a Promising Advocate and an Admirable Golfer. His Handicap was Four. Mr. Justice Foozle, though a Profound Lawyer, was an Indifferent Performer at the Royal and Ancient Game. He had Taken to Athletics Late in Life. His Handicap of Twenty-Four Seldom Enabled him to Secure a Victory. One Easter at the Annual Bench and Bar Tournament, Mr. Slasher Found himself Drawn as the Opponent of Foozle, J. The Committee, he was Informed, Considered that he Ought to Concede to the Learned Judge a Stroke a Hole. Mr. Slasher was Undismayed by the Burden so Put upon him. Indeed, he Backed himself to Win, Laying as Much as Three to One with Various Learned Friends. The Day of the Contest Arrived. Mr. Slasher, being a Tactful Person, Held himself in Reserve. He Permitted Mr. Justice Foozle to Win Eight of the first Sixteen Holes, Confident that he could Get the Seventeenth and Eighteenth on his Head. Thus he would Inflict on Foozle, J., a Defeat which Carried with it no Humiliation. But at the Short Seventeenth an Unexpected Event Occurred. Foozle, J., was on the Extreme Edge of the Green with his Third. Mr. Slasher, as the Result of a Beautiful Iron Shot, Laid his Ball Dead with his Second. As the

Learned Judge's Ball was a Good Three Yards from the Pin it was Clear that only a Miracle could Save him. After Examining the Position Closely, Mr. Justice Foozle, with a Look of Extreme Innocence, Uttered the Word "Halved" and Picked up his Ball. Mr. Slasher was so Taken Aback by the Tactics of Foozle, J., that he Topped his Drive to the Eighteenth, Sliced into the Rough with his Second, Was out of Bounds with his Third, and Ultimately was Down in Nine. Whereas Mr. Justice Foozle, Greatly Heartened by the Halved Seventeenth, Did a Magnificent Five and Won the Match. The Result of it all was that Mr. Slasher Lost Twenty Odd Pounds that he could Ill Afford. Did Foozle, J., Exhibit Any Remorse? None whatever. And when Mr. Slasher next Appeared in Judge's Chambers, Mr. Justice Foozle Addressed him as "Mr. Tompkins," and Ordered him to Pay the Costs in Any Event.

Moral.—*Play Up*.

THE MATURE JUNIOR AND THE
DILIGENT PUPIL

THE MATURE JUNIOR AND THE
DILIGENT PUPIL

∽

AMATURE Junior had a Diligent Pupil who
Wanted to Know All about Everything. So
Insatiable was his Thirst for Knowledge that
the Patience of the Mature Junior was Sorely Tried.
From Morning till Night the Diligent Pupil Plied
him with Questions about Practice and Procedure,
Professional Etiquette, Case-Law and Legal Biography till his Head Span. The Time Came when
the Mature Junior Felt he Could not Stand It Much
Longer. One Fine Day the Mature Junior was Unex-
pectedly Deserted by his Leader at a Critical Moment.
The Case had Taken a Nasty Turn and the Leader
Suddenly Remembered that he had to Send a Tele-
gram. The Diligent Pupil (who was Sitting Behind
the Mature Junior) Asked him whether the Leader
would Soon Come Back, and Expressed the View
that the Judge Seemed to be Rather Against them.
He also Begged to be Told the Name of the Leader on
the Other Side. When the Mature Junior was about
to Address the Jury the Diligent Pupil Wanted to
Know why the Judge was Wearing Violet Robes.
He Thought the Mature Junior had Told him they
were Never Worn in Jury Cases. The Case was
Part Heard when the Court Rose and the Mature
Junior was Feeling Distinctly Irritable. In Particular he was Worried about his Engagements for the

Following Day. As Soon as he Got Back to his Chambers the Diligent Pupil Asked him when his Case would be Reached in the Court of Appeal, what he Would Do if it Came on before the Part-Heard Case was Finished, and Whether the Diligent Pupil could Join more than one Circuit. The Mature Junior Saw Red, and Struck the Diligent Pupil a Heavy Blow with a Blunt Instrument, to wit, the Poker. When the Diligent Pupil had Recovered Consciousness the Mature Junior Ordered him, on Pain of Death, never to Reappear in his Chambers.

Moral.—*Suffer Pupils Gladly.*

THE JUNIOR WHO LUNCHED AT THE CLUB,
THE BALD OLD GENTLEMAN, AND
THE HEAVY BRIEF

THE JUNIOR WHO LUNCHED AT THE CLUB, THE BALD OLD GENTLEMAN, AND THE HEAVY BRIEF

∽

A JUNIOR sat in his Chambers after Lunching at the Club. There was a Good Fire, and the Arm-Chair was Comfortable. Suddenly a Bald Old Gentleman of Dignified Appearance Stood before him. He Carried a Black Bag. Having Wished the Junior a Good Afternoon he Observed that he was Leaving a Brief for him, and that he would Like to Tell him Something about the Case. It was a Big Affair in the Commercial Court, and there would be Three Leaders who had all Pledged their Word to be Present throughout the Hearing. "You will have," the Bald Old Gentleman Proceeded, "another Junior with you. He has already Settled the Pleadings." "The Case," he Proceeded, "must Last for at Least Three Weeks, and it is bound to Go to the Court of Appeal and the House of Lords. And when the Questions of Principle have been Decided there will be Further Heavy Litigation hereafter." The Bald Old Gentleman then Drew Out his Fountain-Pen and a Cheque-Book, and Said that the Clients Wished that all the Brief-Fees should be Paid forthwith. Just as he was Asking the Junior whether he could Tell him what was Two-Thirds of Two Thousand Five Hundred Guineas, the Clerk Crashed into the Room and Woke the Junior up.

The Clerk Wished to Remind the Junior that the Petty-Cash was Exhausted, and that if he Wanted to be in Time for the County Court Case To-morrow Morning he would have to Catch the Eight Twenty-Two at Fenchurch Street. The Junior Swore Horribly and, Composing himself once more to Slumber, Sought to Recapture this Delicious Dream.

Moral.—*Dormientibus Felicitas Venit.*

BEEFY THOMAS AND ANÆMIC HENRY

BEEFY THOMAS AND ANÆMIC HENRY

THOMAS and Henry were Barristers-at-Law who Shared Chambers in the Temple. Thomas was of Beefy Build but Mediocre Intelligence. Henry was an Anæmic and Brainy Person of Insignificant Appearance. When the European War Broke Out, Anæmic Henry and Beefy Thomas, being of Military Age, Determined to Do their Bit. Anæmic Henry Joined Up, and Proceeded to Flanders, Gallipoli, and Mesopotamia, where he was Gassed, Shelled, Machine-Gunned, Frozen, and Baked during the Ensuing Three Years. Beefy Thomas was Less Precipitate. He Stayed at Home and Made Recruiting Speeches, which were so Manly and Eloquent that Hundreds Flocked to the Colours. The Authorities Soon Rewarded him with the Position of Legal Adviser to the Margarine and Fatty Extracts Ministry. As Legal Adviser, Beefy Thomas Exhibited Great Industry in Drafting Orders-in-Council. After an Unsuccessful Endeavour to Explain to a Law-Officer the Meaning of Margarine Order No. 643, his Further Promotion was Decided upon. Beefy Thomas Became Deputy-Assistant-Supervisor of the Naval and Military Stores (Detraining and Dispatch) Department, with the Temporary Rank of Brigadier-General, and Went to France. For Two Years he Discharged his Duties at Boulogne-Sur-Mer with Quiet Efficiency. He Looked Very Fine in his

Uniform and Decorations. On One Occasion he had the Pleasure of Doing Anæmic Henry a Service. Anæmic Henry was Returning to the Front, and Beefy Thomas Found him an Empty Cattle-Truck to Travel in. When the War Came to an End Beefy Thomas Stood for Parliament. He Got in on his Head. Anæmic Henry went Back to the Temple in a C.3 State of Health. He Found that his Clients had Forgotten him. But Happily the Influence of Beefy Thomas was able to Secure for Anæmic Henry the Attorney-Generalship of the Lower Cannibal Islands, and if Anæmic Henry Can Stand the Climate he will Become Chief Justice in Due Course.

Moral.—*Be Brave.*

YOUNG MR. TITTLEBAT, THE LEADING
SOLICITOR, AND THE UNEXPECTED
VICTORY

YOUNG MR. TITTLEBAT, THE LEADING SOLICITOR, AND THE UNEXPECTED VICTORY

୶

YOUNG Mr. Tittlebat was Visited One Evening in his Chambers by a Leading Solicitor. He Wanted Mr. Tittlebat to Take a Brief in a Case which was to be Heard the Next Day. But as the Defendant (for whom Mr. Tittlebat was to Appear) had no Defence, would Mr. Tittlebat Accept a Fee of One Guinea? Mr. Tittlebat, who had Hitherto been Unemployed, Gladly Assented to this Proposal. On Perusing the Papers Mr. Tittlebat (who was not without Intelligence) Detected a Flaw in the Plaintiff's Armour. And, Sure Enough, on the Morrow Mr. Tittlebat Obtained Judgment, with Costs, for the Astonished Defendant. When the Case was Over there was a Scene of Great Enthusiasm in the Corridor, and both the Defendant and the Leading Solicitor Insisted upon Entertaining Mr. Tittlebat at Luncheon. The Leading Solicitor Asked Mr. Tittlebat which Circuit he Went, and whether he had Any Objection to Parliamentary Work. And he Twice took a Note of Mr. Tittlebat's Temple Address. At a Late Hour Mr. Tittlebat Returned to Chambers, Flushed with Victory and Refreshments, Satisfied that his Career was Made. Twenty Years Elapsed and Mr. Tittlebat, now a Bald and Prosperous Person, Received a Visit from the Leading Solicitor.

He did not Bring a Brief with him this Time, but Said he had Just Looked In to Ask Mr. Tittlebat Whether he Remembered that Glorious Victory of Twenty Years Ago. The Leading Solicitor Added that he had Often Wondered how Mr. Tittlebat was Getting On.

Moral.—*Gratitude takes Many Forms.*

THE AUSTRALIAN PLUTOCRAT,
THE MILLIONAIRE'S NEPHEW, AND
THE OLD BAILEY PRACTITIONER

THE AUSTRALIAN PLUTOCRAT, THE MILLIONAIRE'S NEPHEW, AND THE OLD BAILEY PRACTITIONER

∽

ONE Evening an Old Bailey Practitioner was Seated in the Splendid Lounge of the Cosmopolitan Hotel, Smoking an After-Dinner Cigar and Watching the Giddy Throng about him. To his Great Amusement a Gentleman with an Australian Intonation Professed to Recognise him as a Fellow-Traveller on the *Gigantic*. The Old Bailey Practitioner, Anticipating Developments, Encouraged the Stranger to Converse. It Seemed that he was a Wealthy Piano-Manufacturer from Wagga-Wagga Enjoying a Well-Earned Holiday. Before Long, Another Gentleman (with a Cork Accent) Asked whether he might Join them. He was, it Appeared, in a Great Difficulty. His Uncle, a Millionaire in Chicago, had Left him $10,000 to Distribute in Charity, and he Badly Wanted Advice as to the Legal Formalities to be Observed by those who Wished to Present Large Sums to Hospitals. He was Over-joyed to Discover that the Old Bailey Practitioner was a Lawyer; and when the Old Bailey Practitioner (more Amused than ever) Consented to Distribute 500*l.* on his behalf, the Millionaire's Nephew did not Know how to Express his Gratitude. He Said he had the 500*l.* in his Wallet and was Ready to Hand it Over Forthwith. The Australian Plutocrat then

Suggested that the Confidence which Each Reposed in the Other would be Greatly Strengthened if the Old Bailey Practitioner were to Entrust the Millionaire's Nephew with his Purse. The Old Bailey Practitioner (Hardly Able to Restrain his Laughter) said he would Gladly Do So. The Exchange was Quickly Effected and the Australian Plutocrat and the Millionaire's Nephew Declared they would be Back in a Quarter of an Hour. Before they were Fifty Yards from the Hotel the Old Bailey Practitioner had Handed them over to an Intelligent Constable on the Charge of Obtaining Money by means of the Confidence Trick. The Next Day the Old Bailey Practitioner had Two Nasty Shocks. First, the Police Informed him that the Wallet Really Contained 500*l.* Secondly, the Australian Plutocrat and the Millionaire's Nephew Loudly Protested that the Old Bailey Practitioner was the Trickster, and that he had Induced them to Take his Purse in Exchange for the Wallet. And they Pointed Out that whereas their Statement about the Wallet was perfectly True, the Cash in the Purse of the Old Bailey Practitioner Totalled Nine Shillings and Ten Pence in Silver and Bronze. The Magistrate Said that the Old Bailey Practitioner was Lucky not to be in the Dock, and Discharged the Accused. As they Left the Court they Winked in a Knowing Fashion at the Prosecutor. The Old Bailey Practitioner Bitterly Regretted his Hasty Action. It was now Clear to him that this was the Confidence Trick in a New Form. His Anguish was Increased by a Fierce Letter from an Eminent Firm Threatening an Action for Malicious Prosecu-

tion.   The End of it was that the Old Bailey Practitioner had to Pay 100*l.* to the Australian Plutocrat,
the Same Amount to the Millionaire's Nephew, and
50*l.* to the Eminent Firm for their Agreed Costs.

Moral.—*Festina Lente.*

THE JUDGE OF ASSIZE AND THE
OLD SCHOOL FRIEND

THE JUDGE OF ASSIZE AND THE OLD SCHOOL FRIEND

〜

A JUDGE of Assize, when his Circuit Labours were Concluded, Asked the Governor of the Prison to Show him Over his Establishment. When they Got to the Exercise Yard the Judge of Assize, rather to his Dismay, Recognised an Old School Friend. The Old School Friend had been a Financier and was now Taking the Consequences. Having Obtained Permission to do so, the Judge of Assize Addressed the Old School Friend. Assuming an Expression of Melancholy Sympathy, he Expressed a Hope that the Old School Friend was Bearing Up. The Old School Friend Assured him that he was Exceedingly Well. In Fact, he had never been so Well in his Life. He had Done Five Years, and so would be Out in a Few Months. His Future, he was Glad to Say, was Assured, as he had Taken the Precaution of Making a Handsome Settlement on his Wife before the Crash. He Hoped the Judge of Assize would Visit them at their Villa in the South of France if he Happened to be in Those Parts during the Winter. The Old School Friend then Begged to be Informed as to the Health and Happiness of the Judge of Assize. The Latter Sadly Replied that he was Gouty and Rheumatic, Overworked, and still Separated from his Pension by a Period of Nine Years. His Children, moreover, had Given him a Great Deal of Trouble and Anxiety, and he hadn't Saved a Bob. The Old School Friend said it was Too Bad, and Opined that there was a Great Deal to be said for a Financial Career.

Moral.—*There are Two Sides to Every Question.*

THE EMERITUS PROFESSOR OF INTERNATIONAL
LAW AND THE POLICE COURT BRIEF

THE EMERITUS PROFESSOR OF
INTERNATIONAL LAW AND THE
POLICE COURT BRIEF

✍

THERE was once an Emeritus Professor of International Law. His Learning was Stupendous. He was a D.C.L. and LL.D. Many Times Over. The Public Orators of Oxford, Cambridge, Durham, Sheffield, Birmingham, and Aberystwyth (to Mention only a Few) had Striven in Their Best Latin to do Justice to his Erudition when he Presented himself to Receive their Honorary Degrees. One of them Enquired "*Quae Regio Terrae Vestri Non Plena Laboris?*" Another Greeted him as "*Scientiae Pene Novae Inclytus Propugnator.*" A Third Remarked that he was "*Maxime Egregius Philosophus.*" A Fourth that he was "*Spectatissimus Doctor.*" And a Fifth, who Proclaimed him to be "*Juris Inter Omnes Nationes Observandi Peritissimus,*" was Thought to have Hit the Right Nail on the Head. Four Massive Tomes which the Emeritus Professor had Compiled Entitled "Peace and War," "the Doctrine of *Renvoi,*" "The Three-Mile Limit," and "The Declaration of Paris, Its Genesis and Implications," had been Translated into French, German, Spanish, Russian, Urdu, and Chinese. The Emeritus Professor had a Considerable Beard, Large Spectacles, a Weak Voice and Flat Feet.

When he was at the Height of his Fame it

Happened that the Private Secretary of the Baratarian Ambassador, being Short of Cash, Endeavoured to Stabilise his Finances by Means of a Stumer Cheque and so Placed himself within the Grip of the Law. An Intelligent Solicitor, Hastily Summoned to the Embassy, Advised that the Emeritus Professor should be Retained At Once to Defend the Private Secretary. It was Clearly a Case, he said, in which the Privilege of Exterritoriality should be Invoked, and None but the Emeritus Professor could Deal Adequately with that Difficult Topic.

The Emeritus Professor, Duly Briefed, Proceeded to the Mulberry Street Police Court. With him he Took some Two Dozen Volumes of Text-books and Reports.

When the Emeritus Professor Seated himself in the Pen Provided for Counsel the Dock was already Occupied. The Magistrate Asked the Emeritus Professor whether he Appeared for the Accused. He Replied in the Affirmative and Began his Discourse.

The Emeritus Professor Led Off with a Few Pages of *Westlake* and *Hall*, and then, Warming to his Work, Read Several Cogent Passages, from *Grotius*, *Puffendorf*, and *Bynkershoek*. He Dwelt, in Particular, on the Second Half of Chapter XIII. (*"De Foro Legatorum"*) of the last-named Authority. The Magistrate Appeared to the Emeritus Professor to be both Obtuse and Impolite. He Repeatedly Tried to Stop the Emeritus Professor's Argument, and said, More than Once, that he Could not Hear or Understand what the Emeritus Professor was Saying. After Forty-Five Minutes the Magistrate Ordered the

Emeritus Professor to Sit Down. The Emeritus Professor (who by this Time was Referring the Magistrate to Bergbohn's *Staats-Verträge Und Gesetze als Quellen des Volkerrechts*) went on Unmoved. When the Emeritus Professor at last Resumed his Seat, after Reading All the Judgments in *The "Parlement Belge*,"[1] he had been Speaking for an Hour and a Half, and the Magistrate was Foaming at the Mouth. To the Amazement of the Emeritus Professor the Magistrate Told the Defendant that he had Aggravated his Offence by Employing a Lunatic to Defend him, and Sent him to Prison for a Month. It was not till the Next Day that the Emeritus Professor Realised that he had Gone to the Wrong Police Court and that the Defendant on whose Behalf he had Delivered his Oration was an Italian Costermonger who had Obstructed the Traffic with his Barrow and Assaulted the Police.

Moral.—*Choose Your Tribunal Wisely.*

[1] 4 P.D. 129; 5 P.D. 197.

MR. FLEDGLING AND THE APPLICATION FOR
PARTICULARS OF THE STATEMENT OF CLAIM

MR. FLEDGLING AND THE APPLICATION
FOR PARTICULARS OF THE STATEMENT
OF CLAIM

༄

MR. FLEDGLING was Filled with Wild Elation when his First Job Turned Up. It was a Summons in the King's Bench Division. He was to Appear at One-Thirty before a Master of the Supreme Court of Judicature and Apply for Particulars of the Statement of Claim. With regard to Paragraph 1 he was to Insist upon Precise Information as to whether the Alleged Agreement was Oral or in Writing, and, if the Latter, as to the Document or Documents Purporting to Contain it. So far as Paragraph 3 was Concerned, he was to Press for Further Details as to the Alleged Defects in the Said Goods. And the Vagueness of Paragraph 4, he Gathered, Necessitated a Closer Definition of the Loss and Damage Alleged to have been Suffered by the Plaintiff. Two Sleepless Nights were Succeeded by Two Days of Anxious Research, and on the Third Day Mr. Fledgling Tottered to the Field of Battle, Carrying his Books of Reference in a Blue Bag. He Arrived in the Bear-Garden to Find his Elderly Opponent already on the Spot. Mr. Fledgling Noted with Satisfaction that the Elderly Opponent Seemed to be Troubled at the Sight of his Authorities. Whilst Waiting for the Door of the Master's Room to be Flung Open Mr. Fledgling Quietly Went over the

Heads of his Arguments. He was Glad to Find that he was Quite Calm. At last the Dread Moment Arrived and Mr. Fledgling was Standing before the Master with his Elderly Opponent at his Side. The Elderly Opponent said "Good Morning, Master," in a Somewhat Familiar Fashion, but the Master, though rather Formidable in Appearance, did not Appear to Mind. While Mr. Fledgling was Explaining to the Master in a Shaky Voice the Terms of the Order and Rule under which the Application was being Made, the Elderly Opponent said he was Quite Ready to give the Particulars. The Master Observed "All Right" and Wrote a Few Words in a Deplorable Hand on the Summons. Mr. Fledgling Could hardly Believe his Ears. He had Won, Hands Down. When he Got Home that Evening Mr. Fledgling Told his People all about it. They Gathered that Mr. Fledgling had Gone Through a Trying Ordeal; that it had been a Ding-Dong Thing; and that, but for the Grim Determination of Mr. Fledgling and his Refusal to be Browbeaten by the Master or his Elderly Opponent, the Day would have been Lost.

Moral.—*Be Thorough.*

THE PROUD PARENT WHO DID HIS
BEST FOR ALFRED

THE PROUD PARENT WHO DID HIS
BEST FOR ALFRED

∽

A PROUD PARENT was Determined that his Son Alfred should Succeed at the Bar. He therefore Consulted the Wisest of his Friends upon the All-important Question of how Alfred should be Trained to this End. They All Advised him Fully. And the Proud Parent Followed their Advice. Alfred Began by Doing three Trips on a Tramp Steamer in the Mediterranean; then he Went to Learn Colloquial French in the Cathedral City of Tours (because the Touraine Accent is so Perfect); and thereafter he Acquired Conversational German at Bonn (where the University Discipline is so Helpful to the Young). Alfred next Proceeded to Pick Up Business Methods in a Big Commercial House. Four Years having thus Sped by, Alfred did Twelve Months with a City Solicitor, a Second Twelve Months in the Chambers of a Conveyancer in Lincoln's Inn, and a Third Twelve Months in those of a Stuff-gownsman in the Temple. All would, no doubt, have been Well with Alfred's Career at the Bar had he been Able to Get Through the Examination in Roman Law. But, despite the Persistent Efforts of the Most Accomplished Coaches, he could not Perform this Feat. Driven to Select an Alternative Occupation for Alfred, the Proud Parent Answered a Number of Advertisements in the Public Journals; and Alfred is now in Charge of a Chicken Farm near Eye, in the County of Suffolk, where he also Breeds Angora Rabbits.

Moral.—*Consult Your Friends.*

THE IDLE APPRENTICE AND THE
INDUSTRIOUS DITTO

THE IDLE APPRENTICE AND THE
INDUSTRIOUS DITTO

∽

TWO Apprentices to the Law Shared Chambers together. The One was Idle; the Other was Industrious. The Latter Rose Early, Abstained from Strong Drink and Tobacco, Read the Law Reports, Attended Debating Societies, and Held Briefs for his Learned Friends. The Former Stayed in Bed till Mid-day, Arrived at Chambers at One, Lunched from Two to Four, Borrowed Sums of Money from his Acquaintances, Consumed Considerable Quantities of Alcohol between his Abundant Meals, and Devoted his Spare Time to Studying the Sporting Papers and Spotting Winners. The Industrious Apprentice was Ultimately Rewarded for his Virtuous Conduct. After Twenty-Three Years of Unrequited Toil, he Attracted the Favourable Notice of a Silk, who Gave him a Room and a Hundred a Year for Noting his Briefs. Far Different was the Fate of the Idle Apprentice. He Made Friends with a Moneyed Person, Got into Polite Society, Married a Charming Wife, and is now the Managing Director of the Amalgamated Continental & Asiatic Tea, Rubber, Tin & Indigo Syndicate, Limited, with an Annual Salary of Twelve Thousand Pounds.

Moral.—*Work Hard.*

THE YOUNG SOLICITOR AND THE
SAGACIOUS OLD BUFFER

THE YOUNG SOLICITOR AND THE
SAGACIOUS OLD BUFFER

∾

THERE was Once a Young Solicitor who Began to Fear that he would Never Get On. He Worked Hard, but, Try as he Might, he Could not Learn any Law. Persons who Sought his Advice were Clearly Disappointed when the Young Solicitor Told them he would Look it Up and Let Them Know To-morrow. The Young Solicitor therefore Determined to Consult a Sagacious Old Buffer whose Name was a Household Word in the Profession. The Street in which the Old Buffer's Palatial Offices were Situate was Blocked from Morning to Night by the Rolls-Royces of the Bankers, Ladies in Distress, Shipowners, Jockeys, and Dignitaries of the Church who Desired his Assistance. The Old Buffer Made them Pay through the Nose, but they all Went Away Satisfied that they had Received Good Value for their Money. Nor was this Surprising. For the Old Buffer Possessed both a Dignified Appearance and a Sympathetic Manner, and was Never at a Loss when a Complicated Legal Problem had to be Solved. The Old Buffer Always Remembered that Baron Parke, or Cairns, or Blackburn had Discussed the Topic in an Old Case. He would then Tell his Clerk to Bring him "2 Meeson & Welsby," "6 Term Reports," or "4 Barnewall & Cresswell";

and, Lo and Behold, the Volume was Sure to Contain Something Apposite and Helpful. When the Client Expressed his Astonishment at the Old Buffer's Amazing Feat of Memory he would Smile Quietly and Say it was Nothing. The Old Buffer Received the Young Solicitor with the Utmost Courtesy and Listened Attentively to his Story. When he had Finished, the Old Buffer Locked the Door and Whispered to the Young Solicitor that, if he would Swear Never to Divulge it to a Soul, he would Impart to him the Secret of his Success. "Like you," said the Old Buffer, with Tears in his Eyes, "I Knew no Law and Could not Learn any of the Beastly Stuff. But One Day I found on a Railway Book-Stall an Admirable Work Entitled 'Law for the Million.' It Cost Two Shillings and Six Pence. I Saw at once that it was a Mine of Useful Information. I Purchased Three Copies and had them Rebound. One is Called '2 Meeson & Welsby,' Another is '6 Term Reports,' and the Third is '4 Barnewell & Cresswell." When I am Asked to Advise about a Charter Party, a Bill of Sale, a Gambling Debt, or a Faculty I Turn Up the Appropriate Heading with the Happiest Results. I Strongly Advise You to Do the Same. The Book is Arranged Alphabetically," the Old Buffer Concluded, "so that it is Quite Easy to Find what you Want."

The Young Solicitor Thanked the Old Buffer Warmly and Withdrew.

Within Five Years the Young Solicitor was a Knight, a Member of Parliament, the Owner of Three Cars, and a Resident in Carlton House Terrace. And if the Old Buffer had not Retired from Practice meanwhile (with a Cool Quarter of a Million) the Young Solicitor would Assuredly have Cut him Out.

Moral.—*Bind Your Books Carefully.*

THE JUDGE WHOSE APPEARANCE
TERRIFIED THE PUBLIC

THE JUDGE WHOSE APPEARANCE
TERRIFIED THE PUBLIC

∽

ON the Opening Day of the Michaelmas Sittings no Figure in the Judicial Procession was More Awe-Inspiring than that of Mr. Justice Mildew. His Lordship's Grim Countenance Struck Terror into All Beholders. As he Walked up the Central Hall of the Royal Courts of Justice, Barristers, Managing Clerks, Office-Boys, and Flappers Shook in their Shoes and Thanked their Stars they were not Standing before him in the Dock. It was Clear to All of them that Mr. Justice Mildew had Something of Grave Importance on his Mind, and that he was Thinking Deeply. They were Right. Mr. Justice Mildew was Reflecting, as the Procession Started, that the Champagne at the Lord Chancellor's Breakfast was (for a Light Wine) Uncommonly Good, that it was a Pity he had not Taken a Third Glass, and that he had Better Find Out Where it Came From before he went Circuit. Half-way up the Hall, Mr. Justice Mildew was Wondering whether the Port at Forty-Two Shillings (of which a Considerable Quantity had been Left Over from the Last Circuit) would be Good Enough for the Bar when they Came to Dinner, and was Sincerely Hoping that his Brother Judge would be a Bit more Lively than his Colleague at the Recent Assizes. And during the last Five Yards, when his Expression became Particularly

Fierce, Mr. Justice Mildew was Internally Debating whether he should Purchase a "Wilfred" or a "Gollywog" for his Youngest Grand-Daughter, and Trying Hard to Remember whether her Birthday was on Tuesday or Wednesday.

Moral.—*Look Impressive*.

MR. BUFFLE, THE YOUNG PERSON, AND
THE SEEDY INDIVIDUAL

MR. BUFFLE, THE YOUNG PERSON, AND THE SEEDY INDIVIDUAL

∽

MR. BUFFLE was a Barrister of Thirty Years'
Standing, a Bencher of his Inn, and a
Devoted Husband and Father. One Saturday Afternoon Mr. Buffle Sat in his Chambers Working Hard on the Proof-Sheets of the Second Edition
of his Invaluable Work, "The Law Relating to
Vaccination."

At Five O'Clock, Feeling somewhat Exhausted, he
Refreshed himself with a Cup of Tea. It then
Occurred to him that it would be Pleasant to Take a
Stroll in the Beautiful Garden of the Outer Temple
and there Smoke a Cigarette. Mr. Buffle Made for
the Seat under the Catalpa Tree (his Usual Resting-
Place), and Found to his Surprise, that it was Already
Occupied by a Young Person. Mr. Buffle Surmised
that she was a Nursery-Maid, for she was Accompanied by a Perambulator. It also Struck him that
her Appearance was Quite Agreeable. She Wore a
Small Black Bonnet, with Strings Tied in a Bow under
her Chin, a Lilac Print Dress with Spots, and a Very
Becoming Sort of Black Mantle. Mr. Buffle further
Noticed that the Young Person Seemed to be in
Distress; and, as he Drew Near, a Distinct Sob Broke
upon his Ear. Though Elderly, Mr. Buffle was Full
of Gallantry. Seating himself beside the Young Person, he Begged her to Tell him whether he could be

of Any Assistance. The Young Person Replied that she had Just had a Nasty Accident. Which a Splinter from the Pram had Run into her Finger, and the Pain was Somethink Awful, and she didn't Know, she was Sure, how she could Put Up with it Much Longer, and did Mr. Buffle Think he could Find a Doctor? Mr. Buffle Said a Few Comforting Words and Assured the Young Person that he could Deal with the Splinter himself. The Young Person, Still Sobbing, Extended a Plump Hand, and Mr. Buffle without any Difficulty Drew Out the Offending Particle. So Simple was the Operation that Mr. Buffle Rather Wondered why the Young Person had not Performed it herself. After a Little Chat, Mr. Buffle Withdrew to his Chambers and Resumed his Labours. This was Positively All that Happened.

Three Days later a Seedy Individual Waited upon Mr. Buffle in his Chambers. He Explained that he was a Professional Photographer, and was Anxious to Show Mr. Buffle his Collection of Views of the Temple. Mr. Buffle (Feeling a Little Troubled) said he would Greatly Like to See them. The Seedy Individual thereupon Displayed Several Photographs. There was One of Lamb Building, Another of the Middle Temple Hall, a Third of Pump Court, and a Fourth of the Catalpa Tree, with a Close-Up of Mr. Buffle and the Young Person in the Foreground. The Picture had been Taken at a Moment when the Young Person was Looking Exceedingly Coy. Mr. Buffle Looked at the Seedy Individual and the Seedy Individual Looked at Mr. Buffle. After a Pause, Mr. Buffle said he Admired the Photograph of the Catalpa

168

Tree Enormously, and Asked whether he could Buy not only the Photograph but the Film. The Seedy Individual Agreed that the Photograph of the Catalpa Tree was one of his Most Successful Efforts, but said he was Afraid he could not Part with the Film as he had Contracted to Sell the Copyright to a Newspaper Syndicate. But if Mr. Buffle Thought it was Worth 50*l.* (as he, the Seedy Individual, did) he would Brave the Indignation of the Newspaper Syndicate and Face any Legal Proceedings they might Take. Did Mr. Buffle Hesitate? Not for a Moment. At the Request of the Seedy Individual he Made the Cheque an Open One. Directly the Seedy Individual had Departed, Mr. Buffle Tore the Photograph and the Film into a Thousand Fragments and Flung them Out of the Window. As he did so, he Observed the Seedy Individual and the Young Person in Animated Conversation Hurrying Together in the Direction of the Bank.

Moral.—*Send for the Doctor.*

THE TWO TEMPLARS AND THE LONG
VACATION

THE TWO TEMPLARS AND THE
LONG VACATION

〜

TWO Templars Met at the Railway Station on their Return from the Long Vacation. The First Templar had been Shooting and Fishing in Scotland. The Second Templar had been Doing the Cathedrals of France and Italy. Each Begged the Other to Give a Full Account of his Adventures. The First Templar at once Became Eloquent about the Wildness of the Birds, the Heavy Cost of Beaters, and the Discomforts of the Inn to which he had been Recommended. He also Gave a Spirited Account of the Salmon he had Lost on the 3rd September, and the Thirty-Two Pounder he had Landed with a Light Trout Rod only Last Week. While the First Templar was Imparting this Information, the Second Templar was Explaining what a Rough Crossing his Party had on the 15th August, how Impressed he was with Chartres, what Gigantic Railway Reforms had been Carried through by Mussolini, how much he Preferred Assisi to Florence, and how his Wife's Niece had Unfortunately Contracted Measles in Genoa. As Neither of them Heard what the Other was Talking about, Both Templars Enjoyed their Chat Immensely. They Ultimately Parted with a Mutual Threat to Exchange Further and Better Particulars at a Later Date.

Moral.—*Don't Listen.*

THE CAUTIOUS SOLICITOR AND THE
CHINESE WITNESS

THE CAUTIOUS SOLICITOR AND THE
CHINESE WITNESS

∽

THERE was Once a Solicitor who was both Learned and Cautious. He never Allowed Himself to be Taken by Surprise; and he Invariably had his Tackle in Order. Whilst Preparing for the Trial of a Case of Great Importance, the Cautious Solicitor Suddenly Realised that Mr. Chi-Hung-Chang, the Principal Witness for his Client, was a Chinaman, and that he would have to be Sworn in Whatever might be the Appropriate Fashion. The Cautious Solicitor Made Anxious Enquiries and Gathered that Everything Depended on the Precise Place of Origin of Mr. Chi-Hung-Chang. It appeared that if he Came from the Northern Regions the Breaking of a Saucer was the Central Piece of Ritual; that if he was from Kwei Chow (or the Parts Adjacent thereto) he would Require a Lighted Candle which would be Blown Out at the Critical Moment; and that if he Happened to be a Native of Kwangsi he would not Deem himself Properly Sworn Unless and Until he had Sacrificed a White Cockerel in the Witness Box by Cutting its Throat with a Steel Knife. The Cautious Solicitor Took no Risks. He Procured a Dozen Porcelain Saucers of Various Sizes; a Box of Best Spermaceti Candles and a Box of Superior Quality Wax Ditto; and (from Leadenhall Market) a Cockerel of Unblemished Purity, which Spent the

Night in his Bed-Chamber and Inconvenienced him a Great Deal by Crowing Enthusiastically when the Dawn Broke.   On the Day Fixed for the Hearing of the Case the Cautious Solicitor Conveyed the Saucers, the Candles, and a Hamper Containing the White Cockerel to the Royal Courts of Justice, and there Awaited the Arrival of the Chinese Witness.   When Mr. Chi-Hung-Chang Turned Up he Told the Cautious Solicitor that he had to Catch the Three-Thirty as he was Going to the Grand National.   He also Remarked that *Silly Billy's* Price Seemed to have Shortened a Bit.   On the Cautious Solicitor Enquiring whether he would Prefer a Saucer, a Lighted Candle, or a Cockerel for the purposes of his Oath, Mr. Chi-Hung-Chang Said he had become a Bit of a Christian Scientist at Balliol, and Thought, on the Whole, he would Like to Affirm.   He then Asked the Cautious Solicitor to Come and Have a Drink.

Moral.—*Safety First.*

THE HABITUAL CRIMINAL AND THE
FIRST OFFENDER

THE HABITUAL CRIMINAL AND THE
FIRST OFFENDER

ᔪ

ONE Winter's Evening a "Black Maria" Containing a Habitual Criminal and a First Offender was Proceeding from the Old Bailey towards Wormwood Scrubs. The Habitual Criminal Wore a Cloth Cap, and his Lean Neck was Enveloped in a Handkerchief. The First Offender was Richly Dressed and of Portly Build. On his Head he Carried a Silk Hat, and his Overcoat, which was Lined with Mink, had Cuffs and Collar of the Same Admirable Fur. He was Smoking (by Permission of the Kindly Janitor) a Long and Fragrant Corona. Engaging the First Offender in Conversation, the Habitual Criminal Invited his Sympathy. This was his Tenth Conviction for Stealing and Receiving. He was to Do Seven Years' Penal Servitude and Five Years' Preventive Detention. The Habitual Criminal didn't Suppose he had Pinched Fifty Pounds' Worth from First to Last, and he was Jiggered if he hadn't Done Twenty-three Years altogether. Rotten Luck, the Habitual Criminal Called it. The First Offender Gently Demurred. "You Ought," he said, "to have Shown more Restraint. Habitual Criminality is not to be Tolerated. You have only Yourself to Thank for your Present Unhappy Situation." Throwing away his Cigar, the First Offender Proceeded: "Till a Year ago I Led a Blameless Life. Then, having Dissipated my Fortune in Riotous Living, I Started a Bucket-Shop. My Distinguished Appearance and Perfect Manners Enabled me to Rob Widows, Orphans, Clergymen, and University Professors of a Sum Approaching a Hundred Thousand Pounds; and, but for the Treachery of a Trusted Clerk, I should Still be Going Strong. The Judge who Tried me was a Man of Intelligence and Discernment. He very Properly Reminded me that the Disgrace I had Brought upon my Family, my Public School, and my University was in itself a Severe Punishment, and he Directed, as it was my First Offence, that I should be Imprisoned in the Second Division for Six Months." When the Kindly Janitor at last Succeeded in Detaching the Habitual Criminal from the First Offender, the Latter was Suffering from a Contused Eye and a Bleeding Nose. He had also Lost Two Front Teeth.

Moral.—*Be Merciful.*

THE ENTHUSIASTIC TOURISTS AND THE
CAPABLE GUIDE

THE ENTHUSIASTIC TOURISTS AND
THE CAPABLE GUIDE

⌒

THERE was Once a Party of Tourists who Hailed from Penn., Mass., Ga., Va., and Other Parts of the Land of Freedom and Prohibition. For a Crowded Fortnight they had been Absorbing the Beauties of the Continent and the British Isles. They had Done France, Stratford-on-Avon, Switzerland, the English Lakes and Cathedrals, Italy, the Flemish Battlefields, the Old Curiosity Shop, the Rhine, the Cheshire Cheese, and the Houses of Parliament. Now, Exhausted but Still Enthusiastic, they were Visiting the Temple. Happily they had Discovered a Capable Guide who could Show Them Everything that was worthy of Notice. First, the Capable Guide Took Them to the Law Courts where King Charles the First and "Bardell *v.* Pickwick" were Tried. Next he Pointed out Pump Court, where Charles Lamb Wrote the "Vicar of Wakefield." In the Garden of the Middle Temple They Saw the Exact Spot (now Occupied by a Concrete Vase Containing Geraniums) where Peace was Signed by King Richard the Third after the Battle of Evesham. And, Finally, he Led them to the Terrace Flanking the Inner Temple Hall, that they might Inspect the Very Rings to which Queen Elizabeth's Barge was Tied Up when Her Majesty Came to Dine with the Benchers of the Honourable Society. The Tourists with Tears of Gratitude in Their Eyes Heaped Largesse upon the Capable Guide.

Moral.—*Miss Nothing.*

THE CAREFUL JUNIOR AND THE
LEADING QUESTION

THE CAREFUL JUNIOR AND THE LEADING QUESTION

∽

A CAREFUL Junior Read his First Brief Again and Again till he Knew its Contents by Heart. He also Took the Precaution of Making Marginal Notes on the Various Proofs of the Witnesses. Thus, he Reasoned, he Could Bring Out the Evidence with Clarity and Effect if it Should Fall to his Lot to Examine Anybody in Chief. In Due Course the Leader Requested him to Take Alfred Grubby, the Independent Witness who had Viewed the Accident through the Window of the "Golden Unicorn." The Careful Junior Rose Trembling to his Feet. The Judge having Written Down the Name of the Witness, the Careful Junior, Reading from his Proof, Asked Alfred Grubby whether he Lived at 48, West Beaconsfield Rise, Tiptree Avenue, Clerkenwell. To the Careful Junior's Horror and Dismay the Witness Furiously Answered in the Negative. With a Cry of Distress the Careful Junior Sunk Unconscious to the Ground.

*　　*　　*　　*　　*

Three Days Later the Careful Junior was Aware of the Roar of Traffic, a Strong Smell of Cabbage, and the Angry Voices of Ministering Angels. He was in a Nursing Home. When the Careful Junior was Well Enough to Discuss Things he was Informed that Alfred Grubby's Furious Demeanour was Due to the Fact that he had Changed his Address after his Proof had been Taken.

Moral.—*Never Lead the Witness.*

THE ATHLETIC TEMPLARS WHO CLIMBED
THE DENT DU CHIEN

THE ATHLETIC TEMPLARS WHO
CLIMBED THE DENT DU CHIEN

∽

TWO Athletic Templars, the Long Vacation having Set In, Proceeded to the Alps as Soon as Their Respective Clerks Permitted them to Do So. For they were Keen Mountaineers. The Athletic Templars Rejoiced in their Freedom. They Laughed Aloud to Think that they had Left Behind them Solicitors, Briefs, Managing Clerks, Statements of Claim, and all the Paraphernalia of the Law. Arrived in Switzerland they Determined to Do, Once More, the Dear Old *Dent du Chien* by the Difficult Route. Across the Glacier, Leaving the *Cuisine du Cardinal* on the Left, Skirting the Moraine, and so Up the South-West Face. Did the Athletic Templars Enjoy the Climb? Of Course they Did. Did they Discuss the Beauty of the Eternal Peaks and the Glory of the Untrodden Snows? By No Means. For the First Four Hours they Debated whether the Judgment of the Court of Appeal in *Finkelheim* v. *Cohenstein* was Correct. Between the Hut and the Summit (Eight Hours) they Compared the Forensic Giants of the Past with the Pigmies of To-day. And During the

Descent (Six Hours) they Speculated as to the Judicial Changes which would Probably Take Place in the Month of October.

Moral.—*Have a Change*.

THE PRUDENT JUDGE AND THE STOUT USHER

THE PRUDENT JUDGE AND THE
STOUT USHER

∽

A GREAT Many Years Ago there Lived a Prudent Judge who Gave Universal Satisfaction. He was a Magnificent Lawyer. Legal Problems, however Complicated and Obscure, Never Caused him the Least Alarm. When the Doctrine of Equitable Subrogation was Mentioned, the Prudent Judge Brightened Up; and Such Topics as Anticipatory Breach of the Contract, the Provisions of the Harter Act, and Covenants Running with the Land Filled him with Joy. And, Wonderful to Relate, the Prudent Judge was Just as Good when it Came to a Question of Fact. As the Prudent Judge was a Bachelor and a Recluse, whose Practice at the Bar had been of the Stuffiest Description, there Appeared to be no Reason for this Phenomenon. But there was. Quite Early in his Judicial Career the Prudent Judge Detected that the Stout Usher in his Court was a Person of Great Good Sense. He therefore Summoned the Stout Usher to his Room, Pressed a Substantial Offering into his Hand, and Begged him to Abandon his Habit of Sleeping throughout the Proceedings, and to Pay Close Attention to the Evidence in Each Case. The Stout Usher Orally Agreed so to Do. Thereafter, when the Court Adjourned, the Prudent Judge would Ask the Stout Usher what he Thought about the Various Witnesses.

The Stout Usher was Never in Doubt. Sometimes he would Say that the Plaintiff was a Bit of a Liar; on Other Occasions he would Pick Out the Defendant as the Ananias of the Piece. Under the Able Guidance of the Stout Usher the Prudent Judge Never Went Wrong. And when At Last the Prudent Judge Retired, the Attorney-General, in a Valedictory Address, Dwelt upon his Uncanny Knowledge of Human Nature and his Marvellous Capacity for Distinguishing Truth from Fiction.

Moral.—*Ask the Usher.*

THE THREE ELDERLY JURISTS WHO MET
AFTER MANY YEARS

THE THREE ELDERLY JURISTS WHO
MET AFTER MANY YEARS

∽

THREE Elderly Jurists who had been Friends in
their Youth Met after Many Years. The
Career of Each had been Distinguished. The
First, whose Treatise on the "Laws and Customs of
the Khojas of the Himalaya Foot-Hills" (Based upon
the *Rajatarangini,* as Summarised by Abu'l Fazl in the
A'in-i-Akbari) is Quoted wherever the Kashmiri
Tongue is Spoken, had Held High Office in the East.
The Second, after Filling a Law-Officership with
Glittering Efficiency, had Climbed to the Topmost
Rung of the Legal Ladder at Home. The Third by
his Activities as a Parliamentary Draftsman had
Earned the Execrations of Several Generations of
Practising Lawyers. The Three Elderly Jurists
Agreed to Dine together and Collate their Varied
Experiences. They Duly Forgathered and Feasted.
Did they Discuss the Bureaucratic Tendencies of
Modern Legislation, the Hindu Law of Succession in
Zanzibar, or the Question of the Lord Chancellor's
Retiring Pension? Yes; for About Ten Minutes.
Then they Turned to Other Topics. With the
Whitebait they were Recalling Happy Evenings they
had Severally Spent in the Defunct Music-Halls of the
Metropolis. While Consuming the Joint they Com-
pared the Respective Charms of Miss Violet Cameron,
Miss Sylvia Grey and Miss Florence St. John. At

the Liqueur Stage of the Proceedings they were Endeavouring (with Some Success) to Reproduce the Words and the Melody of "Two Lovely Black Eyes." And when the Waiter came to Remind them that the Club Closed at One-Thirty, the Three Elderly Jurists were Cordially Agreeing that the Elegant Figure of Miss Nellie Farren in "Little Jack Sheppard" was the Most Precious of all their Memories.

Moral.—*Think Deeply*.

THE NERVOUS YOUTH WHO DID HIS BEST IN
THE CIRCUMSTANCES

THE NERVOUS YOUTH WHO DID
HIS BEST IN THE CIRCUMSTANCES

∽

A NERVOUS Youth, after Waiting and Watching for Many Months, Received his First County Court Brief. The Brief Conveyed to the Nervous Youth that he was to Appear for the Plaintiff, a Merchant in Whitechapel, who Considered that he was Entitled to Commission on the Sale of a Fish-and-Chips Establishment in the Mile End Road. It Seemed, also, that there was Some Doubt as to whether the Claim was Well-Founded, and that the Utmost Discretion in Handling the Plaintiff's Case would be Necessary if a Satisfactory Result was to be Secured. The Nervous Youth Repaired to the County Court, Determined to Do or Die. Owing to the Slow Progress of the Bus in which he Performed his Journey, the Nervous Youth Found, on his Arrival, that he had Kept the Court Waiting and that the Judge was Considerably Ruffled. Much Agitated by the Sharpness of the Judge's Comments, the Nervous Youth Rose to his Feet, to Find that he was Afflicted by a Sudden Condition of Aphasia and Loss of Memory. The Nervous Youth has no Distinct Recollection of what Happened Next; but from the Account of the Proceedings Given to Him by Bystanders, the Nervous Youth Understands that in Faltering Tones he Read Aloud to the Jury the First Two Pages of his Brief, and that, when he Came to the Bit which Recommended that he had Better not Call the Plaintiff, as he had Been in Prison More than Once, the Jury had Stopped the Case.

Moral.—*Take a Taxi.*

THE AGED JUDGE WHO REMEMBERED THE
PAST AND CHANGED HIS MIND

THE AGED JUDGE
WHO REMEMBERED THE PAST AND
CHANGED HIS MIND

ᶜᵔ

ONE Hot Afternoon an Aged Judge Found Himself Growing More and More Irritable as a Tedious Case Dragged On. The Youthful Counsel who Represented the Plaintiff was Nervous and Incoherent. Also he Entirely Declined to Shorten the Proceedings by Adopting the Various Hints offered by the Aged Judge. Stung to Madness, the Aged Judge was About to Let Himself Go and Tell the Youthful Counsel Exactly what he Thought about him, when he Suddenly Remembered an Incident of the Past. The Aged Judge Recalled the Occasion, Fifty Years Ago, when he Held his First Brief; the Savage Appearance of the Judge; his own Terror; his Rage and Humiliation when the Judge Informed him that he didn't Know his Business; the Sleepless Night which Followed; and the Misery of the Lady of his Choice when he Told her all about It. Therefore the Aged Judge Restrained himself; and when, at Long Last, the Case Came to an End, he Declared (Quite Untruly) that he had been Greatly Assisted by the Arguments of the Youthful Counsel, and that the Plaintiff had been Fortunate to Secure his Services. What was the Result? The Youthful Counsel Left the Court in Wild Elation; the Father of his True Love was So Impressed by the Report of the Case in the Papers that he Withdrew his Opposition to the Engagement; and the Youthful Counsel and his Future Bride Invested the Fee (Five and One) in a Lunch at the Savoy, an Arm-Chair, and a Coal-Scuttle. And when the Aged Judge Heard how Fruitful his Kindness had been, he Burst into Tears and Sent the Young People a Handsome Gift.

Moral.—*Remember the Past.*

THE LITIGANTS IN PERSON WHO COMPARED
NOTES

THE LITIGANTS IN PERSON WHO
COMPARED NOTES

〜

TWO Litigants in Person met in the Vaults of the Royal Courts of Justice. Each was Anxious for Refreshment after his Oratorical Efforts. The Lunatic Ordered Roast Potatoes, Two Cold Muffins, and a Double Whisky. The Scientist Thought he would have a Chop. The Litigants in Person then Compared Notes. The Lunatic was Very Happy. It Appeared that, Finding his Incarceration Irksome, he had Escaped from the Asylum in the Laundry Basket. It had then Occurred to him that he was Sane. He therefore Brought Actions against the Doctors who had Certified him (for Negligence) and all his Near Relations (for Conspiracy). No Solicitor would Take up his Case, so he had Appeared in Person. The Judge had been Charming and the Jury Most Sympathetic. In fact, they had Just Awarded him 10,000*l.* Damages. The Scientist Congratulated the Lunatic and Took up the Running. Some Years ago he had Invented a New Explosive. The Dishonest Representative of a Government Department had Stolen it, Used it, and Denied having Done so. The Scientist, Advised by Eminent Lawyers, had Proceeded by Way of Petition of Right and had been Told by the Court that he Ought to have Sued in Tort. Now (as his Money was Gone) he had Sued in Tort in Person and had been Defeated. The

Judge had Suggested to the Jury that he had a Bee in his Bonnet, and the Jury had Stopped the Case. The Lunatic Expressed his Sorrow, and after Firmly Declining to Pay his Bill and Embracing the Waitress, Fled from the Dining-Room. The Scientist Proceeded to his Lodgings in a Bus. The Same Evening the Lunatic Blew his Brains Out because the Asylum Authorities Refused to Re-Admit him, and the Scientist was Taken to the Workhouse.

Moral.—*Lex Lunaticos Amat.*

MR. TITMOUSE, MRS. TITMOUSE, AND THE
CLAIM FOR GOODS SOLD AND DELIVERED

MR. TITMOUSE, MRS. TITMOUSE, AND THE CLAIM FOR GOODS SOLD AND DELIVERED

∽

M R. TITMOUSE, of Pump-Handle Court, was a Barrister and a Happily Married Man. There was but One Fly in the Ointment. Mrs. Titmouse, though Amiable and of Pleasing Appearance, was not a Capable Manager, and Mr. Titmouse Often had Occasion to Complain of her Reckless Expenditure. At last, Mr. Titmouse was Driven to Take the Extreme Course of Putting his Foot Down. Mrs. Titmouse Gathered that if she were County-Courted, she would Jolly Well have to Get the Money out of her Own People. Nor did the Tears of Mrs. Titmouse Cause him to Recede from this Position. A Few Days Later Mr. Titmouse, Armed with a Three and One, was in the Robing-Room of the County-Court which Enjoys Jurisdiction over West Kensington and the Parts Adjacent thereto. To his Delight a Solicitor's Clerk Pressed another Brief into his Hand, Saying that the Case had been Called On and that his Counsel had been Held Up Elsewhere. The Claim, he Explained, was by Messrs. Lingerie, Ltd., for the Price of Goods Sold and Delivered and there was No Defence. Mr. Titmouse Rushed into Court to Find that the Defendant was already in the Witness-Box. She was Conversing Very Sweetly with the Judge. It was Mrs. Titmouse.

Before Mr. Titmouse could Open his Mouth the Judge said he had Ascertained from the Defendant that the Goods in Question had been Ordered on behalf of her Husband, and he Supposed there was no Objection to Substituting him as the Defendant. Mr. Titmouse was so Taken Aback that he Feebly Assented to this Proposal. Judgment was Accordingly Signed against Mr. Titmouse (whose Christian Names Mrs. Titmouse Obligingly Supplied) with Costs. When he Got Home that Evening Mr. Titmouse Took the Line that he had been Moved to this Act of Self-Sacrifice by Pity for Mrs. Titmouse, and Mrs. Titmouse was So Tactful that she Pretended to Believe Him.

Moral.—*Be Firm.*

THE DEAF REPORTER, THE DILIGENT YOUNG
COUNSEL, AND THE GLORIOUS WIN

THE DEAF REPORTER, THE DILIGENT YOUNG COUNSEL, AND THE GLORIOUS WIN

∽

THERE was Once an Old Gentleman who Practised as a Special Pleader in the Early Part of the Eighteenth Century. Being Very Deaf and Extremely Stupid, he Thought he would Take to Reporting. His Reports, by Reason of his Above-Mentioned Disabilities, were Shockingly Bad. As his Contemporaries Knew that the Old Gentleman Heard One Half of the Case and Reported the Other, they Paid No Attention to his Efforts. When the Deaf Reporter had Produced One Volume he Passed Away, much Regretted by his Laundress, to whom (according to Some) he was Secretly Married. Two Hundred Years Rolled by, and a Diligent Young Counsel, who was Accustomed to Go to the Root of Things, Unearthed the Forgotten Volume. To his Joy he Discovered therein an Authority which Exactly Fitted the Difficult Case he had to Argue on the Morrow in the County Court. The Startling Proposition Contained in the Head-Note was Due to the Fact that the Deaf Reporter had Omitted the Word "Not" when Taking Down the Observations of Mr. Justice Punt in the Court of Common Pleas. The Diligent Young Counsel Waited till the County Court Judge Showed Signs of Wobbling and then Loosed Off his Splendid Find. The County Court

Judge, who was Anxious to Catch his Train, was in no Critical Mood.   Thus the Diligent Young Counsel had a Glorious Win and Sowed the Seeds of a Large and Lucrative Practice.

Moral.—*Si Auctoritatem Requiris Circumspice.*

THE DISTINGUISHED ARCHITECT AND THE
PALACE OF JUSTICE

THE DISTINGUISHED ARCHITECT
AND THE PALACE OF JUSTICE

∽

THERE was Once a Distinguished Architect who Won an Open Competition for the Best Design for a Palace of Justice. He was an R.A. His Plans Carried Out the Best Architectural Traditions. The Palace of Justice, which Cost Several Millions, was in the Norman-Jacobean-Early-English Style. Each of the Thirty Courts was Extremely Lofty. The Gallery for the Waiting Jurors was Approached by a Tortuous Stairway. The Jury-Box was a Structure into which the Twelve Good Men and True could Just Fit if they Held their Breath. The Judge's Seat was Half-Way up the Wall. The Seats for Counsel were so Arranged that they Could not Get In or Out without Injuring Each Other; and the Desks so Sloped that their Briefs and Papers Fell to the Floor unless Held on by Main Force. The Witness Occupied a Box so Far Removed from both Counsel and the Jury that the Witness had to Shout his Answers if he was to be Heard. The Doors Clapped Noisily when they were Opened or Shut. The Floors Contained Concealed Steps down which the Unwary Fell with a Crash. Everybody Agreed that the Palace of Justice was a Miserable Failure. When a Great Many Years had Gone by the Palace of Justice, owing to some Defect in its Patent Heating Apparatus, was Burned to the

Ground.   There was Universal Rejoicing, for it was Felt that now At Last the Errors of the Distinguished Architect Could be Put Right.   Were they?   They were Not.   The Authorities Unearthed the Distinguished Architect (now in a State of Senile Decay) and Paid him an Immense Sum of Money to Reproduce his Old Plans.   Thus the New Palace of Justice Proved to be the Twin of its Predecessor, except that the Courts were Ten Feet Higher and the Judge was Placed Still Nearer to the Ceiling.

Moral.—*It Might be Worse.*

THE LANGUID LEADER AND THE DUCAL
ACTION

THE LANGUID LEADER AND THE
DUCAL ACTION

ﬤ

THERE was Once a Languid Leader. He
Despised Old-Fashioned Methods and did not
Think Much of his Contemporaries. Though
the Languid Leader was both Learned and Industrious
he Preferred to Pose as a Dilettante. Sometimes he
Remarked that he Only Practised at the Bar because it
Provided him with a Certain Amount of Pocket-
Money. Often he would Say that it was an Old
Woman's Job. Shortly after the Languid Leader had
Taken Silk a Painful Dispute Arose between the
Bogglesdale Rural District Council and Duke of
Agincourt. The Rural District Council Asserted,
and the Duke Denied, that there was a Right of Way
over his Grace's Best Grouse-Moor. As the Passage
of Citizens along the Sky-Line would Absolutely
Ruin the Third and Fourth Drives the Duke Con-
sulted his Family Solicitor and a Chancery Action was
Duly Launched. The Duke Retained Mr. Topnot,
K.C., the Great Real Property Lawyer, to Present his
Claim for Damages, a Declaration and an Injunc-
tion. The Rural District Council Delivered a
Defence and Counterclaim which Bristled with Law
and Fact. Two Days before the Case Came On, Mr.
Topnot, K.C., was Attacked by Influenza and
Returned his Large and Well-Marked Brief. Con-
sternation Reigned in the Ducal Camp. The Family

Solicitor, not without Misgivings, Approached the Clerk of the Languid Leader. That Experienced Official Undertook that if the Fee was Substantially Increased (as Time was so Short) his Employer would Give the Matter his Close Attention. On the Eve of the Day Appointed for the Trial the Duke of Agincourt, the Family Solicitor, the Managing Clerk, and the Junior Counsel Attended at the Chambers of the Languid Leader for the Final Consultation. The Languid Leader had Studied the Brief with Care and Knew the Case Inside Out. But he was not Going to Give the Show Away. He Received the Party with Vague Cordiality and Thought it Well to Mistake the Duke of Agincourt for the Managing Clerk. He then Observed that he had Only been Able to Glance at the Pleadings, and Opined that the Case was about a Cargo of Chinese Pickled Eggs. When this Misapprehension was Rectified the Languid Leader Exhibited no Emotion. After the Junior Counsel had Explained the Outstanding Points, the Languid Leader Yawned and Said he was Afraid he must be Going to the House. The Duke of Agincourt Left the Consultation Speechless with Rage and Indignation. On the Morrow the Languid Leader Delivered a Dashing Speech and Cross-Examined the Defendants' Witnesses into Cocked Hats. When All was Happily Over the Languid Leader Received the Congratulations of the Duke of Agincourt with Easy Nonchalance. He Explained that One Case was Much Like Another and that it was Quite Easy to Pick a Thing Up as You Went Along.

Moral.—*Keep It Up*.

THE WISE OLD BIRD WHO RETIRED

THE WISE OLD BIRD WHO RETIRED

∽

THERE was Once a Wise Old Bird who Retired from the Bench the Very Moment he had Done his Fifteen Years. The Wise Old Bird's Friends Assured him he would be Bored to Tears. They also Hinted Darkly that, Deprived of his Customary Employment, he would Probably Pass Away in the Near Future. Were they Right in their Gloomy Prognostications? Did he Miss the Dear Old Courts of Justice? Not a Bit of it. The Wise Old Bird took a Nice Little Place in the Country, and Thought Out an Admirable Routine. He Rose Late, Breakfasted Comfortably, Read *The Times* (Skipping the Law Reports) and had a Look at the Pigs. Then he Lunched and Read a Novel. At Four-Thirty the Wise Old Bird Took a Cup of Tea and had Another Look at the Pigs. At Seven-Thirty he Dined, Finishing Up with Two Glasses of Vintage Port, an Old Brandy, and a Cigar. Before Retiring to Rest he Consumed a Stiff Whisky and Soda, and had Another if he Felt he Wanted it. When in Need of Society he Invited his Niece Emily for the Week-End, but he Always Expected her to Go Home by the Ten-Forty on Monday. The Wise Old Bird Firmly Declined to be Bothered with Quarter Sessions, Petty Sessions, or Any Nonsense of that Kind. He thus Survived to Celebrate his Ninety-Eighth Birthday and had the Extreme Satisfaction of Outliving All his Contemporaries.

Moral.—*Retire.*

THE GREAT LAWYER WHO TOLD HIS
AUDIENCE HOW TO DO IT

THE GREAT LAWYER WHO TOLD HIS AUDIENCE HOW TO DO IT

∽

A GREAT Lawyer Once Attended a Banquet. He was the Principal Guest. The Great Lawyer's Hosts were Budding Members of the Bar who had Formed a Debating Society. They Desired to Pay Honour where Honour was Due and to Learn from One who had Arrived at the Top how the Trick was to be Done. The Great Lawyer, when Responding to the Toast of the Evening, Told them All About It. Individual Effort and Concentration, said the Great Lawyer, were the Only Things that Counted. There were Some, he Believed, who Thought that Luck was an Important Factor in Life. They were Wrong. He who Wished to Succeed must Work—Work—Work. He must Rise Early and Map Out his Day. He must be an Athlete in Strict Training. He must be a Sentry at his Post, Morning, Noon and Night. He must Serve One Master, and One Master Only—his Profession. The Great Lawyer Reminded them of the Emperor Napoleon's Observations on the Subject of Knapsacks and Bâtons, and Assured them that, if Only they would Fight the Good Fight, Each One of them might be a Marshal in the Army of the Law. And in a Moving Peroration the Great Lawyer Attributed his Own Success in Life to a Strict Adherence to the Maxims he was Expounding. In Point of Fact, the Great

Lawyer had been Spoon-Fed by a Near Relative from the Day of his Call; he had Always Taken Things Easily and Done himself Well; he had made a Matrimonial Alliance which Furnished him with Abundant Cash; a Series of Unexpected Political Events had Floated him into a Government; and the Sudden Demise of an Important Personage on the Eve of his Party's Defeat at the Polls had Provided him with the Fat Job which he now Enjoyed. When the Great Lawyer Resumed his seat after Speaking for Forty-Five Minutes, his Innocent Hosts Cheered him to the Echo, and Went Home Grimly Determined to Follow in the Great Lawyer's Footsteps.

Moral.—*Say the Right Thing.*

THE EXPERIENCED JUDGE, THE RUNNING
DOWN CASE, AND THE LAW RELATING TO
CONTRIBUTORY NEGLIGENCE

THE EXPERIENCED JUDGE, THE RUNNING DOWN CASE, AND THE LAW RELATING TO CONTRIBUTORY NEGLIGENCE

∽

THERE was Once an Experienced Judge who Tried a Running-Down Case. The Defendant Pleaded that the Said Accident was Due to the Negligence or Alternatively the Contributory Negligence of the Plaintiff. The Experienced Judge (who was a Person of Robust Intellect) Requested the Jury to Say whether the Disaster in Question was Caused by the Negligence of the Plaintiff or by that of the Defendant. As the Result of an Application for a New Trial the Experienced Judge Gathered that he had Failed to Explain Sufficiently to the Jury the Law Relating to Contributory Negligence. Shortly Afterwards the Experienced Judge had Another Running-Down Case to Try. This Time he Determined there should be no Mistake about the Law. So he Told the Retired Draper, the Lady in Glasses, the Dejected Publican, and the Nine Others who Composed the Jury All About It. They were, he said, to Consider whether (if they Thought that the Motor had in fact been Guilty of Contributory Negligence) the Taxi-Cab could by the Exercise of Reasonable Care have Avoided the Consequences of Such Contributory Negligence. Further, they Must Ask themselves whether it was the Motor or the Taxi-Cab which had the Last Opportunity of Avoiding the Negligence of the Other. Thirdly, they must Enquire whether the Negligence of the Motor, or that of the Taxi-Cab, could be Deemed to be the Proximate, as Distinguished from the Remote, Cause of the Plaintiff's Injuries. Fourthly, they must Tell him whether they Regarded the Negligence of Either as the Efficient or Decisive Cause of The Accident. Lastly, they Must Bear in Mind that if the Confusion of the Driver of the Motor had been Induced by the Want of Skill and Caution on the Part of the Taxi-Cab they should Give Due Weight to that Fact in Forming an Opinion as to the Degree of Responsibility which must be Attributed to the Former. The Experienced Judge then Read to the Jury at Length Various Relevant Cases Contained in the Law Reports including *Dublin, Wicklow & Wexford Railway Co.* v. *Slattery*, 3 App. Cas. 1155; *Radley* v. *L. & N.W. Railway Co.,* 1 App. Cas. 759; and *The Bernina*, 12 P. D. 36. He Finished Up with the Speeches of Their Lordships in *The Volute* [1922] 1 A. C. 129, Adding, however, the Warning that the Jury might Disregard the Provisions of the Maritime Conventions Act, 1911. After an Absence of Four Hours the Jury Announced that there was no Hope of their Agreement. As the Plaintiff's Financial Resources were Now Exhausted the Case gave no Further Trouble.

Moral.—*Explain the Law to the Jury.*

THE MAN OF AFFAIRS, THE INTELLIGENT
SOLICITOR, AND THE PROMISING SON

THE MAN OF AFFAIRS, THE INTELLIGENT SOLICITOR, AND THE PROMISING SON

～

A MAN of Affairs had a Promising Son to Whom he was Devotedly Attached and whose Material Advancement in this Vale of Tears he Fondly Desired. Therefore when the Man of Affairs Next had Occasion to Consult his Solicitor (a Person of Lively Intelligence) he Suggested—Quite Tactfully— at the Close of the Interview that the Solicitor should Send his Son a Brief at the Earliest Possible Moment. The Man of Affairs Added that his Son was a Youth of Parts in whom the Intelligent Solicitor might Repose Absolute Confidence. The Intelligent Solicitor with Cheerful Alacrity said he would At Once Brief the Youth in Question in a Case of Vital Importance, then Pending, in which the Man of Affairs was the Defendant. With a Cry of Agony the Man of Affairs Told him to Do Nothing of the Kind.

Moral.—*Charity Begins at Home.*

MABEL GUDGEON, THE DRESSMAKER'S BILL,
UNCLE PETER AND THE ARTICLED CLERK

MABEL GUDGEON, THE DRESSMAKER'S BILL, UNCLE PETER AND THE ARTICLED CLERK

∽

MABEL GUDGEON, a Beautiful Orphan, Resided with her Uncle Peter in Regent's Park. Uncle Peter was the Senior Partner in the Firm of Gudgeon, Gudgeon & Co. No Solicitor was More Respected in the City of London; but it has to be Admitted that Mabel Sometimes Found him Rather a Grumpy Companion. One Morning, at Breakfast, Mabel was Shocked to Receive a Peremptory Demand for Payment from her Dressmaker. The Figure at the Bottom of the Account Made her Sit Up. She was Still more Horrified when Uncle Peter Required her to Produce the Document for his Inspection. As soon as Uncle Peter had Recovered his Calm he Telephoned for Young Mr. Pott, the New Articled Clerk, and Told him to Settle with Madame Fleurette At Once. Meanwhile Mabel Wept. Young Mr. Pott Came Back in No Time to Say that Madame Fleurette (who was in Fact a Stout Hebrew of the Male Sex) had Agreed to Knock Off Thirty-Three Per Cent. in Consideration of an Immediate Cash Payment. Mabel Rewarded Young Mr. Pott (who was of Good Appearance) with a Tearful but Very Sweet Smile. So Pleased was Uncle Peter that he Asked Young Mr. Pott to Dinner. Can you Guess the Sequel? At First Uncle Peter would not Hear of It; but when he Learned that Young Mr. Pott's Father was a Wealthy Manufacturer of Glue, who had Recently been Made a Baronet, his Opposition Weakened. Uncle Peter then Insisted on a Long Engagement; but After Enduring the Engagement for Six Weeks he Insisted on a Short One. So Henry (for Such was his Christian Name) and Mabel were Married at St. Jude's. It was a Very Pretty Wedding, and the Four Bridesmaids Wore Tight-Fitting Bodices, Tulle Skirts and Court Shoes (All Pink). Mr. and Mrs. Pott at First Occupied a Flat near Earl's Court Station. But Soon, Prompted by Happy Expectations, they Secured a Roomier Abode with Good Nursery Accommodation. And now, Any Morning, Mrs. Pott may be Seen with her String-Bag Shopping Like Anything at John Barker's.

Moral.—*You Never Can Tell.*

MR. SHARP, MR. BRIGHT, AND THE AWARD
STATED IN THE FORM OF A SPECIAL CASE

MR. SHARP, MR. BRIGHT, AND THE AWARD STATED IN THE FORM OF A SPECIAL CASE

ᔥ

M R. SHARP and Mr. Bright, though Barristers-at-law of Twelve Months' Standing, had Positively Nothing to Do. They Decided that it was Essential to Get a Move on. As Clients were so Shy some Public Demonstration of their Learning and Ability Clearly had to be Made. Having Put their Heads together, Mr. Sharp and Mr. Bright Hit Upon an Admirable Plan. Their Clerk should State an Award in the Form of a Special Case. The Facts should be of Intense Human Interest and the Problems Arising therefrom should be Complicated and Obscure. They would Prepare the Arguments on Either Side with the Utmost Care; the Special Case should be Set Down for Hearing; and, Instructed by Friendly Young Solicitors (whom they could Readily Discover), Mr. Sharp and Mr. Bright would Electrify the Court. There was no Reason why the Case should not be Carried to the House of Lords. All Went Well. The Special Case, Skilfully Drafted by Mr. Sharp and Mr. Bright, was Set Down (at a Trifling Cost) for Hearing in the Special Paper. It was a Masterpiece. The Incidents Narrated were Thrilling but Improbable. The Robust Style of Mr. Edgar Wallace was Wedded to the Quaint Fancy of Robert Louis Stevenson. A Marriage, Invalid by the Law of England, but Valid by the Law of Tibet (in which Country the Wife had been Domiciled as an Infant), had Resulted in the Birth of an Expectant Heir. After Mortgaging his Reversion to his Mother's Tibetan Estates to a Money-Lender the Expectant Heir had Insured his Life. The Policy he had Assigned to a Person who (Intending his Death) Chartered an Unseaworthy Yacht in which the Expectant Heir was Drowned. Before being Drowned the Expectant Heir (when Slightly Intoxicated) had Made a Will Devising the Mortgaged Lands to a Society for the Abolition of Gaming, Wagering and Church Establishments. The Mother of the Expectant Heir had then Married a Clergyman in Shropshire who Obtained a Divorce and thereafter Married the Money-Lender's Widow. The Opinion of the Court was Asked upon the Various Nice Questions to which these and other Collateral Events Gave Rise. Unfortunately When Mr. Sharp Rose to Argue on behalf of the Claimants, the Judge Said that Large Sums Appeared to be Owing to the Revenue for Stamps; that the Case ought to Go Back to the Arbitrator for his Finding upon Several Matters which he had Left Obscure; and that he would Send all the Papers to the Director of Public Prosecutions in order that the Criminal Law might be Set in Motion. Thus the Labours of Mr. Sharp and Mr. Bright were Wasted.

Moral.—*Stick to the County Court.*

THE DISGRUNTLED PRACTITIONER WHO
THOUGHT POORLY OF EVERYBODY

THE DISGRUNTLED PRACTITIONER
WHO THOUGHT POORLY OF
EVERYBODY

෮

THERE was Once a Disgruntled Practitioner who Complained Loudly of Everybody. Whilst he was a Junior he Thought very Poorly of the Leaders. The Disgruntled Practitioner Wondered why such a Collection of Gumps were ever Briefed at all. After a Case had been Disposed of he would Remark that the Blighter had Made a Mess of it, or that the Ass had Thrown Away the Verdict, or that the Idiot had not Understood the Point. After the Disgruntled Practitioner had Taken Silk he Discovered that the Juniors were, without Exception, Half-Wits who Expected him to Do their Work for them. In the Fullness of Time the Disgruntled Practitioner became a Judge. Now he Found that his Colleagues were Mostly Duds and that the Court of Appeal (which Often Reversed him) was Deplorably Weak. He Often Explained to his Clerk that the Legal System of the Country was Doomed, for, Bad as the Bench was, there was Nobody at the Bar who was Fit for Promotion to a Judgeship. His Clerk, who had his own Views on the Subject, Respectfully Agreed with him. But when the Disgruntled Practitioner at last Disappeared it didn't Seem to Matter very Much, and the Legal System Got on Quite Comfortably without him.

Moral.—*Cheer Up.*

THE BARONY OF DE MONTAZURE AND
FRONT-DE-BŒUF, THE COMMITTEE FOR
PRIVILEGES, AND THE SWEET YOUNG LADY

THE BARONY OF DE MONTAZURE AND FRONT-DE-BŒUF, THE COMMITTEE FOR PRIVILEGES, AND THE SWEET YOUNG LADY

∽

THE Barony of De Montazure and Front-De-Bœuf had long been in Abeyance. Whether the Original Baron De Montazure and Front-de-Bœuf had Ever been Summoned to the Parliament of King Edward III, Holden at Wallingford in the Year 1369, was a Matter of Debate. Indeed, Some Peerage Lawyers of Note Declared that the Nobleman in Question had Never Existed, while Others Held that the Alleged Parliament was in Fact a Court Heriot Summoned by the Local Lord of the Manor to Determine the Ownership of a Cow which had Estrayed upon the Waste thereof, and that its One and Only Statute (*De Vacca Detinenda,* 43 Ed. 3, c. 6, Ruff. Stat.) Merely Embodied the Order of that Tribunal "Qe Vache Soit Detenuz en Prisone."[1] Therefore there was Much Interest Amongst Antiquarians when Miss Smythe-Bilkington-Smythe Put Forward her Claim to have the Abeyance Terminated in her Favour as The Baron De Montazure and Front-de-Bœuf's Senior Co-Heiress. She had Wisely Placed her Affairs in the Hands of a Highly Competent Solicitor. The Highly Competent Solicitor Kept a Good Publicity Department, and was Careful to Let the Newspapers Know that Miss Smythe-Bilkington-

[1] See Cott. M.S. 64, § 11, and Rot. Wall. temp. Ed. Tert.

Smythe was not only a Keen Hockey Player, but a Splendid Swimmer and Devoted to Dogs; also, that she would Attend the Hearing of her Claim. When the Parties Appeared at the Bar of the House of Lords the Members of the Committee for Privileges were Present in Full Force. They were Delighted with the Appearance of the Sweet Young Lady who Sat in the Pen Reserved for Counsel. Her Bobbed Hair, her Slender Figure, her Large Grey Eyes, and her Winsome Dignity were Indeed Calculated to Touch the Stoniest Heart. The Sweet Young Lady Paid the Closest Attention to the Proceedings, and from Time to Time Assisted Counsel by Producing the Necessary Year Book, Parliament Roll, or What-Not. On the Afternoon of the Second Day their Lordships were Concerned to Note that the Sweet Young Lady Shewed Signs of Faintness, and the Senior Lord of Appeal Directed the Attendant to Provide her with a Glass of Water. At the Close of the Arguments the Committee, by a Majority of One, Declared that Miss Smythe-Bilkington-Smythe had Made Out her Claim. Miss Smythe-Bilkington-Smythe thereupon Descended from the Remote Gallery in which she had been Quietly Sitting (in Obedience to the Instructions of the Highly Competent Solicitor) to Receive the Congratulations of her Friends. The New Baroness De Montazure and Front-de-Bœuf was Both Stout and Plain. The Highly Competent Solicitor Warmly Thanked the Sweet Young Lady (who was in Fact his Stenographer) for her Invaluable Services, and Raised her Salary on the Spot to 3*l.* 10*s.* a week.

Moral.—*Have the Client in Court.*

MR. JUSTICE HEAVYSIDE AND THE FAITHFUL
CLERK

MR. JUSTICE HEAVYSIDE AND THE
FAITHFUL CLERK

∽

SIR EBENEZER HEAVYSIDE was a Judge of
the High Court of Justice. He had been Ele-
vated to the Bench with the Full Approval of the
Profession. Nor were his Many Admirers Dis-
appointed by his Performances in the Judgment-Seat.
Indeed, it was Clear to All that (if Merit were the
Qualifying Test) Mr. Justice Heavyside would
Shortly be Promoted to the Court of Appeal or the
House of Lords. Heavyside, J., was Gratified that he
Stood so High in Public Estimation; but he had One
Abiding Sorrow. He Suffered Severely from a
Faithful but Incompetent Clerk. Man and Boy, the
Faithful Clerk had been with Mr. Justice Heavyside
for Forty Years. Day by Day his Imbecility Appeared
to Increase; yet his Employer had Never Summoned
Up Courage to Dismiss him. It was when Heavy-
side, J., Travelled on Circuit that the Doings of the
Faithful Clerk became Particularly Infuriating. The
Faithful Clerk could never Remember at what Hour
the Train Started, and he was Liable to Confuse St.
Pancras with Waterloo and Euston with Paddington.
Also he Made it a Practice to Lose the Tickets and
Leave the Depositions Behind. Here you Observe
Heavyside, J., and the Faithful Clerk on the Platform.
Once More the Faithful Clerk has Made a Mess of it.
They have Just Missed the Train. Mr. Justice

251

Heavyside will Arrive at Bodmin Two Hours Late for Dinner and he is Furious. Heavyside, J., is Wearing a Bowler, and the Faithful Clerk is the Gentleman in the Silk Hat.

Moral.—*Appearances are Deceptive.*

THE ESTABLISHED JUNIOR WHO HAD NOTHING
TO COMPLAIN OF

THE ESTABLISHED JUNIOR WHO HAD NOTHING TO COMPLAIN OF

∽

A N Established Junior having Dined Comfortably in his Flat Proceeded to Compare the Present with the Past. Thirty Years Ago, the Established Junior Reflected, he had Lived Laborious Days. He had Devilled, Reported, Coached Coloured Pupils, Written for the Papers, Compiled Legal Treatises, and Perspired in County Courts. Then, at Long Last, he had Turned the Corner. His Cases had Become Heavy and Numerous. Whereas in his Youth he had been Poorly Paid for his Eloquence in Courts of Inferior Jurisdiction, he was now Richly Rewarded for Sitting Silent behind Eminent Leaders in the Higher Tribunals. Instead of Mugging Up his Cases himself, he Allowed a Highly Intelligent Fellow of All Saints' to Do that Disagreeable Job for him. That Afternoon, the Established Junior Recalled with Satisfaction, he had Attended a Consultation with an Ex-Law Officer. After Twice Remarking "Quite," he had Left for Another Consultation with Another Great Man, at which he Looked Important and Said Nothing. It Comforted him to Think that he would be Unable to be Present at the Hearing of Either Matter, as he would be Very Busy Elsewhere, and that his Absence would Only be Regarded by his Client as Evidence of his Worth. The Established Junior Felt that, on the whole, he had Nothing to

Complain of. After All, there was Something to be Said for the Profession. The Established Junior had Another Go of Pre-War Whisky, Lit a Second Corona, and Resumed his Agreeable Meditations.

Moral.—*Stick to a Stuff-Gown.*

THE DOMESTIC TYRANT, THE CRUSHED WORM,
AND THE BIBULOUS BUTLER

THE DOMESTIC TYRANT, THE CRUSHED
WORM, AND THE BIBULOUS BUTLER

～

MR. JUSTICE CRASHER was a Profound Lawyer, a Married Man, and a Domestic Tyrant. Lady Crasher, after Filling the Rôle of Crushed Worm for some Forty Years, Resolved to Strike a Blow for Freedom. Her Chance soon Came. One Monday Morning, after Crasher, J., had Left for the Royal Courts of Justice, an Inspector of Police Informed her Ladyship that her Butler, being at the time Intoxicated, had Pledged with a Neighbouring Pawnbroker a Silver Teapot and other Articles Bearing the Crasher Crest. The Same Evening Lady Crasher Mentioned to her Lord and Master that she had Dismissed the Butler Without Notice, or Wages in Lieu thereof, for Drunkenness and Dishonesty. Crasher, J., Exhibited Violent Displeasure, and Pointed Out that the Butler would Certainly Bring an Action for Wrongful Dismissal. Lady Crasher Listened Unmoved, and did not Disclose the Strength of her Hand. When on Tuesday Morning a Dingy Person Served a Writ upon Lady Crasher in a Suit entitled "Binns *v.* Crasher (Married Woman)" Mr. Justice Crasher Screamed with Passion and Insisted that the Matter must be Settled Forthwith. Lady Crasher's Quiet Reply that she would not Pay the Disgusting Wretch a Farthing and that she would Fight the Case in Person Caused Crasher, J., to Use

Very Ungentlemanly Language. Lady Crasher Gathered from his Remarks that she had, amongst Other Notable Disadvantages, the Temperament of a Mule and the Intellect of a Child of Seven. The Day of Reckoning Arrived and Lady Crasher Appeared in Person. Was she Defeated? Far from it. Lady Crasher Cross-examined the Bibulous Butler Inside Out, and he Never had a Look-in. The Next Day the Newspapers of the Metropolis Rang with the Praises of Lady Crasher. The *Daily Howl* Contained her Portrait; the *Daily Screech* Called her "Portia Rediviva"; and the *Thunderer* had a Leader in which Lady Crasher was Thanked for the Splendid Stand she had made on behalf of the Employers of Domestic Servants. Mr. Justice Crasher took the Dignified Course of Never Alluding to the Victory which Lady Crasher had Won. But his Reign as a Domestic Tyrant was Over, and thereafter Crasher, J., Became a Considerate and Respectful Husband.

Moral.—*Fight*.

1898   1928

THE YOUTH WHO RESOLVED ALWAYS TO
MAKE A CAREFUL NOTE OF THE FACTS

THE YOUTH WHO RESOLVED ALWAYS TO MAKE A CAREFUL NOTE OF THE FACTS

~

THERE was Once a Youth who was Instructed to Appear for the Crown in a Case at Quarter Sessions. Being both Industrious and Prudent the Youth Made a Careful Note from which to Open the Facts and the Law to the Jury. The Note in its Final Form was Completed at 2 a.m. on the Day Fixed for the Trial. The Youth Sat Up Late because he was Very Anxious that it should be both Full and Accurate. The Note (which was on Two Sheets of Paper United by a Fastener) was as follows:—

CHARGE { (*a*) Larceny of boots.
        { (*b*) Receiving same well knowing
        {   to be stolen.

N.B.—Onus on Crown; but *no reasonable doubt*.

FACTS: 6th October, 1897—10.15 a.m.

Prisoner seen near shop by

(1) J. Brown.

(2) J. Brown, jun.

Both struck by Prisoner's appearance.

(*a*) Black Eye.

(*b*) Limp.

Same Evening—11.45 p.m. (about)

☞ *Crash heard.*

J. Brown goes downstairs.

☞ *Sees Prisoner escaping from window.*

Next Day.

Prisoner Arrested by P.C.

N.B.—actually wearing boots.

Statement to P.C.:

"I done it."

Submit onus discharged:

(1) Wearing of boots.

(2) Admission to P.C.

Shaking All Over the Youth Opened the Case. On the Whole it Went Very Well. There was an Awkward Pause at One Moment because the Youth Could not Read the Words "Crash Heard," but Ultimately the Mists Cleared Away, and he was Able to Resume his Interrupted Address.

Pleased with his Performance, the Youth Resolved that he would Never Go into Court without a Careful Note of the Facts and the Law.

Thirty Years Later the Youth (now a K.C.) had to Open a Running-Down Case. After a Short Chat with his Junior he Wrote on the Back of his Brief (which he had not Read) the words "How Much?" He then made a Fluent and Convincing Speech. In the Course of his Address he Referred to the Plaintiff More than Once as "this Poor Old Gentleman." The Plaintiff in Truth was an Elderly Widow. But this Little Misapprehension didn't Matter a Bit and he Got a Nice Verdict.

Moral.—*Stick to Your Note.*

THE BEGINNER WHO THOUGHT HE WOULD
DO IT HIMSELF

THE BEGINNER WHO THOUGHT HE
WOULD DO IT HIMSELF

〜

A BEGINNER, in the Temporary Absence of his Leader, Found himself Opposed to a Big Pot in the Commercial Court. Though Greatly Alarmed, the Beginner Bore himself Bravely. To his Surprise and Delight the Beginner Managed to Cross-Examine the Big Pot's Principal Witness with Such Effect that he Needed a Good Deal of Rehabilitation. Rising to Re-Examine, the Big Pot Airily Observed to the Principal Witness: "I Suppose What You Meant by Your Last Answer was This," and Proceeded to Tell the Principal Witness Quite Clearly what he Meant. When the Beginner made a Dignified Protest the Judge Smilingly Suggested that the Big Pot might Shape his Question rather Differently. The Next Day the Beginner was in a County Court. The Plaintiff (for whom the Beginner Appeared) having Made an Awkward Admission to his Learned Friend on the Other Side, the Beginner Thought he would Employ the Excellent Formula of the Big Pot. He Did so. The Scene that Followed Beggars Description. The County Court Judge in a Voice of Thunder Ordered the Beginner to Sit Down. He then Rebuked the Beginner for his Gross Misconduct and Discussed the Question whether he would Commit him for Contempt, or Merely Report him to the General Council of the Bar. Finally he Expressed the Hope that the Incident would be a Lesson to the Beginner and Directed that the Case should be re-Heard on a Later Date before a Fresh Jury.

Moral.—*Wait till You're a Big Pot.*

THE CALLOW YOUTH, THE BRIEF IN THE
DIVORCE COURT, AND THE WEEPING LADY

THE CALLOW YOUTH, THE BRIEF IN
THE DIVORCE COURT, AND THE
WEEPING LADY

∽

A CALLOW Youth Shortly After his Call Caused his Name to be Inscribed on the Roll of Counsel Desirous of Representing Poor Persons. He was Soon Rewarded with Instructions to Appear on behalf of a Female Petitioner in the Divorce Court. The Callow Youth Perused the Brief and Learned that the Female's Husband had been Going On Anyhow. Not Only had he Preferred the Society of Two Other Ladies to that of the Female Petitioner, but on various Occasions he had Treated her with Physical Violence. The Case, which was to be Tried on the Morrow, Appeared to be Plain Sailing. After Dining Quietly at "The Cock" the Callow Youth Returned to his Chambers to have a Final Look at the Brief. Turning Up the Light he Observed a Middle-Aged Lady Seated in the Arm-Chair. She Wore a Straw Boater and a Macintosh, and she was Weeping Quietly. The Callow Youth saw At Once what had Happened. It was Clear that his Client had Come for a Conference about the Case. Approaching the Arm-Chair the Callow Youth Begged the Weeping Lady to be Calm and Spoke a Few Tactful Words of Sympathy. The Weeping Lady with a Slight Hiccup Said Something about "a Couple." She then Sank into Complete

Unconsciousness. The Callow Youth Redoubled his Attentions and, Recalling the First Aid Lectures he had Once Attended, Did What he Deemed Necessary to Restore her to Life. As he was Engaged upon his Work of Mercy a Furious Cry Assailed his Ear. Turning Round, the Callow Youth Found himself in the Grasp of a Gigantic Male. While the Callow Youth was Staunching the Flow of Gore from his Injured Nose he Gathered that the Weeping Lady was the Laundress in charge of the Chambers; that she was Intoxicated, not for the First Time; and that her Husband (the Gigantic Male) had Come to Take her Home. The Callow Youth Retired to Rest a Poorer but a Wiser Man.

Moral.—*Don't Jump to Conclusions.*

THE CAREFUL LAWYER WHO COULD NOT
MAKE UP HIS MIND

THE CAREFUL LAWYER WHO COULD
NOT MAKE UP HIS MIND

᷍

THERE was Once a Careful Lawyer who, as the Result of a Variety of Unexpected Circumstances, Found himself Elevated to the Bench. The Careful Lawyer was not Entirely Satisfied that he had the Necessary Qualifications for Judicial Office, and his Misgivings were Shared by those who Knew him Best. For, Most Unfortunately, he could not Make Up his Mind. In Chambers the Careful Lawyer Got on Well Enough by Affirming the Order of the Master and Directing that the Costs should be Costs in the Cause. And in Jury Cases the Careful Lawyer Discovered that it was not a Bad Plan to Read over the Evidence to the Jury and Ask them Such Questions as Counsel Suggested. But as a Rule the Careful Lawyer Found himself Sadly Puzzled. On Circuit he Spent Sleepless Nights Wondering whether the Prisoner ought to Have Two Months with Hard Labour or Three Months in the Second Division; and when he Tried a Non-Jury Case it was his Custom to Reserve his Judgment for so Long a Period of Time that he Often Forgot what the Case had been About. One Day, for a Change, they Put the Careful Lawyer in a Divisional Court. It was Hoped that he would Find the Job an Easy One. But the Careful Lawyer was so Bothered by Trying to Decide, whilst the Other Judgments were being

Delivered, whether he should Say that he Agreed with Them or that he Concurred with them, that he had a Nervous Breakdown from which he Never Recovered.

Moral.—*Toss Up.*

THE SILK WHO KNEW HOW TO MAKE A
GOOD SHOW

THE SILK WHO KNEW HOW TO MAKE
A GOOD SHOW

～

THERE was Once a Plaintiff who Brought an Action in the Hope that the Defendant would Prefer not to Fight. But the Defendant Plucked Up Courage and Briefed a Silk whose Fame as a Cross-Examiner was World-Wide. As the Plaintiff, apart from being a Bad Egg in a General Way, had Spent Several Years in Penal Servitude, it was Clear that the Silk would have Some Material to Work Upon. A Week before the Case Came On the Silk Presided over a Consultation at which the Question of Evidence was Discussed. How was the Black Record of the Plaintiff to be Established? The Junior Suggested that the Certificate of his Conviction Duly Produced in Court would Suffice. The Silk Curtly Rejected this Proposal, and Gave Other Directions. When the Time Came for the Silk to Cross-Examine the Plaintiff the Court was Crowded with Expectant Members of the Public and Representatives of the Press. The Silk First Asked the Plaintiff whether he was in Good Health. Having Learned that the Plaintiff's Physical Condition was All that Could be Desired, the Silk Enquired where the Plaintiff Lived. After Ascertaining that he Resided in Tooting, the Silk Begged to be Informed Whether he Ever Went to the Country or the Sea-Side. If so, Which Place did he Like Best? The

Silk then Took the Plaintiff Through a Long List of Inland and Marine Health-Resorts and Gathered that he Usually Spent his Holidays at Margate. Did the Plaintiff Care, by any Chance, for Devonshire? What did he Think of the Moors of Devonshire? Did he Know them Well? Had he Found them Salubrious? Had he Found them So Salubrious that he had Lived on them for Seven Years? Did he Know the Stout Gentleman Standing Up at the Back of the Court? Was the Stout Gentleman a Warder at the Dartmoor Convict Establishment? Did he Know the Gentleman with a Broken Nose Standing Up in the Gallery? Was he a Fellow-Convict with the Plaintiff at the said Convict Establishment? Were the Plaintiff and the Gentleman with the Broken Nose Employed in the Quarries at the Same Time? When the Plaintiff had Given Satisfactory Answers to these Various Queries, the Silk Resumed his Seat. Was his Reputation as a Cross-Examiner Enhanced? It was. The Daily Journals Reported his Masterly Performance Word for Word, and the Public Wondered Once More at the Amazing Skill with which the Silk Managed to Worm the Truth out of a Cunning Scoundrel.

Moral.—*Do it in Style.*

MISS SNAFFLETON (INFANT) AND THE
OLD-FASHIONED JUDGE

MISS SNAFFLETON (INFANT)

AND

THE OLD-FASHIONED JUDGE

∽

THERE was Once a Judge of the Chancery Division of the High Court of Justice who had Old-Fashioned Views about Everything. In Particular, about the Young. He did not Like the Goings-On of the New Generation. Their Want of Respect, their Indifference to the Conventions, their Slangy Talk, and their Cocktail Parties were, in his Opinion, Positively Intolerable. Therefore when the Old-Fashioned Judge Received a Breezy and rather Ungrammatical Letter from his Ward of Court, Miss Snaffleton (Infant), Saying that she Wanted to See him *At Once* about a Matter of *Urjent Importence*, he Determined to Give her a Piece of his Mind. The Old-Fashioned Judge had Already Informed Master Pooter (who Took the S to Z Business) that he had been Far too Indulgent to Miss Snaffleton (Infant) in the Matter of Finance. The Following Monday Miss Snaffleton Blew In. She was Costumed for the Game of Golf and was Furnished with a Cigarette. Miss Snaffleton (Infant) At Once Took Control of the Situation. After Telling the Old-Fashioned Judge that he Looked a Dear in those Funny Clothes, she Said she was Sure he was Going to be Sweet. The Fact was she Wanted to be Married. Tommy was Absolutely It and the Poor Lamb had Quite Given

Up Lifting His Elbow. He had an Interest or Something in a Motor Business and was Doing Terribly Well, Would the Old-Fashioned Judge be an Absolute Angel and Give his Consent? Did the Old-Fashioned Judge Take a Firm Line ? He Did. The Old-Fashioned Judge Insisted that the Marriage should not Take Place till a Fortnight had Elapsed (in Order that Miss Snaffleton might be Sure she Knew her Own Mind) and Declined to Allow her More than 3,000*l.* a year Until she had Satisfied him that this Amount was Insufficient for her and Tommy's Requirements. He also Agreed to Buy One of Tommy's Cars and to Give Miss Snaffleton (Infant) Away at the Hymeneal Altar.

Moral.—*Be Firm.*

MRS. SARAH STOUT, THE LAST WILL OF
MR. BUFFIN, AND THE DRAFT AFFIDAVIT

MRS. SARAH STOUT, THE LAST WILL OF MR. BUFFIN, AND THE DRAFT AFFIDAVIT

～

WHEN Mr. Buffin, of 1, Plum Tree Court, Temple, E.C.4, Passed Away in his Eighty-Ninth Year, his Last Will and Testament could not be Discovered. This Circumstance Annoyed his Nephews and Nieces Greatly; for Mr. Buffin was a Bachelor and the Nephews and Nieces had Expectations. And when, as the Result of a Diligent Search in a Glory-Hole Containing the Rubbish of Years, Mrs. Sarah Stout, the Laundress, Unearthed the Missing Document, the Anxieties of the Nephews and Nieces were not at an End. For, Owing to the Attentions of a Mouse with a Morbid Appetite, the Name of the Second Attesting Witness had Disappeared, and the First Attesting Witness was Dead. What was to be Done? Mrs. Sarah Stout again Came to the Rescue, for she Well Remembered about Three Years ago Poor Mr. Buffin Saying Would she Come and Sign her Name Here Next his Clerk's Name, which the Clerk he Signed it Too the Same as What Mrs. Sarah Stout did, and it was a Damp, Foggy Day, and she Noticed Poor Mr. Buffin had a Nasty Cough and she Said to Herself, she Said, Well, she Said, she Hoped Mr. Buffin wasn't Really Ill, and he Got through the Winter Nicely After All, and that Poor Clerk he was the First to Go, and a Pleasant

Man he was, though a Little Too Fond of a Quick One. While Mrs. Stout was Telling this Tale, the Solicitor in Charge of Mr. Buffin's Affairs was Making a Careful Note of her Observations. In Due Course Mrs. Stout Received the Affidavit which she was to Swear. In Successive Paragraphs it Related that Mrs. Stout had Long been Acquainted with the Testator and his Clerk; that She Well Remembered the 4th November, 1927, as the Weather was Peculiarly Inclement; that on that Date the Testator Requested her to Witness his Last Will and Testament; that the Testator also Informed her that his said Clerk would be the First Attesting Witness; that she had thereupon Signed her Name in the Presence of the Testator and of his said Clerk, and that his said Clerk had Likewise Signed his Name in the Presence of Herself and of the Testator; that she Recognised the Document (now Produced to her and Marked " S.S.1.") as a Copy of the Document which she had so Signed together with the said Clerk of the Testator; that the Testator to the Best of her Belief was on the said Date of Sound Mind and of Testamentary Capacity; and that she was Informed and Believed that the said Clerk of the Testator was now Deceased. Mrs. Sarah Stout was so Delighted by the Purity of her Language and the Perfection of her Style that she forthwith made up her Mind to Adopt a Literary Career.

Moral.—*Magna est Veritas.*

THE KINDLY JUDGE AND LITTLE EFFIE

THE KINDLY JUDGE AND LITTLE
EFFIE

～

A KINDLY Judge (of the Chancery Division)
Found himself Confronted by a Difficult
Problem. Was Little Effie (a Ward of Court)
to go to School, or Not?

Counsel Representing Little Effie's Grandmother
Contended that Little Effie, by Reason of her Nervous
Temperament, was not Fitted for Contact with the
Rough Companions whom she would Doubtless En-
counter at the Proposed Educational Establishment.

The Advocate Voicing the Opinions of the Maiden
Aunt Took the Line that Little Effie was a Perfectly
Normal and Healthy Child who would Derive Im-
mense Benefit from the Discipline and Gaiety of
School Life.

The Kindly Judge Wisely Suggested that before
Reading the Affidavits he should Interview Little
Effie in his Private Room.

When Little Effie Presented herself the Kindly
Judge (who was a Family Man) Found himself
Attracted by her Cropped Head and her large Blue
Eyes. To Put Little Effie Completely at her Ease the
Kindly Judge Invited her to Try on his Wig and to
Observe the Effect in his Looking-Glass. After a
Pleasant Little Chat the Kindly Judge Resumed his
Wig and Returned to Court. Counsel Thereupon
Set to Work.

"A Month Ago," ran Paragraph One of the Grandmother's Affidavit, "Effie Suffered from a Bad Attack of Ring-Worm and her Head had to be Shaved." The Kindly Judge forthwith Adjourned the Proceedings *Sine Die*, and Sent his Clerk Out for a Bottle (Large Size) of Condy's Fluid.

Moral.—*Read the Affidavits First.*

MR. BOBBY CHUMP, THE SUCCESSFUL
DEFENCE AND ITS SINGULAR CONSE-
QUENCES

MR. BOBBY CHUMP, THE SUCCESSFUL DEFENCE AND ITS SINGULAR CONSEQUENCES

∾

MRS. BOBBY CHUMP was Greatly Pleased when the Judge at the Old Bailey Asked her Bobby to Defend a Prisoner. Her Pleasure was all the Greater when Bobby Telephoned to Say that the Prisoner had been Acquitted, and that the Judge had Invited Him to Dinner. He did not Add that the Jury had Stopped the Case before Bobby had Cross-examined Anybody or Delivered the Eloquent Speech which he and Mrs. Chump had Prepared in Consultation.

When Bobby Returned to the Flat at Midnight Mrs. Bobby was greatly Alarmed by his Manner and Appearance. Something had Happened. Bobby's Gait was Unsteady; his Words, which were Imperfectly Formed, Came in Strange Sequence; and he had a Fixed and Feeble Smile. It was Clear to Mrs. Bobby that he Must be Got to Bed at Once.

The Next Day Bobby was Very Much Better. And to Mrs. Bobby's Great Relief, Bobby was Able to Assure Her at Breakfast that his Experience of the Night Before was Not Uncommon at the Bar. Advocacy, he Explained, Exposes the Nervous System to a Tremendous Strain. Some Speakers Suffer before, Some after, the Making of the Oratorical Effort. Bobby, she Gathered, Belonged to the Latter Class; Brougham, Russell, and Birkenhead to the Former.

Moral.—*Take Sanatogen.*

295

THE PROFOUND LAWYER WHO RECEIVED
A SUBPŒNA *AD TESTIFICANDUM*

THE PROFOUND LAWYER WHO
RECEIVED A SUBPŒNA *AD*
TESTIFICANDUM

∽

A PROFOUND Lawyer, Whose Fame as an Orator and a Cross-Examiner was of the World-Wide Order, once Chanced to Observe a Collision between a Taxi-Cab and a Bus. When a Stout and Peremptory Policeman Demanded his Name and Address the Profound Lawyer Gladly Gave the Desired Particulars. He was Well Pleased to Have an Opportunity of Entering the Witness-Box and Showing Everybody how Evidence Ought to be Given. A Month Later the Profound Lawyer was Visited by a Managing Clerk of Unprepossessing Appearance and Considerable Intelligence. Invited by his Visitor to Give a Proof, the Profound Lawyer Proceeded to Dictate an Accurate Account of the Disaster, Prudently Retaining a Copy of the Resultant Document so that he might from Time to Time Refresh his Memory before the Hearing of the Cause. In Due Course the Profound Lawyer Received a Subpœna Requiring him to Testify on behalf of the Plaintiff in the King's Bench Division of the High Court of Justice.

Was the Evidence of the Profound Lawyer a Success? Far from it.

When the Profound Lawyer was Asked to Mention the Date of the Accident he was Quite Unable to

Remember it. So Confidential were the Tones in which he Began his Story that the Judge Sharply Ordered Him to Speak Up. When the Plan was Handed to the Profound Lawyer he Held it Upside Down. Twice he Endeavoured to Tell the Court what he had Said to his Wife when he Got Home in the Evening. His Reservations and Qualifications were so Abundant that it Appeared Doubtful Whether he had seen Anything at All. A Short Cross-Examination Elicited the Fact that he had Learnt his Proof by Heart. In his Summing-Up the Judge Told the Jury to Dismiss from their Minds the Evidence of the Profound Lawyer, as it was Entirely Worthless.

Moral.—*Look the Other Way.*

THE HIGH SHERIFF'S CHAPLAIN AND THE
ASSIZE SERMON WHICH GAVE UNIVERSAL
SATISFACTION

THE HIGH SHERIFF'S CHAPLAIN AND THE ASSIZE SERMON WHICH GAVE UNIVERSAL SATISFACTION

∽

A HIGH Sheriff's Chaplain, whose Sermons on Various Occasions were Greatly Admired, Determined that when he Preached before the Judge of Assize his Lordship should not be Disappointed. He accordingly Composed with the Utmost Care a Dignified Dissertation in which Scholarship, Dogma, and Respect for the Judicial Office were Suitably Blended. In Due Course the High Sheriff's Chaplain Climbed into the Pulpit, and the Judge of Assize, with a Sinking Heart, Prepared for the Worst.

When he Opened his Manuscript the High Sheriff's Chaplain had the Shock of His Life. He Realised with Horror that his Wife had Furnished him with an Address which he had Intended for the Annual Parochial Outing of the Boy Scouts and Girl Guides. There was Only One Thing to be Done. The High Sheriff's Chaplain Mumbled through the First Page, which Dealt with the Evils of Cigarette Smoking (Boy Scouts) and the Evils of Gossip (Girl Guides), and Tottered into the Vestry. The Whole Thing was Over in Three Minutes.

Was the Sermon a Success? It was. The Same Evening the Judge of Assize Told the High Sheriff's Chaplain at the Bishop's Dinner-Table that he had

Never Enjoyed a Sermon so Much, and that he Should Certainly Mention the Name of the High Sheriff's Chaplain to the Prime Minister in Connection with the Vacant Deanery of Porchester.

Moral.—*It Doesn't Matter.*

THE BRILLIANT PERSON, THE VULGAR IN-
DIVIDUAL WITH A COCKNEY ACCENT AND
THE TWO MALEFACTORS

THE BRILLIANT PERSON, THE VULGAR INDIVIDUAL WITH A COCKNEY ACCENT AND THE TWO MALEFACTORS

∽

THERE was Once a Brilliant Person who Regretted the Decay of Eloquence at the Bar. He had Studied the Subject of Rhetoric and was Himself a Splendid Performer. The Brilliant Person Knew all about Proem, Narrative, Arguments and Peroration; furthermore, he was both Skilled in the Use of Metaphor and a Master of Expression. So far as Style was Concerned the Brilliant Person Preferred Lysias to Antiphon.

The Brilliant Person (whose Practice was on the Small Side) Felt that His Chance had Come when he was Briefed to Defend One of Two Alleged Malefactors. He Determined that he would Show those Duds at the Old Bailey how to Do the Trick.

The Malefactors were Charged with Receiving Goods Well Knowing them to have been Stolen. The Brilliant Person Learned that Malefactor Number Two was to be Represented by a Vulgar Individual with a Cockney Accent. This Annoyed the Brilliant Person a Good Deal, for it was Clear to him that, while his Own Client was Certain of Acquittal, the Case of Number Two Needed Delicate Handling. It was a Pity, the Brilliant Person Reflected, that the

Destinies of Both Prisoners had not been Entrusted to him. The Case Came on.

The Brilliant Person Made a Masterly Speech in which he Expounded the Law, Analysed the Evidence, and Explained to the Jury the Vital Distinction between Actual and Constructive Notice. In his Concluding Sentences the Brilliant Person Invoked the Spirit of Justice. He also Called Three Witnesses to Character.

The Vulgar Individual Began his Observations by Wishing the Jury a Happy New Year. He then Told them a Story about a Scotchman and a Jew. During the Course of his Rollicking Address, which Filled the Brilliant Person with Shame, the Vulgar Individual made no Attempt to Grapple with the Difficulties of the Case. Nor (inasmuch as the Second Malefactor had been Repeatedly Convicted) did he Call any Witnesses to Character.

But, to the Unspeakable Fury of the Brilliant Person, the Jury, without Leaving the Box, Convicted the Brilliant Person's Client and Acquitted Number Two.

Moral.—*Acquire a Cockney Accent.*

LORD PUSHLEIGH OF RUNNYMEDE AND
HIS COAT-OF-ARMS

LORD PUSHLEIGH OF RUNNYMEDE
AND HIS COAT-OF-ARMS

↪

MR. SAMUEL PUSHLEIGH, having been Called to the Bar, Quickly Realised that if he was to Get to the Top he must Take Part in Political Life. So Mr. Pushleigh Became a Friend of the Downtrodden and Oppressed and Joined the Forward Party. He had a Bust of Danton on his Book Case; he Laughed Hoarsely when the House of Lords was Mentioned; and he Spoke on Countless Platforms in a Loud Tone of Voice in Favour of Votes for Minors, the Destruction of Capitalism, a Single Chamber, the Abolition of the Army and the Navy, and the Nationalisation of Everything that was Left Over.

Thirty Years later Mr. (now Sir) Samuel Pushleigh, K.C., Reached the Zenith of his Career. When Title and Coat-of-Arms had to be Decided Upon, Sir Samuel Pushleigh Recalled that an Ancestor (Maternal) was Believed to have Fought by the Side of the Black Prince. His Suggestion that he should be the First Baron Crécy of Poictiers was, to his Annoyance, Rejected by the Authorities, and Ultimately he was Gazetted as Lord Pushleigh of Runnymede. But the Coat-of-Arms, which Arrived with the Coronet and Robes, was All that Lord Pushleigh Could Desire. The Crest (a Crowned Cross-Bow, *Gules*) Surmounted a Shield on which were Quartered First, Three

Leopards of England, Proper, Charged with the Fleurs-de-Lys of France, *Argent*, Secondly, Two Bowmen, Mourant, *Sable*, on a Chevron *Topaz*, between Three Arrow-Heads in Pale. Emblematical Figures Representing Truth and Justice were the Supporters. On a Label beneath Ran the Proud Motto: *Pour Roy et Loy*.

Moral.—*Why not?*

THE JUDICIAL PERSONAGE WHO DISAPPROVED
OF CINEMAS AND SENSATIONAL LITERATURE

THE JUDICIAL PERSONAGE WHO
DISAPPROVED OF CINEMAS AND
SENSATIONAL LITERATURE

ᔐ

A JUDICIAL Personage of Ripe Experience Held Decided Views on the Subject of Cinemas and Sensational Literature. He Felt that they were the Main Causes of the Demoralisation of the Working Classes, the State of Unrest in India, and the General Decadence of the Present Generation. Whenever a Suitable Opportunity Presented itself the Judicial Personage Let Fly at Both of these Weapons of the Evil One. If Informed by the Police Officer in Charge of the Case that the Oaf or Flapper in the Dock had been a Constant Attendant at the Flicks or a Regular Reader of Detective Tales the Judicial Personage Preached an Impressive Sermon and Gave the Offender not Less than Nine Months. And when Responding at a Public Dinner for the Bench, the Guests of the Evening, or What Not, the Judicial Personage did not Fail to Say a Few Forcible Words on Each of these Topics.

Though, Greatly to his Disappointment, his Sermons Seemed to Fall upon Deaf Ears, the Judicial Personage Manfully Continued to Sow the Good Seed.

Once a Week (on Saturday Afternoons) the Judicial Personage Allowed himself a Little Relaxation. He Lunched at the Megatherium, Took a Two-and-

Fourpenny Seat at Whatever Cinema the Hall-Porter Recommended, and Returned to his Club to Tea. During the Latter Refection he Read the Last Edgar Wallace.

Moral.—*Quite Right Too.*

THE FIERCE ADVOCATE WHO REALLY HAD
A SOFT HEART

THE FIERCE ADVOCATE WHO
REALLY HAD A SOFT HEART

～

THERE was Once a Fierce Advocate Who Carried All before him. He was Very Alarming in Court. When he Opened the Case for the Plaintiff or the Defendant his Eye Flashed, and he Said Such Nasty and Sarcastic Things about the Other Side that the Jury were Quite Anxious to Give him a Verdict Then and There. While the Fierce Advocate's Eye was Flashing and he was Saying the Nasty and Sarcastic Things, the Other Side Did its Best to Look Unconcerned.

When it was his Turn to Cross-Examine, The Fierce Advocate Usually Began by Asking the Witness a Few Simple and Direct Questions—whether he was not a Dirty Dog, or a Swindling Scoundrel, or Something of that Sort—and then he Took the Witness through the Details of his Discreditable Past. Company Promoters and Money Lenders Shook in Their Shoes when the Fierce Advocate Got Going, and Experienced Leading Ladies Tottered in a Fainting Condition from the Box. Only the Most Courageous of the Judges Ventured to Criticize his Methods, for it was Well Known that the Fierce Advocate Enjoyed a Breeze with the Bench.

Did the Fierce Advocate Behave in Like Fashion in Private Life? He did not. The Fierce Advocate had Lived in the Same Uncomfortable Rooms for

Thirty Years because he was Afraid to Tell the Proprietor he Wanted to Go Away. His Companions were two Canaries, three Cats and a Parrot, to which Birds and Beasts he was Devotedly Attached. And the Fierce Advocate's Favourite Bed-Side Books were "Jessica's First Prayer" and "Froggy's Little Brother," with one of which he Cried himself to Sleep Every Night.

Moral.—*Be Fierce.*

THE BRILLIANT ORATOR WHO WON FAME
AS A DEFENDER

THE BRILLIANT ORATOR WHO WON
FAME AS A DEFENDER

∽

A BRILLIANT Orator once Shot like a Comet across the Legal Firmament. His More Obvious Endowments were a Commanding Presence, a Rich Voice and a Piercing Eye. The Brilliant Orator's Law was a little Shaky, but he Made Up for This by Knowing All about Everything Else. As a Defender of Important Criminals the Brilliant Orator was Admitted to be *Facile Princeps*. No Murder Case was Complete Without Him. The News that the Police had Arrested the Suspected Person and that the Brilliant Orator had been Retained for the Defence would Appear Simultaneously in the Evening Papers.

At or about the Same Time Enterprising Publishers would Purchase the Serial and Other Rights in the Autobiography of the Suspected Person. The Common Form of Agreement Required that the Suspected Person should Furnish the Completed Manuscript within Three Days after the Conclusion of the Proceedings, and that the Proceedings should be Deemed to be Concluded on the Dismissal of the Suspected Person's Appeal (if any) by the Court of Criminal Appeal. The Brilliant Orator's Favourite Line was that the Murdered Individual was an Undesirable Citizen who had Got no more than his Deserts, but that the Suspected Person had, in fact,

Fired the Revolver by Accident, or Picked Up the Wrong Bottle in the Dark.

When the Suspected Person was a Female of Agreeable Appearance this Defence Went Off very Well indeed.

It was in his Perorations that the Brilliant Orator was Heard at his Best. After Reminding the Jury that the Chain of Evidence was as Strong as the Weakest Link in it, that it was for the Crown to Establish the Case against the Prisoner beyond the Scintilla of a Reasonable Doubt, and that the Doctor who had Conducted the Post-Mortem Examination had Very Fairly Said that he could not Swear that the Murdered Individual was not a Man of Violent Temper, the Brilliant Orator, in a Final Crash of Eloquence, would Ask them to Remember that it was Better that Ninety-nine Innocent Persons should be Convicted than that One Guilty Person should be Acquitted. The Jury, however, always Understood what he Meant. At the Close of his Address the Brilliant Orator would Sink into his Seat in a State of Collapse. There were Cavillers who said that the Brilliant Orator had Secured the Conviction of Several of his Clients; but the Public Knew Better.

Moral.—*Perorate*.

DIEHARD AND STICKIT, JJ.

DIEHARD AND STICKIT, JJ.

E ARLY in the Nineteenth Century Young Mr.
Diehard and Young Mr. Stickit, Barristers-at-
Law, Observed with Concern that the then
Members of the Judiciary Exhibited a Tendency to
Cling to Office Long After the Process of Physical
and Mental Decay had Set In. Mr. Diehard and Mr.
Stickit Regretted on Public Grounds both the
Incompetence and the Immortality of these Judicial
Limpets.

Years Rolled by, and Mr. Diehard and Mr. Stickit,
now of Middle Age, Received the Reward of Merit
and Took their Seats upon the Bench. More Years
Rolled by, and Diehard, J., and Stickit, J., Began to
Note that Youthful Counsel would not Speak Up,
that Leaders Insisted on Mumbling, and that the Bar
was Deteriorating Day by Day.

When Ninety-Three and Ninety-Four Respectively,
Diehard and Stickit, JJ., were Still Going Strong.
They often Assured Each Other that they were Best
Serving the Interests of the Country by Holding on
to their Jobs; that of all Judicial Qualifications Ripe
Experience was the Most Precious; and that if they
were to Retire the Lord Chancellor would Look In
Vain for Anybody who was Fit to Succeed Either of
Them.

Moral.—*Don't Desert the Gold Standard.*

MR. BLUEBAG, MR. BERT BAUMSTEIN AND
"THE OLD JUDGE"

MR. BLUEBAG, MR. BERT BAUMSTEIN
AND "THE OLD JUDGE"

〜

MR. BLUEBAG having Ample Leisure after his Call to the Bar Took to Visiting the Pictures. Sickened by the Foolishness of the Plots Unfolded before him, Mr. Bluebag Took Pen in Hand to See whether he could Emulate the Imbecility of their Authors. The result was Excellent.

Mr. Bluebag's Film Began with the Old Judge, Fully Robed, Returning on Christmas Eve to his Chambers in Pump Court, after a Hard Day's Work. It was Snowing. To the Old Judge's Amazement he Found a Newly-Born Infant (Female) on the Doorstep. Wrapping the Infant Tenderly in his Full-Bottomed Wig, the Old Judge Carried her to the Fire-Side, where, with the Help of his Old Clerk (with White Hair), he Bathed and Fed her.

As the Infant had Brought a New Joy into his Life —for he was Lonely—he Adopted her.

When a Beautiful Young Woman of Eighteen the Infant Produced a Sealed Letter which she had Always Worn Round her Neck. It Informed the Old Judge that she was the Child of his Son, who had been Shipped in Disgrace to the Antipodes and Never Heard of Again.

On the Nineteenth Anniversary of her Discovery on the Doorstep, an Exhausted and Dying Woman

Knocked at the Old Judge's Door. She was Covered with Snow, for it was Snowing. In Faltering Accents she Confessed that the Infant was no Relation of the Old Judge, but her Own Deserted Child. She then Passed Away in the Old Judge's Arms. Was the Old Judge Distressed by her News? No. He had Lost a Grand-Daughter, but he had Won a Bride. And on the Next Christmas Eve there was a Wedding (in the Snow) of Surpassing Splendour at Westminster Abbey, Attended by the Lord Chancellor, the Lords of Appeal, the Lords Justices, the Judges of the High Court, the County Court Judges, and the Three Official Referees. Throughout the Performance (Ran the Instructions of Mr. Bluebag) "Goodnight, Sweetheart" and "Always" were to be Played upon a Mechanical Organ.

Hardly had Mr. Bluebag Completed the Manuscript when Mr. Bert Baumstein, of The Universal Amalgamated Flicks Inc., was Ushered in. He Wished to Consult Mr. Bluebag on the Subject of a Broken Contract. While he was Perusing the Contract Mr. Bluebag was Startled by the Sound of Muffled Sobs. Looking Up, he Observed Mr. Baumstein Quietly Weeping over "The Old Judge." Mastering his Emotion, Mr. Baumstein Enquired whether Mr. Bluebag was Free to Dispose of the Performing Rights in the most Human, Inspiring, Touching and Elevating Scenario he had ever Read. If he were a Willing Vendor Mr. Baumstein could offer Fifty Thousand Pounds (Spot Cash) and a Ten per cent. Royalty. Mr. Bluebag Closed. "The Old Judge" has had a Phenomenal Run in London, New

328

York, Rome, Paris, Vienna, Budapest, Constantinople and Leningrad, and will shortly be Generally Released.   Mr. Bluebag has Retired from the Bar.

Moral.—*Go to the Flicks.*

MR. POTTLE'S NASTY ACCIDENT, THE
SAGACIOUS COOK, AND THE ACTION AT LAW

MR. POTTLE'S NASTY ACCIDENT, THE SAGACIOUS COOK, AND THE ACTION AT LAW

∽

WHEN Mr. Pottle was Beginning to Recover from his Nasty Accident on the Escalator he Very Properly Consulted his Lawyer. The Opinion of Eminent Counsel was Taken, and Mr. Pottle was Assured that if he were to Issue a Writ his Prospects of Success were Good. The Underlying Note of the Opinion was that the Escalator was in the Nature of a Trap, and that Mr. Pottle had not been Given Sufficient Warning of its Dangerous Qualities, whether by the Railway Company or its Servants and Agents.

When Mr. Pottle's Sagacious Cook Came to Take the Orders for the Day, Mr. Pottle Told her of the Encouraging Advice he had Received and Invited her Views. The Sagacious Cook Replied that, for her Part, she would have Nothing to do with those Lawyers who would Go and Say that the Notice Said You were to Step Off with Your Right Foot; that she was Sure Mr. Pottle had Stepped Off with his Left Foot; and that it had All Happened (if Mr. Pottle didn't Mind her Saying so) because Mr. Pottle had Left his Spectacles at Home. Mr. Pottle Smiled Kindly at the Simplicity of the Sagacious Cook.

Twelve Months having Elapsed the Action Came

on for Hearing, and Mr. Pottle Recovered Heavy Damages.

Fifteen Months later a New Trial was Ordered as the Judge had Misdirected the Jury on the Law relating to Invitees and Licensees.

Two Years having Rolled by, a Second Judgment in Mr. Pottle's Favour was Upheld by a Majority in the Court of Appeal. Three Years afterwards the House of Lords Reversed it by a Majority of One.

In the Speech of the Lord Chancellor it was Pointed Out that a Notice Exhibited at the Foot of Escalator Warned Passengers to Step Off with the Right Foot; that the Evidence Clearly Established that Mr. Pottle had Stepped Off with his Left Foot; and that if Mr. Pottle had not Unfortunately Left his Spectacles at Home the Accident would not have Happened.

Moral.—*Ring the Bell.*

THE CHANCERY JUDGE WHO OBSERVED
THAT THE INTELLECT OF HIS COMMON-
LAW BROTHER WAS FAILING

THE CHANCERY JUDGE WHO OBSERVED THAT THE INTELLECT OF HIS COMMON-LAW BROTHER WAS FAILING

ᔆ

ONE Day a Chancery Judge Met a Common-Law Brother in the Judge's Corridor as the Latter was Hurrying towards the Luncheon Room. Full of the Interesting Point which was being Developed in His Court, the Chancery Judge Stopped his Common-Law Brother so that he might Secure the Benefit of his Opinion. Button-holing his Colleague, the Chancery Judge Explained that the Main Question was whether the Appointment of the Land to Trustees for Sale was Good. This Depended upon whether the Will of the Testator had Effected a Conversion of the Land into Personalty. The Underlying Difficulty of the Matter, he said, was Due to an *Obiter Dictum* of Mr. Justice Cockwitch in an Unreported Case which Seemed to Throw an Entirely Fresh Light on the Statute of Uses. The Chancery Judge Observed, as his Narrative Proceeded, that his Common-Law Brother Seemed both Listless and Apathetic. And when the Chancery Judge Asked his Common-Law Brother what he Thought about the Problem and his Common-Law Brother Replied, "The Answer is a Lemon," the Chancery Judge was Reluctantly Driven to the Conclusion that the Intellect of his Common-Law Brother was Failing.

Moral.—*Read Snell.*

335

THE HUSBANDS WHO MET IN THE
ELYSIAN FIELDS

THE HUSBANDS WHO MET IN THE
ELYSIAN FIELDS

～

MEETING in the Elysian Fields, Two Husbands Proceeded to Exchange their Melancholy Experiences in the Divorce Court.
Eighteen-Hundred-and-Sixty was Happily Married,
but One Fine Day he Accompanied a Lady from Hyde
Park to the Recently-Opened Railroad Terminus at
New Cross in a Four-Wheeled Cab. His Wife, Hearing of the Incident, Presented a Petition in the
Divorce Court. The Judge Promptly Decided that
Opportunity for Misconduct having been Afforded
by the Expedition in the Four-Wheeled Cab, there
was a Presumption that Eighteen-Hundred-and-Sixty
had been Unfaithful to his Marriage Vow. Thus his
Home had been Broken Up.

Nineteen-Hundred-and-Thirty said that he had
no Such Luck. Desiring the Dissolution of his Marriage (for his Wife was both Ill-Tempered and Plain)
he Visited the Hotel Magnifique, Shrimpton-on-Sea,
with a Sympathetic Companion. They had not been
Formally Introduced. Their Room was Number 27.
Tea was Brought to them in the Morning by the
Chambermaid. The Judge Decided without Hesitation that in all the Circumstances there was no Satisfactory Evidence of Matrimonial Misconduct on the
Part of Nineteen-Hundred-and-Thirty. In Fact, the
Presumption was that it was a Put-Up Job. Eighteen-

Hundred-and-Sixty Opined that Times had Changed Since his Day and Suggested that they should Have a Little Refreshment at the Adjacent Bar. Nineteen-Hundred-and-Thirty Agreed with Alacrity.

Moral.—*Omnia Præsumuntur*.

THE ERUDITE JUDGE AND THE QUESTION
OF DOUBTFUL ADMISSIBILITY

THE ERUDITE JUDGE AND THE QUESTION OF DOUBTFUL ADMISSIBILITY

∽

THERE Lived in the Past an Erudite Judge who Considered that he was Rather Hot Stuff. Nor was his Good Opinion of himself without Justification; for he had the Law at his Finger Ends and he Expounded it in Language which was both Elegant and Precise. When Opportunity Offered the Erudite Judge would Enrich the Law Reports with a Judgment in which he Discussed all the Authorities, Exposed the Fallacies of Deceased Members of the Bench, Corrected the Errors of Legal Writers, and Generally Cleared Things Up for Posterity. One Fine Day, while the Erudite Judge was Trying a Case in the Common Jury List, Counsel for the Plaintiff Asked the Witness What the Charwoman had Said when the Witness Told her that the Plaintiff had Fallen Over the Pail on the Stairs. The Erudite Judge Directed the Witness not to Answer the Question, and Ordered the Jury to Withdraw. After a Protracted Argument as to the Admissibility of the Question the Erudite Judge Adjourned the Hearing so that he might Consider the Matter Fully.

The Next Day the Erudite Judge Loosed Off a Splendid Bit of Work. No Aspect of the Law of Evidence was Left Untouched. Beginning with the Pandects of Justinian, the Erudite Judge Took his

Hearers through the Canon Law and the Year-Books, and thus Traced to its Source the Doctrine of the Inadmissibility of Hearsay Evidence. By Eleven Forty-Five the Erudite Judge had Got to *Whitelocke* v. *Baker* (13 Ves. 514), Declarations by Deceased Persons, Inscriptions on Tombstones, and the Facts Properly to be Regarded as *Res Gestæ*. At Long Last, when the Stenographers were Shewing Signs of Exhaustion, the Erudite Judge Reached the Conclusion that the Question was Admissible.

The Witness having Returned to the Box Counsel for the Plaintiff Once More Enquired: "What did the Charwoman Say when you Told her that the Plaintiff had Fallen Over the Pail on the Stairs?"

The Witness Replied that the Charwoman hadn't said Nothing. He Added that he wasn't Surprised, which the Charwoman was as Deaf as a Post.

Moral.—*Reserve Judgment.*

BOODLE, CASH & CO. AND THE BIG JOB

BOODLE, CASH & CO. AND THE BIG JOB

〜

M R. BOODLE and Mr. Cash were the Senior Partners in the Firm of Boodle, Cash & Co. Various Sons and Nephews, who Showed Up at the Annual Share-Out, were the Co. If a Big Job came along it was Mr. Boodle and Mr. Cash who Tackled it. One Fine Day a Client of Immense Importance Blew In. He was in a State of Great Agitation. Millions were at Stake and he Insisted that the Best Brains at the Bar must be Secured for the Conduct of the Case.

Mr. Boodle and Mr. Cash Dined together the Same Evening to Decide which Eminent Counsel should be Retained. Mr. Boodle was all for Howler, K.C. Mr. Cash Thought Squeaker, K.C., was the Man for their Money. Mr. Boodle Pointed Out that Squeaker, K.C., was Inaudible, and that Howler, K.C., was a Magnificent Cross-Examiner. Mr. Cash Retorted that Howler, K.C., was Quarrelsome, while Squeaker, K.C., was a First-Class Lawyer. Finally Mr. Boodle and Mr. Cash Agreed that they had better Retain them Both.

Did Things go well? They did Not. When the Defendant had to be Cross-Examined, Howler, K.C., was Elsewhere, and when the Law had to be Expounded Squeaker, K.C., was Engaged in the Court of Appeal.

Moral.—*Don't Litigate.*

345

THE LEARNED YOUTH, UNCLE ROBERT
AND THE CONSULTATION

THE LEARNED YOUTH, UNCLE ROBERT AND THE CONSULTATION

ARE Virtue and Industry always Rewarded? They are not. A Learned Youth was Once Entrusted with a Difficult Matter. The Solicitor Instructing him was his Uncle Robert. The Learned Youth Gave his Whole Mind to the Problems Laid before him, and Advised, at length, as to (1) the Cause of Action (if any); (2) the Party or Parties to be Sued; (3) the Possibility of Enforcing a Judgment in the Union of Socialist Soviet Republics; (4) whether the Writ could be Served out of the Jurisdiction; and (5) Generally. Later on the Learned Youth Prepared a Statement of Claim of a very Imposing Character. On the Eve of the Trial a Consultation Took Place in the Chambers of the Great Man who was to Lead the Learned Youth. The Lay Client, Uncle Robert, and Everybody Else Attended.

When the Great Man Opened the Ball by Announcing that in his Opinion the Action was Entirely Misconceived, Uncle Robert Exhibited Symptoms of Incipient Cerebral Hæmorrhage.

Was Uncle Robert Consoled when the Great Man, after Listening Attentively to a Dissertation from the Learned Youth, Humbly Admitted that the Learned Youth had been Perfectly Right throughout? No. Even after Judgment had been Recovered, with Costs, Uncle Robert Continued to Think and Speak of the Learned Youth as the Idiot who had Nearly Let him Down.

Moral. *Relations are Readily Strained.*

347

MR. TOMPKYNS, CORINNE BOZIEU AND
THE CLOSE-UP

MR. TOMPKYNS, CORINNE BOZIEU
AND THE CLOSE-UP

∽

MR. TOMPKYNS was all in a Twitter when he Heard that Corinne Bozieu, the Fascinating Vamp, Desired his Professional Assistance in the High Court of Justice. And when Mr. Tompkyns was Told that Corinne would herself Confer with him, his Excitement Knew no Bounds.

Corinne Duly Arrived at Sealing-Wax Buildings. Her Charming Appearance Filled Mr. Tompkyns with the Tenderest Emotion. Fixing her Lustrous Eyes upon Mr. Tompkyns, Corinne Told her Sad Story.

It seemed that she had Fallen Out with the Management and was Seeking Damages for Breach of Contract, Wrongful Dismissal, Slander, and Loss of Publicity. The Whole Trouble had Arisen over a Close-Up, and Corinne was Certain that if Anything had Gone Wrong it was All the Fault of that Silly Electrician.

Mr. Tompkyns Made Careful Notes as Corinne Proceeded with her Narrative, and (being a Prudent Person) Asked Corinne to Tell him what Exactly a Close-Up was.

Corinne Explained that the Gentleman Grasps the Lady's Left Arm with his Right Hand. Meanwhile he Spreads the Fingers of his Left Hand across her Shoulders. He then Draws the Lady in the Direction

349

of his Waistcoat and Embraces her Tenderly for Some Seconds.

Mr. Tompkyns, Greatly Interested, Said it would Assist him if he could have a Demonstration of a Close-Up, and Intimated that he was Quite Ready to Do the Gentleman's Part. With Becoming Modesty, he Added that he was Afraid Corinne would Find him Very Clumsy.

Corinne Agreed with Alacrity that this was an Excellent Idea, and Proposed, with a Delightful Little Laugh, that they should Ask her Chaperon (who was Waiting in the Clerk's Room) to Join them.

Mr. Tompkyns, though rather Disappointed to Find Corinne so Victorian in her Ideas, did not See his Way to Oppose this Proposition.

The Chaperon was Ushered in. She was Fat, Muscular, Elderly and Spectacled. To the Horror of Mr. Tompkyns, Corinne Ordered the Chaperon to Show Mr. Tompkyns how to Do a Close-Up.

Placing her Bag and Umbrella on the Table, the Chaperon Told Mr. Tompkyns to Come On. And as Mr. Tompkyns did not Do it Right the First Time, the Chaperon Made Mr. Tompkyns Repeat the Close-Up till he was Perfect.

Moral.—*Deal with the Principal.*

THE VOLUBLE PLAINTIFF AND THE
LACONIC INTERPRETER

THE VOLUBLE PLAINTIFF AND THE LACONIC INTERPRETER

〜

ONCE Upon a Time there Appeared in the Royal Courts of Justice a Voluble Plaintiff of Foreign Extraction. His Country, which Owed its Origin to the Treaty of Versailles, was Situated in the Balkan Region. The Claim of the Voluble Plaintiff, which was both Large and Complicated, was Stoutly Resisted by the Defendant.

As the Voluble Plaintiff was Unacquainted with the English Language the Services of an Interpreter were Requisitioned. When The Time Came for his Cross-Examination, Counsel for the Defendant, by Way of Clearing the Decks, Asked the Voluble Plaintiff whether he had not some Three Years ago Made a Fraudulent Claim upon Underwriters. The Question having been Translated, the Voluble Plaintiff Gave a Shrill Scream Resembling that of a Locomotive Engine when Entering a Tunnel and Delivered an Eloquent Speech, in the Course of which he Threw his Arms about in a Terrifying Fashion. At the End of Five Minutes the Voluble Plaintiff Paused for Breath and the Judge Enquired of the Interpreter what the Voluble Plaintiff had said. The Interpreter Cleared his Throat and Replied: "'E Say 'No.'"

Moral.—*Keep it Short.*

THE KING OF THE UPPER AND LOWER
CANNIBAL ISLANDS AND THE REGIUS
PROFESSOR

354

THE KING OF THE UPPER AND
LOWER CANNIBAL ISLANDS AND
THE REGIUS PROFESSOR

～

THE King of the Upper and Lower Cannibal Islands, being an Enlightened Monarch, Determined to Raise the Standard of his Local Legal Tribunals. To this End he Took the Opinions of the Jurists of Other Countries. Arriving in England he was Referred by the Colonial Office to a Regius Professor who had Made the Practice and Procedure of British Courts of Justice the Study of a Lifetime. The Regius Professor Explained to his Majesty that though the British System was an Expensive one it Happily Cost the Country Nothing. For Nobody could Assert or Defend a Claim without Paying through the Nose at Every Stage of the Proceedings. Thus the Litigants Unconsciously and Painlessly Provided the Cash for Heating and Lighting the Courts and Paying the Salaries of the Judges.

The British Courts, Proceeded the Regius Professor, were Famed for their Absolute Fairness. To Demonstrate their Impartiality they Extended Peculiar Indulgence to Blackmailers, Thieves and Lunatics, all of whom were Deemed to be Virtuous and Sane till the Contrary was Affirmatively Established. Further, it was well Understood that if a Defendant Failed to Appear when his Case was Called On, the

Plaintiff must Prove his Claim with the Utmost Strictness, the Presumption being that the Plaintiff was a Fraudulent Person.

Difficult Questions of Fact were Referred to a Jury of Twelve Reasonable Men and Women. If their Verdict Proved to be Entirely Unreasonable, a New Trial (with a Fresh Jury) was Ordered at the Expense of the Parties, in the Hope that a Different Result would be Secured.

When his Majesty Asked how Twelve Reasonable Persons could Arrive at an Unreasonable Verdict the Regius Professor said he would Deal with that Topic a little Later.

Questions of Law, the Regius Professor Mentioned, were Decided by a Judge from whom there was an Appeal to the Court of Appeal and to the House of Lords. An Appellant could not Succeed in the House of Lords unless he had a Majority in his Favour. Thus if their Lordships Chanced to be Equally divided the Appeal was Dismissed. His Majesty Enquired why the Appeal was not Heard Again, and the Regius Professor said he didn't Know. Divorce Cases, the Regius Professor Continued, were Usually Tried by Lawyers who had been Trained Exclusively in the Admiralty Court, for Reasons which he would Subsequently Explain; and Questions relating to the Cost and Quality of Female Garments were referred to Bachelor Judges. As at this Point the Regius Professor Seemed to be Running Down, his Majesty Thanked him Warmly and Observed that he Thought the System Obtaining in the Upper and Lower Cannibal Islands was, on the Whole, to be

Preferred. If, said His Majesty, a Plaintiff Succeeded in his Claim, the Defendant was at once Handed Over to him to be Eaten; and *Vice Versa*. If Claim and Counterclaim were both Dismissed, the Plaintiff and the Defendant were Reserved for Public Consumption on the Next National Holiday. His Majesty Thought, however, that the Plan of Making the Litigants Pay for the Courts and the Judges was a Good One.

Moral.—*Be Just.*

MR. PUMPKIN, K.C., M.P., THE PORTRAIT, AND
THE WEDDING BELLS

MR. PUMPKIN, K.C., M.P., THE PORTRAIT, AND THE WEDDING BELLS

◡

TO Link Together Cause and Effect is not Always an Easy Matter. But there is no Doubt that the Brush of the Artist who Painted the Portrait of Mr. Pumpkin, K.C., M.P., Set the Wedding Bells Ringing.

Mr. Pumpkin, K.C., M.P., was an Elderly Gentleman whose Personal Appearance was on the Ordinary Side. His Features were Wanting in Regularity, and his Figure did not Recall that of the Eros now Happily Restored to Piccadilly Circus. He was accordingly Much Relieved when the Lady Artist (Cheap) who had been Commissioned by his Constituents to Paint his Portrait Produced a Very Pleasing Presentment of a Handsome Advocate in Wig and Gown. The Only Fear of Mr. Pumpkin, K.C., M.P., was that his Friends might Say that the Portrait was Unduly Flattering. Therefore, when his Friend Mrs. Plumply (Widow) Expressed the View that the Likeness was Excellent, but (if he would not Mind her Saying So) that the Artist had *Not* Done Justice to his Eyes, and that it was Positively *Wicked* to have Hidden his Beautifully shaped Head under a Wig, Mr. Pumpkin, K.C., M.P., Plucked Up Courage and Asked Mrs. Plumply to be his.

Moral.—*Lay It on Thick.*

359

MR. SPLASHER, K.C., AND THE BRIEF WHICH
WAS SUITABLY MARKED

MR. SPLASHER, K.C. AND THE
BRIEF WHICH WAS SUITABLY
MARKED

ᔪᕽ

DESIRING to Sue Various Officials of the
Cats' Meat Distributors' Trade Union for
Acts Done in Pursuance of an Alleged Illegal
Conspiracy, an Aggrieved Person was Advised to
Retain Mr. Splasher, K.C. He did so. Mr. Splasher,
K.C., who was of the Conservative Faith, Held the
View that Every Man has a Right to Work; but that
he also has a Duty to Accept with Gratitude such
Wages as his Employer Thinks he can Afford to
Pay him. Mr. Splasher, K.C., also considered that
Attempts by Workers to Raise the Rate of Wages by
Artificial Means were Dishonest, and that the
Modern Machinery of Trade Unionism was a Menace
to the Social Structure. Accordingly Mr. Splasher,
K.C., after Reading the Sad Story of the Aggrieved
Person with a Sympathetic Eye, Composed some
Telling Passages for his Opening Speech. When
Leaving his Chambers Mr. Splasher, K.C., had a Few
Words with his Clerk. He was Pleased to Learn from
that Faithful Official that they had the Same Fee as the
Other Side; that if the Other Side's Fee were Raised
theirs was to be Pushed Up also; that the Special Fee
(as Mr. Splasher, K.C., was not a Member of the
Circuit) was Duly Marked; that a Refresher of a
Hundred had been Agreed; and that their Junior had
Got his Two-Thirds All Right.

Moral—*Down with the Reds.*

361

BEEFY AND BRAWN

BEEFY AND BRAWN

THAT Beefy of St. Polycarp's was the Best Six of his Time was Universally Admitted at Oxbridge; nor did Anybody at Camford Seriously Contend that a More Brilliant Stroke than Brawn of All Hallows' had Ever Shot Barnes Bridge. Small Wonder that Beefy and Brawn Represented their Respective Universities on Four Occasions, and that when they Retired from Aquatics there was General Lamentation in the World of Sport. Years Rolled by, and on a Chilly Morning in the Month of March Beefy of St. Polycarp's (now Mr. Justice Beefy) met Brawn of All Hallows' (now Chief Justice Brawn, K.C.I.E.) at Putney. They were about to Follow the Race on the Old Blues' Steamer. It was a Great Shock to Mr. Justice Beefy to Realise that while he himself had Retained All his Youthful Activity, Poor Old Brawn had Completely Gone to Seed. Chief Justice Brawn, K.C.I.E., Confessed the Same Evening to a Friend at the Club that Poor Old Beefy's Appearance had Greatly Distressed him. He had Never Seen such a Flat-Footed Old Elephant. Chief Justice Brawn, K.C.I.E., Added that he Failed to Understand why, if he himself could Remain Young and Active, Old Beefy Couldn't do so also.

Moral.—*Why Grow Old?*

THE TWO CLERKS WHO EXCHANGED
EXPERIENCES

THE TWO CLERKS WHO EXCHANGED
EXPERIENCES

∽

AN Aged and Retired Clerk, Revisiting the
Glimpses of the Moon, Fell into Conversation
with a Youthful Member of his Species.
"Remember," said the Aged Clerk, "that you are a
Person of no Little Importance to your Employer. I
myself was Clerk to a Barrister who, but for my
Exertions would never have been Heard of. He was,
I Grieve to Say, Idle, Unbusinesslike and Ignorant,
but by Dint of Unremitting Toil and Unfailing Tact I
was Able to Seat him on the Woolsack." "Sir,"
Replied the Youthful Clerk, "What you tell me
Matches my Relatively Short Experience. I am
Junior Clerk to a City Solicitor of Considerable
Eminence. His Success in the Profession is to me a
Mystery, for he is Coarse in his Manners, and entirely
Devoid of Intelligence. Indeed, Were it not for my
Alertness and Devotion, the Whole Blinking Show
would Bust Up." The Youthful Clerk then Hurried
Away to Put Half a Crown on *Bumboat* for the
Three-Thirty; and the Aged Clerk Looked at his
Watch to See Whether the Houses of Entertainment
were Still Closed.

Moral.—*Keep your Eye on Him.*

MR. JUSTICE SNAPPY AND JANE

MR. JUSTICE SNAPPY AND JANE

༄

MR. JUSTICE SNAPPY was the Terror of the Criminal Classes. When the News that he was Coming to the Old Bailey Reached the Cells of that Establishment the Lamentations of their Occupants were Loud and Long. For they were Confident that Protracted Periods of Penal Servitude, Accompanied (in Suitable Cases) by Heavy Doses of the Cat, were in Store for them. Nor did Mr. Justice Snappy Ever Disappoint their Expectations.

One Evening Mr. Justice Snappy, Whilst Awaiting the Sound of the Dinner-Gong, Reflected with Satisfaction that During the Working Day he had Handed Out to the Offenders who had Appeared before him One Hundred and Fifteen Years and Sixty-Four Lashes. His Meditations were Interrupted by Jane, his Younger Daughter, who Enquired in a Peremptory Manner whether he had Bought the Tickets for "*Hullo, Girls!*"

When Mr. Justice Snappy Replied in a Shaky Voice that he had Quite Forgotten to Do So, Jane Told him that his Conduct was Positively Putrid, that she was Absolutely Fed Up with him, and that he Ought to Have a Trained Nurse to Look After him.

Mr. Justice Snappy Trembled Violently and Said he was Very Sorry Indeed.

Moral.—*Warm Them Up.*

367

YOUNG MR. SIMPLE AND THE VENERABLE
SOLICITOR

YOUNG MR. SIMPLE AND THE
VENERABLE SOLICITOR

∽

A VENERABLE Solicitor, Anxious to do Young Mr. Simple a Good Turn, Visited his Chambers for a Conference. Young Mr. Simple, Delighted to be Singled Out by so Eminent a Personage, Received the Venerable Solicitor with Respectful Cordiality and Begged to be Informed as to the Nature of the Problems by which he was Oppressed. With the Object of Telling a Clear and Vivid Story which would Readily be Followed by Young Mr. Simple, the Venerable Solicitor Assumed the Character of his Client. "I am," he said, "an Elderly Gentleman; I have a Large Town-House and a Handsome Place in The Country; my Income from Gilt-Edged Securities is a Comfortable One; but my Faculties are Waning." At this Point Young Mr. Simple Thought it well to Observe, in a Hearty and Reassuring Voice, that the Venerable Solicitor was Taking too Gloomy a View of his Mental Condition. And Young Mr. Simple to this Day does not Know why the Venerable Solicitor Leapt from his Chair, Uttered a Series of Horrid Maledictions, and Disappeared from his Chambers for Ever.

Moral.—*Don't Interrupt.*

MR. JUSTICE LIEN AND MR. JUSTICE DROP

MR. JUSTICE LIEN AND MR. JUSTICE DROP

∽

M R. JUSTICE LIEN (Trained in the Commercial Court) and Mr. Justice Drop (Bred at the Old Bailey) Proceeded Hand-in-Hand to a Northern Assize Town. It was their First Circuit. Lien, J., who was in Charge of the Calendar, Found himself rather At Sea. Nor was Drop, J., at all Happy when he Got to Work on the Causes. Respectively Puzzled, Each Sought the Assistance of the Other.

Drop, J., was thus Enabled to Deliver a Masterly Judgment (Composed by his Brother Lien) on the York-Antwerp Rules and the Doctrine of Subrogation, while Lien, J., Read out to the Jury an Illuminating Dissertation (Drafted by his Brother Drop) on the Nature and Effect of Corroborative Evidence. Was the Result Satisfactory? Not Entirely. For the Court of Criminal Appeal Held without Hesitation that Lien, J., had Misdirected the Jury, and the Lords Justices were Unanimously Agreed that Drop, J., had Failed to Appreciate the Niceties of the Law of Marine Insurance. In the Judgments of both Tribunals it was Tactfully Suggested that Lien and Drop, JJ., had been Grappling Manfully with Unfamiliar Topics.

Moral.—*Cheats Never Prosper.*

THE OLD BUFFER WHO LIVED IN THE
TEMPLE

THE OLD BUFFER WHO LIVED IN
THE TEMPLE

∽

THERE was once an Old Buffer who Occupied a Fourth Floor in Plum-Tree Court. He Always Wore a Top Hat. His Tenancy Dated from 1871. In 1880 the Old Buffer, to his Great Surprise, Received a Brief from a Solicitor (who Thought he was Somebody Else); but, apart from this Adventure, the Old Buffer's Professional Career had been Inactive. The Old Buffer Dined Nightly at the "Stilton Cheese," except during Term Time, when he Fed in the Hall of the Outer Temple. Here he would Tell his Next-Door Neighbour Stories of the Tichborne Case. In 1890 the Old Buffer Began to Write a Book about "The Six Clerks' Office," but when the Great War Broke out he had not got beyond Chapter III. Apart from his Laundress, of whom he was Rather Afraid, the Old Buffer had no Friends. During the Long Vacation he Found Things Rather Dull.

In 1929 the Old Buffer Began to Exhibit Symptoms of Senile Decay. When he Passed Away in 1930 the Only Person who Regretted his Disappearance was a Blind Beggar to whom he Gave Sixpence Every Saturday Morning. The Undertaker's Men Found the Stairs rather Troublesome. The Manuscript of "The Six Clerks' Office" was Used by the Laundress to Light the Fire for the Next Tenant.

373

The Old Buffer Left his Money to Trustees, Directing them to Establish a Home for Aged Cab-Horses. As these Animals were Found to be Extinct the Trustees Sought the Guidance of the Chancery Courts. The Society for the Befriending of Motherless Cats, the Association for the Housing of Homeless Mules, and the Society for the Promotion of Kindness to Pigs all Asked that the *Cy-Près* Doctrine should be Applied in their Favour, and the Proceedings were Protracted and Costly.

Ultimately it was held that Everything went to the Crown. When the Costs had been Paid Everything Amounted to 61*l*. 4*s*. 10*d*. (Sixty-one Pounds Four shillings and Tenpence).

Moral.—*Live in the Temple.*

APPENDIX 1

THE DISTINGUISHED BENCHER
AND THE LOST FABLE
With apologies to "O"

〜

THERE was Once a Distinguished Bencher of Lincoln's Inn who Wrote and Illustrated Forensic Fables. In the Preface to the Third Volume he Promised Not to Do it Again, a Promise he Repeated (In Parentheses) in the Fourth Volume in 1932. Shortly Afterwards he Took Dinner in Hall. His Menu, after Unknown Adventures, was Discovered in 1961 Tucked into a Second-hand Volume, and is Here Reproduced. If the Text is Obscure the Illustrations are Graphic and Characteristic.

Moral.—*Don't Draw on the Menu.*

LINCOLN'S INN HALL

The Rt. Hon. Lord BLANESBURGH, G.B.E., Treasurer.

MENU.

BENCH TABLE.

Clear Soup

Fillet Sole, Meunière

Mutton Cutlet. Reform.

Persillée Potato, French Beans.

Cold Chicken, Ham, or Tongue.

Green Salad.

Fruit Savarin.

Cheese.

Coffee.

APPENDIX 2

SOME CHARACTERS REVEALED

MANY of the "Forensic Fables" are fanciful embroideries on situations familiar in legal practice, or anecdotes divorced from the personalities of whom they were originally related in Inns of Court gossip. Time has buried in oblivion the factual basis of most of them, but several can still be confidently attached, sometimes firmly, sometimes tenuously, to men still identifiable. Before these connections are forgotten it is worth while putting them on record.

*　　*　　*

P 14
THE DOUBLE-FIRST AND THE OLD HAND

The "old hand" was well known to be Martin O'Connor, called to the Bar by Gray's Inn in 1900. He was also a member of the Middle Temple and practised at No 1 Pump Court. He died at Cheam in 1937 aged 67. Strangely for an Irishman with a marked brogue, he had neither humour nor *panache*, but he was a disconcerting adversary, master of all the technical and procedural "tricks of the trade", which he exploited in the lower reaches of litigation. Once, when a particularly blatant impropriety moved a judge to threaten to stop the hearing and start again with another jury, O'Connor protested that his conduct provided no ground for that. "It was merely a gross breach of professional etiquette on my part." The illustration showing O'Connor's wig pushed well back on his head, as it always was, and his challengingly serious expression, is lifelike and recognisable. Before publishing this fable Theo Mathew, the kindest of men, submitted it to O'Connor, a fellow Catholic, who returned it marked "imprimatur", the standard form of ecclesiastical consent to the publication of a Catholic book. Lord Denning believes that he himself was the double-first in the fable.

P 34
THE WITTY JUDGE AND THE BRONCHIAL USHER

Though the drawing is not a portrait, the subject of this fable is clearly Mr. Justice Darling (1843-1936). He was the only judge of his time who was famous (or notorious) as a compulsive jester on the Bench. His levity was often quite unsuitable to a criminal court. Though he had an established reputation as a wit, many of his impromptus were thought to be well prepared.

MR. JUSTICE CATTEMALL AND MR. JUSTICE DEARLOVE

The drawings are not portraits but the personalities certainly represent two contrasting contemporaries, Mr. Justice Day (1826-1908) and Mr. Justice Kennedy (1846-1915) judges of Theo Mathew's younger days, who represented the antitheses of sentencing. Day passed sternly Draconian sentences. Though in private life he was remarkably kind hearted, he was a firm believer in the efficacy of the lash and, as assize judge at Liverpool in 1887 he was credited with having suppressed street violence there by sentencing leaders of the "High Rip gang" to flogging. In search of first-hand evidence of conditions in the slums there, he perambulated them at night with only his marshal and a detective. His sentencing was systematic, passed after full consideration of the defendant's record, and his practice of requiring a complete *dossier* of each prisoner later became universal. Kennedy, by contrast, could never bring himself to impose heavy sentences and he would bind over defendants whom Day would probably have sent to penal servitude.

THE KINDLY JUDGE AND THE LADY BARRISTER

This fable in which the judge mistook the tall good-looking young barrister for a woman is fictitious, but for the illustration Theo Mathew drew the likeness of one of his lady pupils, Miss Monica Geikie-Cobb, MBE, BA, LLB (see "Under the Wigs" p 66, the memoirs of his clerk, Sydney Aylett). She was called to the Bar by the Middle Temple on 17 November 1922, joined the Midland Circuit and practised in the Temple. She last figures in the Law List in 1955.

p 114
THE TEARFUL PERFORMER AND THE PLAINTIFF WITH A PAST

The drawing is not a portrait, for James Campbell, afterwards Lord Glenavy, (1851-1931) was dominating and handsome, but he had the rare gift of opportune tears in his advocacy and Theo Mathew must have had in mind an episode when Campbell, addressing the jury in a divorce case affected to weep. When his opponent, the satirical Tim Healy Q.C., came to reply, he complained of Campbell's exaggerated statement of his client's miseries and said: "My friend was actually moved to tears by the wrongs of his client—the greatest miracle since Moses struck the rock."

p 122
THE MATURE JUNIOR AND THE DILIGENT PUPIL

This must be Theo Mathew himself. He never took silk and, always approachable by the young, was much sought after as a pupil master.

THE CAUTIOUS SOLICITOR AND THE CHINESE WITNESS

This is an embroidery on a story told by Sir Harold Morris Q.C. (1876-1967) President of the Industrial Tribunal from 1926 to 1945. An eminent City solicitor was to call as a witness a highly connected Chinese client. He told his managing clerk to bring to the Law Courts, for the purposes of the oath, a good china plate and a cockerel. When the client was about to go into the witness box he asked him how he wished to be sworn. He replied: "We Balliol men always affirm." The plate long adorned the solicitor's office near Gracechurch Street. The cockerel provided a Sunday dinner for his clerk. Morris had another story of a less distinguished Chinese witness who just said: "Killum cock, breakum plate, smellie book, allee same."

THE DEAF REPORTER, THE DILIGENT COUNSEL AND THE GLORIOUS WIN

Theo Mathew had in mind the status of some of the lesser 18th century reports described by C. G. Moran in "Heralds of the Law." "Some reporters were in such bad repute that judges would not listen to quotations from them. Lord Kenyon reprimanded Sir Alan Park, when he was at the Bar, for citing Keble ... Barnardiston, Banbury and Atkyns Lord

Mansfield forbade to be cited to him. Winfield catalogues the worst as Sidferin, Gilbert, Keble, Cooke, Cumberbach and (a little after Mansfield's time) Espinasse."

p 216
THE DISTINGUISHED ARCHITECT AND THE PALACE OF JUSTICE

This is an unmistakable caricature of George Edmund Street (1824-1881) and his work on the Royal Courts of Justice. His success in the competition to design them was the culmination of a career chiefly devoted to ecclesiastical architecture and the restoration of churches and he used the same methods on the Law Courts. The commission greatly enhanced his reputation but the unpractical character of the design attracted considerable criticism from the lawyers. He died just before the opening of the building and his elaborate memorial stands against the east wall of the Central Hall, which much resembles the Upper Church at Assisi.

p 220
THE LANGUID LEADER AND THE DUCAL ACTION

The languid leader was obviously (both from the text and the drawing) F. E. Smith, later Lord Birkenhead (1873-1930). Casual, off-hand, unembarrassed, unimpressed, insolent, aggressively contemptuous of mediocrity, known as "Don't Care Smith", he yet had great personal charm and could be excellent company when the mood was not on him to be the contrary. His attitude to work he expressed thus: "Much as I detest work I happened to be born in such circumstances as made it necessary that I should work or starve. I know no more persuasive inducement to work. I arrived at the conclusion that, since unfortunately I had to work, it was, on the whole, worth while to work really hard and achieve some substantial result."

P 254
THE ESTABLISHED JUNIOR WHO HAD NOTHING TO COMPLAIN OF

This is certainly Theo Mathew's contented picture of his satisfactory situation in his mature years.

p 278
THE SILK WHO KNEW HOW TO MAKE A GOOD SHOW

This is an undisguised picture of Edward Carson Q.C., later Lord Carson, (1845-1935). He was one of the most commanding and compelling advocates ever to come to the Bar. Tall, strongly built, dark, with piercing eyes. He seemed to exude power. He was a formidable cross-examiner, overwhelming witnesses by the force of his personality.

p 286
MRS. SARAH STOUT, THE LAST WILL OF MR. BUFFIN, AND THE DRAFT AFFIDAVIT

The fable is fantasy but the illustration is a portrait of Theo Mathew's laundress, as cleaners in the chambers of the Inns of Court were called. The memoirs of Sydney Aylett, his clerk, record that "to her huge delight Mrs. Hayden, our laundress, was selected as a model. She didn't raise any objections when later she discovered that in the fable she was called Sarah Stout."

p 320
THE BRILLIANT ORATOR WHO WON FAME AS A DEFENDER

This is an undisguised caricature of Sir Edward Marshall Hall Q.C. (1858-1928). His gift of dramatic oratory is not in doubt and there is irrefutable evidence of the electric atmosphere he generated in court, but his reputation, magnified by the press, stood higher with the public than with the legal profession, in which he was regarded by some as an actor and sometimes a "ham" actor. He had a compulsive urge to show off and exploit his talent for the histrionic. In a sensational libel action against the "Daily Mail" his conduct was so severely criticised in the Court of Appeal in 1901 that his practice declined and took some time to recover. He scored a notable triumph in the Russell divorce case in 1923. Sir

Douglas Hogg Q.C., later Lord Hailsham, who had been in the first trial, told his client: "There is only one man who might pull it off for you. He might win you a brilliant victory and he might make a terrible mess of it." Theo Mathew did not esteem him.

P 340
THE ERUDITE JUDGE AND THE QUESTION OF DOUBTFUL ADMISSIBILITY

The description of the erudite judge corresponds exactly to the characteristics of Mr. Justice McCardie (1869-1933) though the sketch is not a portrait. He was deeply learned and the foremost master of case law of his day. His judgments were of prodigious length, as exhausting as they were exhaustive, (Lord Justice MacKinnon thought more so) for he set out to tidy things up for posterity, dealing with every authority remotely bearing on the point from the earliest times. Curiously enough his own decisions are rarely cited. His judgments are also marked by his belief in himself as a social and moral philosopher. Theo Mathew did not agree. When someone mentioned to him a forthcoming publication called "The Judicial Wisdom of Mr. Justice McCardie" he remarked: "A slender volume, I think."

Francis Cowper

INDEX

A

ACCENT,
    Aberdonian, 70 *and see* MACINTOSH, ALEXANDER
    Cockney, 305

ACCIDENT,
    nasty, 331
    Tearful Performer in Case arising out of, 115

ACQUITTAL,
    of Smart Young Person, 7

ADDITION,
  expected, to prisoner's family, 88

ADDRESS, *and see* REAL NAME
    change of, by Alfred Grubby, 183
    prepared for Annual Outing, 301

ADMIRALTY DIVISION,
    Judge borrowed from, 95

ADMISSIBILITY,
    of question, 341

ADOLPHUS BROWN,
    amazement of, 52
    distaste for law of, 51
    inspiration of, 52
    invitation to, 51
    refreshment taken by, 52
    University Career of, 51
    walks of, with Mr. Justice Grump, 51
    wandering attention of, 52

ADVICE,
    offered to Proud Parent, 155

ADVOCACY,
    nervous system, effect upon, of, 295

ADVOCATE. *See* BARRISTER

AFFIDAVITS,
 anecdote concerning, 19
 of grandmother, 292
  Sarah Stout, 288
 read by Common-Law Junior, 65

AFTERNOON,
 hot, 201

AGED CONVEYANCERS,
 interchange of good stories between, 19
 luncheon of, 19
 noisy behaviour of, 19

AGINCOURT, DUKE OF,
 action by, 221
 attends consultation, 222
 congratulations of, 222
 mistaken for managing clerk, 222
 rage and indignation of, 222

AGREE,
 Careful Lawyer's doubt as to whether he should concur or,
  275

AGREEMENT,
 common form of, 321

A'ĪN-I-AKBARĪ, OF ABU'L FAZI, 193

ALCOHOL. *See* APPRENTICE

ALL HALLOWS',
 Brawn of, 363

ALL SAINTS,
 Fellow of, 255

ALLIANCE,
 matrimonial, of great lawyer, 228

ALPHABETICAL,
 arrangement, of "Law for the Million," 160

ALPS,
 visited by Athletic Templars, 185

ALTAR,
 hymeneal, 284

"ALWAYS,"
  played on mechanical organ, 328

AMALGAMATED UNION OF FRIENDLESS FEMALE
  WORKERS,
  Irene assisted by, 39

AMBITIOUS YOUTH. *See* YOUTH, AMBITIOUS

ANÆMIC HENRY,
  appointed Attorney-General of Lower Cannibal Islands,
    132
  braininess of, 131
  C 3 state of health of, 132
  gassing of, 131
  machine-gunning of, 131
  shelling of, 131
  travels of, in cattle-truck, 132

ANCESTOR,
  maternal, 309

ANCIENT LIGHTS,
  Real Property Lawyer and, 79

ANGORA,
  rabbits, bred by Alfred, 155

ANY EVENT,
  costs in, 120

APPEARANCE,
  unprepossessing, of managing clerk, 297

APPETITE,
  morbid, of mouse, 287

APPRENTICE,
  Idle, alcohol taken by, 157
      borrowings of, 157
      lunch of, 157
      Managing Directorship of, 157
      marriage of, 157
      salary of, 157
  Industrious, abstemiousness of, 157
        early rising of, 157
        reading of, 157
        reward of, 157

391

"ARCHBOLD'S CRIMINAL PLEADING,"
Consulted by Catternall, J., 95

ARCHITECT, DISTINGUISHED,
Palace of Justice, burning of, 217
                    defects of, 217
                    designed by, 217
                    rebuilding of, 218
reproduction of plans by, 218
senile decay of, 218

ARGUMENT,
protracted, 341

ARM-CHAIR,
purchase of, 202

ARROW-HEADS,
in pale, 310

ASSISI,
visited by Templar, 171

ASSIZES,
visit of Circuiteer to, 9

ATTACHMENT,
to Charming Young Person, of Utter Barrister, 61

ATTORNEY-GENERAL,
Exchequer suit on information of, 109
valedictory address by, 190

AUNT JANE,
application of Miss Jones on behalf of, 27
appointment of, as Female Sanitary Inspector, 28
visit of, to Elderly Junior, 28

AUSTRALIAN PLUTOCRAT,
meeting of Old Bailey Practitioner and, 139

AWARD,
in form of Special Case, 241

AWKWARD SITUATION,
dealt with by Tactful Magistrate, 13

BALD OLD GENTLEMAN,
    appearance of, in Junior's Chambers, 127
    brief brought by, to Junior, 127
    gratifying statements of, to Junior, 127

BANK OF ENGLAND,
    reputation of, 75

"BARDELL *v.* PICKWICK,"
    referred to by capable Guide, 181

"BARNEWALL & CRESSWELL,"
    referred to by Sagacious Old Buffer, 159, 160

BARONET, *and see* GLUE, MANUFACTURER OF,
    Sir Moses Blumenkopf, first, 80

BARONY OF DE MONTAZURE AND FRONT-DE-
    BŒUF,
    abeyance of, 247
    claimed by Miss Smythe-Bilkington-Smythe, 247
    doubt as to existence of, 247

BARRISTER. *See* COUNSEL

BATONS,
    Napoleon on, 227

BATTLEFIELDS,
    visited by Enthusiastic Tourists, 181

BAUMSTEIN, BERT,
    emotion of, 328
    Mr. Bluebag consulted by, 328
    sale of scenario to, 328

BEARD,
    red, of Alexander MacIntosh, 70
    worn in Chancery Court, 66

BEARDED JURYMAN,
    conversation between Blushing Beginner and, 57
    effect upon, of Blushing Beginner's peroration, 57
    fierce expectoration of, 58
    nephew of, 58
    reference of, to Blinking Blighters, 58
    visit of, to "Blue Pig," 58

393

BEAR GARDEN,
    visited by Mr. Fledgling, 151

BEARER BONDS,
    and coupons, disposed of by White-haired Trustee, 75

BED-SIDE BOOKS,
    of Fierce Advocate, 318

BEE. *See* BONNET

BEEFY AND BRAWN,
    achievements of, 363
    meeting of, 363
    shock to and distress of, 363

BEEFY THOMAS,
    elected Member of Parliament, 132
    inability of, to explain Order, 131
    industry of, in Margarine Ministry, 131
    influence of, 132
    manly recruiting speeches of, 131
    mediocre intelligence of, 131
    promotion of, 131
    service rendered to Anæmic Henry, 132
    uniform and decorations of, 131

BEGGAR, BLIND,
    sixpence given to, 373

BEGINNER,
    ordered to sit down, 267
    successful cross-examination by, 267
    unsuccessful re-examination by, 267

BEN JONSON,
    quoted by Sound Lawyer, 98

BENCH,
    unfitness of barristers for, 245

BENCHER,
    distinguished, unkept promise of, 375

BILL OF EXCHANGE,
    action by Holder in Due Course of, 3
    Mr. Algernon FitzCholmondely acceptor of, 69

BINKS & CO.,
    plaintiffs in Exchequer Suit, 109

BIRD, WISE OLD,
  declines to go to Quarter Sessions, 225
  nice little place taken by, 225
  niece Emily, visit by, to, 225
  novel read by, 225
  outliving of contemporaries by, 225
  pigs visited by, 225
  port, brandy and cigar consumed by, 225
  retirement of, 225
  routine thought out by, 225
  skipping of law reports by, 225

BIRKENHEAD,
  oratorical effort of, 295

"BLACK MARIA." *See* HABITUAL CRIMINAL

BLACKMAILERS,
  indulgence extended to, 355

BLAMELESS LIFE,
  of K.C., M.P., 91

BLINKING BLIGHTER,
  reference of Bearded Juryman to, 58

BLOWHARD, K.C.,
  continued popularity enjoyed by, 55
  decay of faculties of, 55
  large earnings of, 55
  methods of, 55
  popularity of, 55
  rivalry between Footle, K.C., and, 55

BLUE EYE,
  mild, of Advocate, 101, 102

"BLUE PIG," *and see* LICENSED PREMISES
  visited by Bearded Juryman, 58

BLUEBAG, MR.,
  ample leisure of, 327
  retirement from Bar of, 328
  scenario composed by, 327

BLUMENKOPF,
  Sir Moses. *See* BARONET

395

BLUSHING BEGINNER,
    brief of, 57
    interview between, and Bearded Juryman, 57
    peroration of, 57
    speech of, 57
    studies of, 57

BODICES,
    tight-fitting, worn by bridesmaids, 238

BODMIN,
    train for, missed, 251

BONN,
    visited by Alfred, 155

BONNET,
    bee in, 206
    with strings, worn by Young Person, 167

BOODLE, MR.,
    discussion between Mr. Cash and, 345

BOOK, OF QUOTATIONS,
    purchased by reporters, 98
    used by Judge, 98

BOOK-WORM,
    Real Property Lawyer not a mere, 79

BOOTS, STOLEN,
    worn by prisoner, 264

BOWLER,
    worn by Heavyside, J., 252

BOWMEN, MOURANT, 310

BOULOGNE-SUR-MER,
    duties discharged at, by Beefy Thomas, 131

BOZIEU, CORRINE,
    delightful little laugh of, 350
    explanation of Close-Up by, 349
    visit of, to Mr. Tompkyns, 349

BRAWN,
    brilliance of, as stroke, 363

396

BREAKFAST,
Bobby Chump better at, 295
comfortable, of Wise Old Bird, 225

BREATH,
pause for, 353

BRIDGE, BARNES,
shooting of, 363

BRIEF,
delivered by Leading Solicitor, 135
devilled by Inexperienced Advocate, 3
offered by Bald Old Gentleman, 127
received by Blushing Beginner, 57
Common Law Junior, 65
Double-First, 15
Enthusiastic Beginner, 31
Old Buffer, 373

BRIGHT, MR.,
and Special Case, 241

BRONCHIAL USHER,
characteristics of cough of, 35
rebuked by Witty Judge, 36
transferred to Commercial Court, 36

BROTHER,
Common-law, answer of, to Chancery Judge, 335
explanation of interesting point to, 335
failing intellect of, 335
listless and apathetic demeanour of, 335
Froggy's Little, read by Fierce Advocate, 318

BROUGHAM,
oratorical effort of, 295

BROWN, OLD,
friendship of Grump, J., for, 51

"BUBBLE & SQUEAK." *See* K.C., M.P.

BUDAPEST,
run of film in, 328

397

BUFFER,
Old, brief received by, 373
charity of, 373
dinner of, 373
fourth floor occupied by, 373
stories of, 373
top hat of, 373
will of, 374
writing of book by, 373
Sagacious Old. *See* SAGACIOUS OLD BUFFER

BUFFIN, MR.,
last will of, 287
nasty cough of, 287

BUFFLE, MR.,
assistance rendered by, 168
cheque signed by, 168
cup of tea taken by, 167
humorous observation attributed to, 19
literary work of, 167
meeting of, with Young Person, 167, 168
purchase of photograph by, 168
visited by Seedy Individual, 168

"BULLEN & LEAKE." *See* OLD STAGER

BUMBOAT,
backed for three-thirty, 365

BUNDLEPUMP,
John Marmaduke, address of Tactful Magistrate to, 13

BUS,
collision between taxi-cab and, 297

BUTLER,
drunkenness and dishonesty of, 259

BYNKERSHOEK,
cited by Emeritus Professor, 148

C

CAB,
four-wheeler, drive to New Cross in, 337
horses, aged, home for, 373, 374

CABBAGE,
    strong smell of, 183

CALEDONIAN,
    extraction, Judge of, 69
    from Judæa, 70
        Scotland, 70

CALM,
    of Mr. Fledgling, 151

CAMERON, VIOLET,
    charms of, 193

CANARIES, 318

CANDLES,
    purchased by Cautious Solicitor, 173

CANNIBAL ISLANDS,
    Lower, Attorney-General of, 132
        Chief Justice of, 132
        climate of, 132
    Upper and Lower, King of, 355
            legal system of, 357

CANON LAW,
    referred to by Erudite Judge, 341

CAPABLE GUIDE,
    largesse bestowed upon, 181
    observations of,
        on "Bardell v. Pickwick," 181
            Battle of Evesham, 181
            Charles Lamb, 181
            Charles the First, 181
            Queen Elizabeth, 181
            Richard the Third, 181
            "Vicar of Wakefield," 181

"CARDINAL, CUISINE DU." *See* TEMPLARS, ATHLETIC

CARLTON HOUSE TERRACE,
    removal to, of Young Solicitor, 160

CASE,
    Special, award in form of, 241

399

CASE (*continued*)
    unreported, of Cockwitch, J., 335

CASH,
    Mr., discussion between Mr. Boodle and, 345
    spot, 328

CATALPA TREE,
    meeting of Mr. Buffle and Young Person under, 167, 168

CATS,
    affection of Fierce Advocate for, 318
                  Snappy, J. for, 367
    motherless, Society for befriending of, 374

CATHEDRALS,
    visited by Enthusiastic Tourists, 181

CATTEMALL, J.,
    appeals to Court of Criminal Appeal from, 95
    gratified by lamentations of prisoner's relatives, 95
    petitions against sentences of, 95

CAUSE,
    decisive, 232
    efficient, 232
    proximate, 232
    remote, 232

CAUTIOUS SOLICITOR,
    enquiries by, 173
    interview of, with Chinese Witness, 174
    invited to have a drink, 174
    methodical habits of, 173
    purchase by, of candles, 173
                  saucer, 173
                  White Cockerel, 173

CELLS,
    visit of Youthful Barrister to, 7

CENTRAL HALL,
    of Royal Courts of Justice, 163

CESTUIS QUE TRUSTENT,
    confidence of, in White-haired Trustee, 75

CHAMBERMAID,
    tea brought by, 337

CHAMBERS, *and see* ELIGIBLE CHAMBERS
    read in by Circuiteer, 9
    sought by Ambitious Youth, 73
CHAMPAGNE,
    regrets of Mildew, J., as to, 163
CHANCERY,
    Leader, absence of, in House of Lords, 65
    Old-Fashioned Judge of, 283
    proceedings in, possibility of, 80
CHANGES,
    judicial, 232
CHAPERON,
    order to Mr. Tompkyns, 350
    personal appearance of, 350
CHAPLAIN, HIGH SHERIFF'S,
    and Deanery of Porchester, 302
    dissertation composed by, 301
    mumbling of, 301
    shock of, 301
    success of sermon of, 301
CHARWOMAN,
    silence of, 342
CHEQUE, *and see* STUMER,
    filling up of Counterfoil of, 105
    handed to Seedy Individual, 169
CHESHIRE CHEESE,
    visited by Enthusiastic Tourists, 181
CHICKEN FARM,
    Alfred in charge of, 155
CHI-HUNG-CHANG,
    a Christian Scientist, 174
    affirmation by, 174
    arrangements of, to see Grand National, 174
    drink suggested by, 174
    on prospects of "Silly Billy," 174
"CHIEN, DENT DU." *See* TEMPLARS, ATHLETIC
CHOP,
    ordered by Scientist, 205

401

CHOSES IN ACTION,
    contained in bag, 75
"CHUBBY,"
    carried by Smart Young Person, 7
CHUMP, BOBBY,
    eloquent speech prepared by, 295
    gait of, 295
    nervous strain upon, 295
    manner and appearance of, 295
CHUMP, MRS. BOBBY,
    alarm of, 295
    explanation of Bobby to, 295
    relief of, 295
CICERO,
    quoted by Sound Lawyer, 98
CIGAR,
    offer of, to Circuiteer, 9
    smoked by Nice Old Buffer, 9
CIGARETTES, 301
CINEMA,
    disapproved of by Judicial Personage, 313
    recommended by Hall Porter, 314
    visited by Judicial Personage, 314
CIRCUITEER,
    change of profession of, 10
    conversation of, 9
    horror of, 10
    meeting of, with Nice Old Buffer, 9
    offer of cigar to, 9
CITY MERCHANT,
    failure of, to fill up Counterfoil, 105
CLERK,
    experienced and active, 73
    incompetent, loss of depositions by, 251
                        tickets by, 251
                    silk hat worn by, 252
    managing, unprepossessing appearance of, 297
    of Mr. Buffin, 287
    zealous, 21

CLERKS, THE TWO,
    exchange of experiences between, 365
CLOSE-UP,
    explained by Corinne Bozieu, 349
    practised by Mr. Tompkyns, 350
CLOVES,
    smell of, left by Stout Stranger, 84
CLUB,
    tea at, 314
COAL-SCUTTLE,
    purchase of, 202
COAT-OF-ARMS,
    Lord Pushleigh of Runnymede, 309, 310
COCKED HATS,
    witnesses cross-examined into, 222
COCKEREL,
    crowing of, 174
    White, purchased by Cautious Solicitor, 173
COCKTAIL PARTIES,
    disapproved of, 283
COCKWITCH, J.,
    obiter dictum of, 335
COLD SUPPER,
    of Real Property Lawyer, 79
COLLEAGUE, *and see* TACTFUL MAGISTRATE
    adventure of Much-Respected, 13
COLOURED GENTLEMAN,
    offer of, to Ambitious Youth, 73
COMMENTS,
    sharpness of Judge's, 197
COMMERCIAL COURT,
    transfer of Bronchial Usher to, 36
COMMON PLEAS,
    Court of, 213
COMPANION,
    sympathetic, 337

COMPANY PROMOTER,
    cross-examination, 317

CONCUR,
    Careful Lawyer's doubt as to whether he should agree or,
        276

CONDUCT,
    putrid, of Snappy, J., 367

CONDUCTOR,
    negligence of, 15

CONDY'S FLUID,
    ordered by Kindly Judge, 292

CONFERENCE,
    between Venerable Solicitor and Mr. Simple, 369

CONFESSION,
    modest, of Old Stager, 111

CONFIDENCE,
    in White-haired Trustee, 75
    reposed in Old Bailey Practitioner, 140

CONGRATULATIONS,
    to Languid Leader, 222

CONSEQUENCES,
    of financial career, 143

CONSTANTINOPLE,
    run of film in, 328

CONSULTATION,
    with Silk, 222, 279

CONTEMPT,
    for leader, felt by Junior, 31

CONTINENT,
    sale of securities on, 76
    visited by White-haired Trustee, 76

CONVICTION,
    certificate of, 279

COOK, SAGACIOUS,
    views upon lawyers of, 331

CORK,
    accent of Millionaire's Nephew, 139
CORONA,
    smoked by Established Junior, 256
            First Offender, 177
COSTERMONGER, ITALIAN,
    charge against, 149
COSTS,
    agreed, of eminent firm, 141
    in any event, 120
COUGH,
    quality of Bronchial Usher's, 35
COUNSEL. *See* PASSIM
COUNTRY WALK,
    taken by Real Property Lawyer, 79
COUNTY COUNCIL,
    case concerning, 52
COUPONS. *See* BEARER BONDS
COURT, DIVISIONAL,
    experiences of Careful Lawyer in, 275, 276
COURT OF APPEAL,
    engagement in, of Squeaker, K.C., 345
    judgment of, in Finkelheim *v.* Cohenstein discussed, 185
    win of Miss Mary Poppleton in, 102
COURTS,
    heating and lighting of, 355
CRASH,
    heard, 263, 264
CRASHER, J.,
    domestic tyranny of, 259
    reform of, 260
    ungentlemanly language to Lady Crasher of, 259, 260
    violent displeasure of, 259
CRASHER, LADY,
    successful appearance in person of, 260
CRASHING,
    of Junior's Clerk, 127

405

CRÉCY OF POICTIERS,
    Barony of, 309
CRÈME-DE-MENTHE,
    consumed by K.C., M.P., 91
                Lady Member of "Pongo's," 91
CREST,
    of Lord Pushleigh of Runnymede, 309
CROSS-BOW, CROWNED, 309
CROSS-EXAMINATION,
    damaging, of Mr. FitzCholmondely, 70
    experiences of Profound Lawyer under, 298
    offensive, of Defeated Litigant, 43
    powerful, of Mrs. Tompkyns, 40
    successful, of Holder in Due Course, 3
CROSSING,
    rough, of Templar, 171
CROWN,
    determination in favour of, 374
"CUISINE DUE CARDINAL." *See* TEMPLARS, ATHLETIC
CY-PRÈS DOCTRINE,
    application of, 374

D
DALRYMPLE, POPSIE, MISS,
    charming appearance of, 52
DAMAGES,
    recovered by Mr. Pottle, 332
    tender of, by Real Property Lawyer, 80
DARTMOOR,
    acquaintance of plaintiff with, 280
DATE, of accident, 297
DAWN,
    breaking of, peroration as to, 57
DEAFNESS,
    of Charwoman, 342
DEANERY,
    of Porchester, 302

DEARLOVE, J.,
    binding over by, 95
    gentleness of, towards old offenders, 95
    kindness of, towards young offenders, 95
    tears shed by, 95

DEBENTURE-HOLDERS' ACTION,
    humorous story concerning, 19

DECAY, SENILE,
    symptoms of, 373

"DECLARATION OF PARIS," 147

DECORATIONS,
    of Beefy Thomas, 131

DEER-PARK,
    of Sir Moses Blumenkopf, Baronet, 80

DEFEATED LITIGANT,
    approached by Rash Attendant, 43
    calculation by, 43
    horrid oaths of, 43
    offensive cross-examination of, 43
    state of mind of, 43

DEFENDANT,
    substitution of, 210

DEFENDANTS,
    joinder of trustees of marriage-settlement as, 19

DEMEANOUR,
    furious, of Alfred Grubby, 183

DEMISE,
    of important personage, 228

DESKS,
    of Counsel, 217

"DEVIL,"
    desire of Ambitious Youth to, 73
    performance of Inexperienced Advocate as, 3

DICTUM, OBITER,
    of Cockwitch, J., 335

DIEHARD, J., *and see* STICKIT, J.
    best interests of country served by, 325
    holding on to job by, 325
    merit of, rewarded, 325
    regrets of, 325

DIGESTIVE BISCUITS,
    eaten by Miss Jones, 28

DIGNITY,
    winsome, of Sweet Young Lady, 248

DILAPIDATED STATE,
    of Traveller, cause of, 49

DILIGENT,
    counsel, discovery of authority by, 213
    pupil, Mature Junior irritated by, 124
        order to, by Mature Junior, 124
        questions of, to Mature Junior, 123
        recovery of consciousness by, 124
        struck with poker by Mature Junior, 124

DINNER,
    Mr. Pott invited to, 237

DIRECTOR OF PUBLIC PROSECUTIONS,
    papers sent to, 242

DISCOVERY,
    menu, of, 375

DISHONESTY,
    of butler, 259

DISMISSAL,
    wrongful, 349

DISTRICT COUNCIL, RURAL,
    action against, 221

DIVISION, SECOND,
    three months in, 275

DIVORCE,
    question relating to, tried by Admiralty lawyers, 356

DOCTOR'S FEE,
    paid by Much-Respected Colleague, 13

DOG,
    dirty, 317
    growls of ill-looking, 80

DOGMA,
    in sermon, 301

DOMESTIC SERVANT,
    negligence of, 62

DOMINIONS,
    beyond the seas, laws of, 61

DOOR,
    locked by Sagacious Old Buffer, 160

DOORS,
    noisy clapping of, 217

DOUBLE-FIRST,
    brief delivered to, 15
    epigrams of, 15
    successful application for stay of execution by, 16
    treatment of, by Old Hand, 16

DOZE,
    gentle, of Experienced Judge, 23

DRAFT AFFIDAVITS,
    humorous story as to, 19

DRAFTSMAN, PARLIAMENTARY,
    execrated, 193

DRONING,
    of Counsel, cessation of, 25

DROP, J.,
    masterly judgment of, 371
    reversed by Lords Justices, 371

DRUNKENNESS, *and see* INTOXICATION
    of butler, 259

DUDS,
    judicial colleagues regarded as, 245

EAR-TRUMPET,
>of Promising Equity Junior, 1

EASEMENTS IN GROSS,
>knowledge of Real Property Lawyer as to, 79

EATING,
>of Defendant by Plaintiff, 356
>>Plaintiff and Defendant, 357
>>>by Defendant, 356

EFFORT,
>oratorical, 295

EIGHTEEN-HUNDRED-AND-SIXTY,
>experiences of in Divorce Court, 337

ELBOW,
>lifting of, 284

ELDERLY PERSON,
>not a teetotaller, 73

ELEPHANT,
>flat-footed old, 363

ELIGIBLE CHAMBERS,
>Clerk attached to, 73
>occupants of, 73
>secured by Ambitious Youth, 73
>sought by Ambitious Youth, 73

ELOQUENCE,
>Quintilian on, 57

EMBRACE,
>tender, 350

EMERITUS PROFESSOR,
>address of, to Magistrate, 148
>authorities cited by, 148, 149
>beard of, 147
>briefed in Police Court, 148
>described as lunatic, 149
>flat feet of, 147
>honorary degrees of, 147
>of international law, 147

EMERITUS PROFESSOR (*continued*)
  published works of, 147
  spectacles of, 147
  weak voice of, 147

EMPHYTEUTIC LEASE,
  case concerning, 31

EMOTION,
  of Tearful Performer, 116

ENGAGEMENT,
  long, insisted upon, 238
  short, insisted upon, 238

ENGINE,
  locomotive, 353

ENGLISH LAKES,
  visited by Enthusiastic Tourists, 181

ENQUIRIES,
  made by Industrious Youth, 84

ENTERTAINMENT,
  houses of, closed, 365

ENTHUSIASTIC,
  Beginner, briefed in Privy Council, 31
      contempt of, for Leader, 31
      determination of, to follow Leader, 31
      second thoughts of, 32
  Tourists, address of Capable Guide to, 181
      crowded fortnight of, 181
      largesse heaped upon Capable Guide by, 181
      visit of, to Temple, 181

EPILEPTIC FIT. *See* FIT

EQUITY,
  Draftsmen, luncheon of, 19
      noisy behaviour of, 19
      old brandy consumed by, 19
      stories told by, 19
      And see AGED CONVEYANCERS
  Leader. *See* LEADER

411

ESCALATOR,
> Mr. Pottle's accident on, 331

ESTATE PUR AUTRE VIE,
> case as to, 65

ESTOPPEL,
> point of, argument of Enthusiastic Beginner upon, 31

EVESHAM,
> battle of, 181

EVIDENCE,
> corroborative, Lien, J., on, 371
> Erudite Judge on law of, 341
> of Profound Lawyer, worthlessness of, 298

EXAMINATION-IN-CHIEF, 183

EXCEEDINGLY PAINFUL CASE. *See* SMART YOUNG PERSON

EXCHEQUER SUIT,
> on information of Attorney-General issuing out of Petty-Bag, 109, 110

EXHAUSTION,
> signs of, shewn by Stenographers, 342

EXPECTATIONS,
> happy, of Mr. and Mrs. Pott, 238

EXPERIENCE,
> ripe, 325

EXPERIENCED,
> Advocate, failure of, to fill up counterfoils, 105
>> half-year's rent demanded from, 105
>> indignation of, 105
>> three wins of, 105
> Judge, affirmed in the House of Lords, 24
>> boredom of, 23
>> compliment of Lord Chancellor to, 24
>> gentle doze of, 23
>> judgment of, affirmed in the Court of Appeal, 24
>> presence of mind of, 23
>> profound sleep of, 23
>> trial of complicated case by, 23

EXPLOSIVE,
    invented by Scientist, 205

EXTERRITORIALITY,
    doctrine of, 148

EYE, *and see* SUFFOLK
    black, of Prisoner, 263
    contused, of First Offender, 178
    mild blue, of fragile creature, 101
    sympathetic, 361

EYES, *and see* JONES, MISS
    justice not done to, 359

F

FACT,
    difficult questions of, 356

FACULTIES,
    waning, of Elderly Gentleman, 369

FAINTING,
    of Counsel in Chancery Court, 66

FAINTNESS, SIGNS OF,
    shewn by Sweet Young Lady, 248

FAIRNESS,
    of British Courts, 356

FAMILY,
    addition to, expected by Prisoner's wife, 88

FANCY,
    quaint, 241

FARREN, NELLIE,
    elegant figure of, 194

FEARS,
    realisation of Middle-Aged Junior's Worst, 28

FEE, *and see* FIVE AND ONE
    increase of, 222
    special, marked, 361

FEET FLAT,
    of Emeritus Professor, 147

413

FEMALE,
 Journalist, occupying chambers on top floor, 73
 Sanitary Inspector, appointment of Aunt Jane as, 28

FEME COVERTE,
 humorous story concerning, 19

FICTION,
 truth distinguished from, 190

FIELDS, ELYSIAN,
 meeting of husbands in, 337

FIERCE ADVOCATE,
 bedside books of, 318
 canaries, cats and parrot of, 318
 methods of, 317
 soft heart of, 318

FIERCE-LOOKING OPPONENT,
 of Fragile Creature, 101

FIGURE, SLENDER,
 of Sweet Young Lady, 248

FINANCIAL CAREER,
 of Old School Friend, 143

FINKELHEIM *v.* COHENSTEIN. *See* COURT OF APPEAL

FIRE,
 destruction of treatise by, 62

FIRM OF HIGH STANDING,
 cashing up by, 111
 sued, 109
 terror of, 110

FIRST OFFENDER,
 address of, to Habitual Criminal, 177
 attacked by Habitual Criminal, 178
 bucket-shop of, 178
 cigar smoked by, 177
 observations of Judge to, 178
 richly dressed, 177
 sentence upon, 178

FIT,
 epileptic, simulated by William Shakespeare, 35

FITZCHOLMONDELY, ALGERNON, MR.,
    birth-place of, 70
    borrowing transactions of, 69
    judgment obtained against, 70
    original name of, 70
FIVE AND ONE,
    investment of fee of, 202
FIVE YEARS,
    on each count, given by Cattemall, J., 95
FLAT,
    near Earl's Court, 238
    of Mr. and Mrs. Bobby Chump, 295
FLEDGLING, MR.,
    account given by, to his family, 152
    briefed on application for particulars, 151
    elderly opponent of, 152
    researches of, 151
    sleepless nights of, 151
    success of, 152
FLEUR-DE-LYS,
    of France, 310
FLEURETTE, MADAME. *See* HEBREW, STOUT
FLORENCE,
    visited by Templar, 171
FLUID, CONDY'S,
    ordered by Kindly Judge, 292
FLY,
    in ointment, 209
FOOTLE, K.C.,
    continued popularity of, 55
    decay of faculties of, 55
    large earnings of, 55
    popularity of methods of, 55
    rivalry between Blowhard, K.C., and, 55
FOOZLE, J.,
    an indifferent golfer, 119
    a profound lawyer, 119
    conduct of, at seventeenth hole, 119, 120

FOOZLE, J. (*continued*)
    drawn against Mr. Slasher, 119
    eight holes won by, 119
    eighteenth hole done in five by, 120
    handicap of, 119
    match won by, 120
    order of, in Chambers, 120

FORCEFUL OBSERVATIONS,
    made for Defendants, 24

FORENSIC FABLES,
    second-hand volume, unusual contents of, 375

FORESHORE,
    case concerning, 52

FRAGILE CREATURE,
    mild blue eyes of, 101
    squeaky voice of, 101

FRANCE,
    visited by Enthusiastic Tourists, 181

"FRASER ON LIBEL,"
    consulted by Judge, 45

FRIENDLESS FEMALE WORKERS,
    Amalgamated Union of, assists Irene, 39

"FROGGY'S LITTLE BROTHER." *See* "BROTHER, FROGGY'S LITTLE"

FROU-FROU, MADAME. *See* SHAFTESBURY AVENUE

FUR COAT,
    of First Offender, 177

FUR-TRIMMED COAT,
    of Smart Young Person, 7

FURY, UNSPEAKABLE,
    of Brilliant Person, 306

G

GA.,
    tourists from, 181

GALLERY,
    descent from, 248

GARMENTS, FEMALE,
    cases as to, 356
GENERATION,
    new, 283
GENOA,
    measles contracted in, 171
GENTLEMAN,
    Stout, 280
    with broken nose, 280
GERMAN, CONVERSATIONAL,
    acquired by Alfred, 155
GIANTS, FORENSIC,
    of past, 185
"GIDDY GOAT." *See* K.C., M.P.
GIFT,
    of Aged Judge, 202
    over on Compound Event, case as to, 65
GLUE,
    Manufacturer of, 238 *and see* BARONET
GOGGLING,
    of Adolphus Brown, 52
"GOLDEN UNICORN,"
    accident seen through window of, 183
"GOLLYWOG,"
    reflections of Mildew, J., upon, 164
"GOODNIGHT, SWEETHEART,"
    played on mechanical organ, 328
GOOD STORY,
    told by Aged Conveyancer, 19
GOSSIP,
    evils of, 301
GOVERNMENT DEPARTMENT,
    dishonesty of, 205
GRAND NATIONAL,
    Chi-Hung-Chang and, 174

417

GREY, SYLVIA,
    charms of, 193
GROTIUS,
    cited by Emeritus Professor, 148
GROUSE,
    wildness of, 171
GROUSE-MOOR,
    right of way over, 221
GROWLS,
    of ill-looking dog, 80
GRUBBY, ALFRED,
    furious answer of, 183
    leading question put to, 183
GRUMP, J.,
    invitation of, to Adolphus Brown, 51
    retirement to rest of, 52
    sudden question by, 52
    taciturnity of, 51
    talkativeness of, 52
    well-ordered narrative of, 52
GUDGEON, MABEL,
    dressmaker's demand upon, 237
    engagement of, 238
    flat of, 238
    horror of, 237
    shopping expeditions of, 238
    smile of, 237
    string-bag of, 238
    tears of, 237
    wedding of, 238
GUIDES, GIRL, 301

                    H
HABITUAL CRIMINAL,
    address of First Offender to, 177
    conversation of, in "Black Maria," 177
    violent assault by, upon First Offender, 178
HÆMORRHAGE, CEREBRAL,
    symptoms of, 347
                    418

HAIR,
Bobbed, 248

HALL-PORTER,
cinema recommended by, 314

HAND, WELL-SHAPED. *See* Jones, Miss

HANDKERCHIEF,
no dry, in Court, 115

HEAD,
beautifully shaped, 359
kept by Tactful Magistrate, 13

HEAD-NOTE,
of Deaf Reporter, 213

HEART,
proof learnt by, 298

HEATING APPARATUS,
patent, 217

HEAVY JOB,
offered by Stout Stranger, 83

HEAVYSIDE, J.,
fury of, 252
headgear of, 252
incompetent clerk of, 251
merits of, 251
train missed by, 251
want of courage of, 251

HEBREW, STOUT,
Madame Fleurette in fact a, 237

HEIR, EXPECTANT,
life of, insured, 242

HENRY. *See* Pott, Mr. Henry

HEREDITAMENT. *See* Messuage

HICCUP,
of Laundress, 272

HIGHLY-PLACED OFFICIAL,
advice of, to Elderly Trustee, 76
retirement of, on pension, 76

HIMALAYA,
    Khojas of, 193
HISTRIONIC DISPLAY,
    of Inexperienced Advocate, 4
HOLDER IN DUE COURSE,
    admissions of, 4
    cross-examination of, 3
    judgment against, 4
    loss of nerve by, 3
    red nose of, 3
HOT STUFF. *See* REAL PROPERTY LAWYER
HOTEL MAGNIFIQUE,
    visit to, 337
HOUSEKEEPER,
    displeasure of, incurred by Real Property Lawyer, 81
HOWLER, K.C.,
    absence of, 345
    cross-examining powers of, 345
"HULLO, GIRLS!"
    failure to buy tickets for, 367
HUSBANDS,
    discussion of experiences between, 337
    meeting of, in Elysian Fields, 337
    refreshment taken by, 337

I

INDIVIDUAL, VULGAR,
    acquittal of malefactor defended by, 306
    Cockney accent of, 305
    rollicking address of, 306
    story told by, 306
INDUSTRIOUS,
    Apprentice. *See* APPRENTICE, INDUSTRIOUS
    youth. *See* YOUTH, INDUSTRIOUS
INEXPERIENCED ADVOCATE,
    alarm of, 3
    delight of solicitor instructing, 4
    dropping of jaw of, 3

420

INEXPERIENCED ADVOCATE (*continued*)
    employed as "devil," 3
    glazing of eye of, 3
    unexpected success of, 4

INFANT. *See* SNAFFLETON, MISS (INFANT)

INJURIES,
    of plaintiff, 232

INN,
    visited by Real Property Lawyer, 79

INNER TEMPLE HALL,
    visited by Queen Elizabeth, 181

INNOCENCE,
    Foozle J.'s look of extreme, 120

INSCRIPTIONS,
    on tombstones, 342

INSPECTOR,
    record of prisoner produced by, 88
    thumb moistened by, 88

INSURANCE COMPANIES,
    effect of Tearful Performer upon, 115

INTELLECT,
    failure of, 335

INTELLIGENCE,
    solicitor devoid of, 365

INTERNATIONAL LAW,
    Emeritus Professor of, 147

INTERPRETER, LACONIC,
    services of, requisitioned, 353
    question interpreted by, 353

INTOXICATION,
    of butler, 259
    of laundress, 272
    slight, of Expectant Heir, 242

IRENE MUGG,
    damages recovered by, 40
    grit of, 39
    libel action by, 40

421

IRENE MUGG (*continued*)
    licensed house taken by, 40
    visit to, of Young Man, 39

IRISH,
    Free State, laws of, 61
    Protestant, marriage between Roman Catholic and, 52

IRON SHOT,
    beautiful, of Mr. Slasher, 119

IRRITABILITY,
    of Mature Junior, 123

ITALY,
    visited by Enthusiastic Tourists, 181

J

JANE,
    opinion expressed by, of Snappy, J., 367

JANITOR OF "BLACK MARIA,"
    detaching of Habitual Criminal from First Offender by, 178
    kindliness of, 177

JAVELIN-MEN,
    reception of Stuffin, J., by, 10

JENKINSON, MRS.,
    enquiry by, as to Irene's character, 39
    resident in Putney, 39

"JESSICA'S FIRST PRAYER,"
    read by Fierce Advocate, 316

JESTS,
    concerning mothers-in-law, 98
               Scotchmen, 98

JOB,
    put-up, 337
    tackling of big, 345

JOHN BARKER'S,
    shopping at, 238

JOINING UP,
    by prisoners in 1914 . . ., 88

422

JOKE,
ancient, alluded to by Elderly Conveyancers, 19
enthusiastic reception of, 35
made by Counsel, 35
prepared by Witty Judge, 35

JONES, MISS,
attraction of Elderly Junior towards, 27
eyes of, 27
figure of, 27
reference of, to Aunt Jane, 28
tripping off of, 28
visit of, to Elderly Junior, 27
well-shaped hand of, 28

JUDÆA,
Caledonian from, 70

JUDGE,
aged. *See* JUDGE, AGED
boredom of, 23
Chancery. *See* JUDGE, CHANCERY
congratulations to, by Lord Chancellor, 24
doze of, 23
Erudite. *See* JUDGE, ERUDITE
kindly. *See* JUDGE, KINDLY
of Assize. *See* JUDGE OF ASSIZE
Caledonian extraction, 69
old-fashioned. *See* JUDGE, OLD-FASHIONED
presence of mind, 24
profound sleep of, 23
prudent. *See* JUDGE, PRUDENT
questions of, to Holder in Due Course, 4
relations of, with Marshal, 51
stay of execution granted by, 24
                refused by, 70

JUDGE, AGED,
fruitful kindness of, 202
hints of, disregarded, 201
irritation of, 201
past remembered by, 201
tears of, 202
untruthful compliment paid by, 201

JUDGE, CHANCERY,
    explanation of interesting point by, 335
    meeting of, with Common-Law Brother, 335
    opinion as to mental condition of Common-Law Brother
        of, 335

JUDGE, ERUDITE,
    Canon Law referred to by, 341
    jury ordered to withdraw by, 341
    on declarations by deceased persons, 342
        inscriptions on tombstones, 342
        res gestæ, 342
    Pandects of Justinian referred to by, 341
    splendid bit of work of, 341
    question admitted by, 342

JUDGE, KINDLY, *and see* LADY BARRISTER
    adjournment of proceedings by, 292
    attracted by Effie, 291
    determination of, to assist Lady Barrister, 101
    misleading of, 101
    severity of, towards advocate on other side, 101
    wig of, tried on by Effie, 291

JUDGE OF ASSIZE,
    arrival of, 23
    children of, 143
    congratulations of, to High Sheriff's Chaplain, 302
    conversation of, with Old School Friend, 143
    enjoyment of sermon by, 302
    gout of, 143
    inability of, to save, 143
    preparation of, for worst, 301
    rheumatism of, 143
    sinking heart of, 301
    visit of, to prison, 143

JUDGE, OLD-FASHIONED,
    interview of, with Miss Snaffleton, 283, 284

JUDGE, PRUDENT,
    agreement between Stout Usher and, 189
    kept straight by Stout Usher, 190
    legal attainments of, 189

JUDGE, PRUDENT (*continued*)
 retirement of, 190
 satisfaction given by, 189
 Stout Usher summoned by, 189
 stuffy practice of, 189
 valedictory address by Attorney-General to, 190

JUDGE'S ORDER,
 if necessary, 46

JUDGES,
 Bachelor, duties of, 356
 County Court, attendance of, at wedding, 328
 High Court, of, attendance of, at wedding, 328
 salaries of, 355

JUDGMENT, *and see* STAY OF EXECUTION,
 enforcement of, in U.S.S.R., 347
 for defendant, 4
  plaintiff, 15, 24, 40, 70
 not reserved, 24
 signed against Mr. Titmouse, 210

JUDICIAL HONOURS,
 despised, 55

JUNIOR,
 address of Bald Old Gentleman to, 127
 appearance of Bald Old Gentleman in chambers of, 127
 Careful. *See* JUNIOR, CAREFUL
 Common Law. *See* JUNIOR, COMMON LAW
 Elderly. *See* JUNIOR, ELDERLY
 Established. *See* JUNIOR, ESTABLISHED
 horrible swearing of, 128
 lunch of, 127
 Mature. *See* JUNIOR, MATURE
 Promising Equity, success of, 1, *and see* JUNIOR, PROMISING
  EQUITY
 reminder by Clerk of, 128
 renewed slumber of, 128
 waking up of, 127

JUNIOR, CAREFUL,
 in nursing home, 183
 leading question of, 183
 unconsciousness of, 183

JUNIOR, COMMON LAW, *and see* ORIGINATING SUMMONS,
    briefed in Chancery Division, 65
    collapse of, 66
    faltering accents of, 3
    recovery of, 4, 66
    sudden question to, 65

JUNIOR, ELDERLY,
    favourable impression created upon, 27
    gallant reply of, 28
    visit of Miss Jones to, 27
    worst fears of, realised, 28

JUNIOR, ESTABLISHED,
    past of, 255
    present of, 255
    professional engagements of, 255
    reflections of, 255
    refreshments consumed by, 256

JUNIOR, MATURE,
    deserted by leader, 123
    inability of, to stand it much longer, 123
    order to Diligent Pupil, 124
    patience of, tried, 123
    questions addressed to, by Diligent Pupil, 124
    striking of Diligent Pupil by, 124

JUNIOR, PROMISING EQUITY,
    briefed with Common Law Leader, 1
    ear-trumpet of, 1
    inability of, to hear Common Law Leader, 1
    success of, 1

JURISTS, ELDERLY,
    distinguished careers of, 193
    meeting of, 193
    melody of "Two Lovely Black Eyes" recaptured by, 194
    Miss Nellie Farren, admiration of, for, 194
    subjects discussed by, 193

JURY,
    box for, 217
    case stopped by, 198
    fresh, ordered, 268

JURY (*continued*)
  unable to agree, 232
  withdrawal of, ordered, 341

JUSTICE,
  emblematical figure of, 310
  Palace of, burning of, 217
                    defects of, 217
                    rebuilding of, 218
  spirit of, invoked, 306

JUSTINIAN,
  Pandects of, 341

K

K.C. M.P.,
  bill for suppression of night clubs of, 91
      paid by, 91
  dancing lessons given to, by Madame Frou-Frou, 91
  explanation to police by, 92
  mingling with orchestra of, 92
  scrapping of bill by, 92
  successful ballot of, 91
  supper taken by, with lady member, 91
  visit of, to "Bubble and Squeak," 91
              "Giddy Goat," 91
              "Pongo's," 91
              "Tiddlywinks," 91
  wig and moustache hired by, 91

KASHMIRI,
  tongue, 193

KENSINGTON GARDENS,
  perambulator upset in, 49

KHOJAS,
  laws and customs of, 193

KING OF UPPER AND LOWER CANNIBAL ISLANDS,
  enlightenment of, 355
  explanation of local legal procedure by, 356, 357
  preference expressed by, 356, 357
  referred to Regius Professor, 355
  Regius Professor's lecture to, 355, 356

KNEES,
    shakiness of Counsel at, 3
KNOWLEDGE,
    of human nature, 190

L

LABOUR, HARD,
    two months, 275

LADIES, LEADING,
    fainting condition of, 317

LADY BARRISTER,
    mistaken identity of, 102
    treatment of, by Kindly Judge, 101

LADY MEMBER OF "PONGO'S,"
    K.C., M.P. dances with, 91

LADY PUPIL, *and see* JONES, MISS
    Elderly Junior and, 27

LAMB,
    Building, photograph of, 168
    Charles. *See* CAPABLE GUIDE

LAMENTATIONS,
    of Prisoner's relatives, 95

LAND,
    appointment of, to trustees for sale, 335
    conversion of, into personalty, 335

LANGUAGE,
    Sarah Stout's purity of, 288

LARCENY,
    of boots, 263

LAUGHING,
    of case out of Court, desirability of, 31

LAUNDRESS,
    intoxication of, 271, 272
    of Old Buffer, 373
    secret marriage of, 213

428

LAW,
    appeal to House of Lords on questions of, 356
    failure of Speaker, K.C., to expound, 345
    shaky, of Brilliant Orator, 321
"LAW FOR THE MILLION,"
    bought by Sagacious Old Buffer, 160
LAW OFFICER,
    glittering efficiency of, 193
    Margarine Order explained to, 131
LAW OF PROPERTY ACT, 1925,
    bill for further amendment of, 92
LAWYER, CAREFUL,
    elevated to Bench, 275
    methods of, 275
    misgivings of, 275
    nervous breakdown of, 276
LAWYER, GREAT,
    after-dinner speech of, 227
    cheered by innocent hosts, 228
    invitation to, 227
LAWYER, PROFOUND,
    experience of, as witness, 297
LEADER, *and see* SILK
   absence of Chancery, 65
   Common Law, briefed with Promising Equity Junior, 1
               important case of, in another Court, 1
   despised by Junior, 32
   engagement of Common Law, 21
   Languid, congratulated, 222
         consultation with, 222
         dashing speech of, 222
         observations of, 222
         old-fashioned methods despised by, 221
         retained by Duke of Agincourt, 222
         show not given away by, 222
         substantial fee of, 222
         undertaking by clerk of, 222
         vague cordiality of, 222
         yawning of, 222
429

LEADING SOLICITOR,
>   enthusiasm of, 135
>   Mr. Tittlebat briefed by, 135
>   questions of, to Mr. Tittlebat, 135
>   visit of, to Mr. Tittlebat, after twenty years, 135
LEG-UP,
>   to Lady Barrister given by Kindly Judge, 101
LEGAL ARGUMENT,
>   pointed, of Fierce-Looking Opponent, 101
LEMON,
>   referred to by Common-Law Brother, 335
LENINGRAD,
>   run of film in, 328
LEOPARDS, OF ENGLAND, 309
LIBEL,
>   action for, by Irene Mugg, 40
LICENSED PREMISES,
>   taken by Irene, 40
>   visited by Bearded Juryman, 58
LICKBARROW *v.* MASON,
>   inability of Adolphus Brown to remember point in, 52
LIEN, J.,
>   reversed by Court of Criminal Appeal, 371
LIGHT, FRESH,
>   on Statute of Uses, 335
LIMP,
>   of prisoner, 263
>   Real Property Lawyer, 81
LINCOLN'S INN,
>   Bencher of, dinner in Hall, 375
>   pride of, in Real Property Lawyer, 79
>   reading of Alfred with Conveyancer in, 155
LITERATURE,
>   sensational, 313
LITIGANT IN PERSON. *See* LUNATIC *and* SCIENTIST
"LITTLE JACK SHEPPARD,"
>   jurists' memories of, 194

LOAN,
suggested by Stout Stranger, 83

LONDON,
run of film in, 328

LONG VACATION,
meeting of Templars after, 171

LORD CHANCELLOR,
compliment of, to Experienced Judge, 24
patronage of, 325
speech of, 332

LORD OF APPEAL,
courtesy of, 248

LORDS, HOUSE OF,
appeals on question of law to, 356
Court of Appeal reversed by, 332

LORDS JUSTICES,
attendance of, at wedding, 328

LORDS OF APPEAL,
attendance of, at wedding, 328

LOST GRANT,
doctrine of, 31

LOWER CANNIBAL ISLANDS. *See* CANNIBAL ISLANDS

LUNATIC,
actions brought by, 205
cold muffins ordered by, 205
damages recovered by, 205
double whisky ordered by, 205
escape of, in laundry basket, 205
not so found by inquisition, case as to, 52
roast potatoes ordered by, 205
sorrow of, 206
suicide of, 206
waitress embraced by, 206

LUNCH,
at Megatherium, 313
taken by Idle Apprentice, 157

431

M

MACINTOSH, ALEXANDER, MR.,
  accent of, 70
  appearance of, in witness-box, 69
  judgment obtained by, 70
  money-lending transactions of, 69

MACINTOSH *v.* FITZCHOLMONDELY,
  action of, 69

MAGISTRATE. *See* TACTFUL MAGISTRATE

MAGNIFIQUE HOTEL,
  visited, 337

MALEDICTIONS,
  horrid, of Venerable Solicitor, 369

MALEFACTORS,
  defence of, 305

MAN OF AFFAIRS,
  cry of agony of, 235
  promising son of, 235

MANUSCRIPT,
  fire lit with, 373

MARGATE,
  visited by Plaintiff, 280

MARITIME CONVENTIONS ACT, 1911 . . . 232

MARRIAGE,
  in Amsterdam between Roman Catholic and Protestant, 52

MARRIAGE SETTLEMENT,
  trustees of, joined as defendants, 19

MARSHAL,
  experiences of Adolphus Brown as, 51

MASS,
  tourists from, 181

MASTER, OF SUPREME COURT,
  deplorable handwriting of, 152

MATRIMONIAL PROSPECTS,
  impaired by disfigured *tibia,* 16

MEAN CONDUCT,
of John Marmaduke Bundlepump, 13

MEASLES,
contracted by niece of Templar's wife, 171

"MEESON & WELSBY,"
referred to by Sagacious Old Buffer, 159, 160

MEGATHERIUM,
luncheon of Elderly Conveyancers at, 19
Judicial Personage at, 313

MEMORIES, PRECIOUS,
of Jurists, 194

MEMORY,
refreshment of, 297
Stout Stranger's loss of, 84
sudden loss of, 197

MENTAL PATIENT. *See* LUNATIC

MENU,
adventures of, 375
discovery of, in 1961 . . . 375

MESSUAGE. *See* HEREDITAMENT

MIDDLE TEMPLE HALL,
photograph of, 168

MILDEW, J.,
awe-inspiring appearance of, 163
hopes of, as to brother judge, 163
internal debate of, 163, 164
reflections of, as to champagne, 163
port, 163

MILLIONAIRE'S NEPHEW,
meeting of Old Bailey Practitioner and, 139

MINISTER, PRIME,
patronage of, 302

MISCONDUCT,
gross, of Beginner, 267
matrimonial, 337
evidence of, 337
opportunity for, 337

433

MISDIRECTION,
>by Judge, 332

MISS JONES. *See* JONES, MISS

MODESTY,
>of Old Stager, 111

MONEY-LENDER,
>marriage of widow of, 242
>mortgage of reversion to, 242

MONEY-LENDERS,
>cross-examination of, 317

MONEY-LENDING,
>transactions of Mr. Alexander MacIntosh, 69

MOTHERS-IN-LAW,
>Sound Lawyer's views upon, 98

MOTOR,
>contributory negligence of, 231, 232

MOTTO,
>proud, 310

MOUNTED POLICEMAN, *and see* POLICEMAN
>recommended by Old Stager, 110

MOUSE,
>morbid appetite of, 287

MUCH-RESPECTED COLLEAGUE,
>adventure of, 13
>fine imposed upon, 13
>mistaken confidence of, 13
>payments of doctor's fee by, 13

MUG,
>Mr. Whitewig described as, 88

MUGG. *See* IRENE MUGG

MUGS,
>reference of Bearded Juryman, 58

MULES, HOMELESS,
>Association for Housing of, 374

MUSSOLINI,
>railway reforms of, 171

434

NAMES, CHRISTIAN,
  of Mr. Titmouse, 210

NAPOLEON,
  on Knapsacks, 227

NASTY,
  jar, experienced by Adolphus Brown, 52
  turn, taken by case, 123

NATURE, HUMAN,
  knowledge of, 190

NECKLACE,
  Irene's explanation as to loss of, 39
  libel action resulting from loss of, 40
  missing after Young Man's visit, 39
  owned by Mrs. Tompkyns, 39
  successfully disposed of, 40

NEGLIGENCE,
  of Conductor of tram, 15
    domestic servant, 49
    nursery maid, 49

NEGLIGENCE, CONTRIBUTORY,
  fully expounded, 231, 232
  insufficiently explained, 231
  law relating to, 231

NEPHEW. *See* MILLIONAIRE'S NEPHEW

NERVE,
  loss of, by Holder in Due Course, 3

NEW CLIENT,
  admiration of, for Strident Person, 113
  dissatisfaction of, with Prudent Counsel, 113

NEW YORK,
  run of film in, 328

NEWGATE STREET,
  Cough of Bronchial Usher heard in, 35

NEWSPAPERS,
  effect of Tearful Performer upon, 115

NICE OLD BUFFER,
    amiability of, 9
    cigar of, 9
    reception on platform of, 10
NIGHT CLUBS,
    visited by K.C., M.P., 91
NINETEEN-HUNDRED-AND-THIRTY,
    experiences of, in Divorce Court, 337
NOISY BEHAVIOUR,
    of Elderly Conveyancers, 19
NONCHALANCE,
    easy, of Languid Leader, 221, 222
NORTHERN IRELAND,
    laws of, 61
NOSE,
    bleeding, of First Offender, 178
    payment through, 355
    powdered, of Smart Young Person, 7
NOTE, CAREFUL,
    form of, 263, 264
    made by Junior, 263
            Leader, 264
NOTICE,
    actual, 306
    constructive, 306
    disregarded by Real Property Lawyer, 1
NOVEL,
    read by Wise Old Bird, 225
NURSERYMAID, *and see* YOUNG PERSON
    negligence of, 49
NURSING HOME,
    Careful Junior in, 183

O

OAF,
    cigarette smoked by, 73
    employed as clerk, 73
    squint of, 73
436

OATH,
>Chinese form of, 173
>of Junior, 128
>>Surly Gamekeeper, 80

OCTOBER,
>judicial changes in, 186

OFFERING,
>substantial, to Stout Usher, 189

OFFICIAL REFEREES, *and see* REFEREES, OFFICIAL,
>attendance of, at wedding, 328

OINTMENT,
>fly in, 209

OLD BAILEY,
>practitioner. *See* OLD BAILEY PRACTITIONER
>transference of Bronchial Usher from, 36
>trial of W. Shakespeare at, 35

OLD BAILEY PRACTITIONER,
>amusement of, 139
>exchange of purse for wallet by, 140
>magistrate's opinion of, 140
>meeting of, with Australian Plutocrat, 139
>>>Millionaire's Nephew, 139
>nasty shocks to, 140
>payment of, to Australian Plutocrat, 141
>>>Eminent Firm, 141
>>>Millionaire's Nephew, 141
>regret of, 140

OLD BIRD,
>intelligent, 1

OLD CLIENT,
>alarm of, 21
>brief offered by, 21
>removal of brief by, 21
>visit of, to Silk, 21

OLD CURIOSITY SHOP,
>visited by Enthusiastic Tourists, 181

OLD HAND,
    application for protection of witness by, 16
    conduct of case by, 15
    Double-First opposed by, 15
    harmless appearance of, 15
    speech of, to jury, 16

OLD OFFENDERS,
    gentleness of Dearlove, J., towards, 95

OLD SCHOOL FRIEND,
    financial career of, 143
    good health of, 143
    invitation of, to Judge of Assize, 143
    settlement on wife by, 143

OLD STAGER,
    advice of, sought by solicitor, 109
    devout aspirations added by, 110
    draft prepared by, 109
    familiarity of, with "Bullen & Leake," 10
    modest confession of, 111
    recommends Exchequer Suit, 109
    statutes referred to by, 110

OLD-FASHIONED JUDGE,
    firmness of, 284
    interview of Miss Snaffleton with, 283
    views of, 283

ONE, QUICK,
    Clerk fond of, 288

OPINION,
    of counsel, 331

ORATOR, BRILLIANT,
    collapse of, 322
    peroration of, 322
    piercing eye of, 321
    rich voice of, 321
    shaky law of, 321

ORDERS-IN-COUNCIL,
    drafted by Beefy Thomas, 131

ORGAN,
    mechanical, 328

438

ORIGINATING SUMMONS,
        called on out of turn, 19
        Common Law Junior briefed in, 65
        conduct of, by Common Law Junior, 65

OUTING,
        parochial, 301

OVERSEERS OF PARISH OF CRIGGLESWICH *v.* MUD-
        BANK-SUPER-MARE DOCKS AND HARBOUR
        TRUSTEES,
        referred to, 23

P

PAIL,
        on stairs, 341

PARALYSIS,
        anticipated by Old Hand, 16

PARAPHERNALIA,
        of law, 185

"PARLEMENT BELGE," THE,
        referred to by Emeritus Professor, 149

PARLIAMENT,
        Houses of, visited by Enthusiastic Tourists, 181
        Roll, production of, 248

PARIS,
        run of film in, 328

PARROT, 318

PART-HEARD CASE,
        mature Junior engaged in, 123

PARTICULARS OF STATEMENT OF CLAIM,
        application for, 151

PASSAGES,
        telling, 361

PAST,
        plaintiff with a, 115

PATENT. *See* HEATING APPARATUS

PEAKS, ETERNAL,
        beauty of, 185

439

PENAL SERVITUDE,
    desire of White-haired Trustee to avoid, 7
PENN.,
    Tourists from, 181
PERAMBULATOR,
    upsetting of, in Kensington Gardens, 49
PERFORMANCE, MASTERLY,
    of Silk, 222
PERJURY,
    conviction of Plaintiff for, 115
PERORATION,
    of Blushing Beginner, 57
PERSISTENT EFFORTS,
    of Coaches, 155
PERSON, BRILLIANT, *and see* SMART YOUNG PERSON
    masterly speech of, 305
    Spirit of Justice invoked by, 306
    unspeakable fury of, 306

PERSONAGE, JUDICIAL,
    disappointment of, 313
    nine months sentence passed by, 313
    relaxation of, 313
    response for guests by, 313
    views of, on cinemas, 313
                    sensational literature, 313

PERSONS,
    deceased, declarations by, 342
    reasonable, unreasonable verdict of, 356

PETER, UNCLE,
    grumpiness of, 237
    insistence of, upon short engagement, 238
    inspects dressmaker's bill, 237
    Mr. Pott summoned by, 237
    opposition of, to niece's engagement, 238

PETTY BAG. *See* EXCHEQUER SUIT

PHOTOGRAPH OF CATALPA TREE,
    purchased by Mr. Buffle, 169

PHYSICIAN,
> failure of, to elicit facts, 49
> horror of, at Traveller's appearance, 49
> visit of, to Traveller, 49

PIGS, KINDNESS TO,
> Society for Promotion to, 374

PIGMIES,
> of to-day, 186

PITY,
> self-sacrifice induced by, 210

PLACE,
> handsome, in country, 369

PLAINTIFF,
> acquaintance of, with Dartmoor, 280
> answer of voluble, 353
> origin of voluble, 353
> presumed to be fraudulent, 356
> question to voluble, 353
> required to prove case, 356
> resources of, exhausted, 205, 232

PLAN,
> admirable, of Mr. Sharp and Mr. Bright, 241
> held upside down by Profound Lawyer, 298
> pool of blood indicated on, by Old Hand, 15

PLEADER, SPECIAL. *See* REPORTER, DEAF

PLUMPLY, MRS.,
> criticisms of, 359

POLICE-COURT,
> visited by Emeritus Professor, 148

POLICEMAN, *and see* MOUNTED POLICEMAN
> stout and peremptory, 297

"PONGO'S." *See* K.C., M.P.,

POOTER, MASTER,
> S to Z business taken by, 283

POPPLETON, MISS MARY. *See* LADY BARRISTER

PORCHESTER,
    deanery of, 302
    Terrace, residence of Real Property Lawyer in, 79

PORT,
    considered by Mildew, J., 163

PORTRAIT. *See* PUMPKIN, K.C.

POST,
    charwoman deaf as, 342

POT, BIG,
    re-examination by, 267

POTATOES, ROAST,
    ordered by Lunatic, 205

POTT, MR. HENRY,
    articled to Gudgeon, Gudgeon & Co., 237
    engagement of, to Mabel Gudgeon, 238
    good appearance of, 237
    parentage of, 238
    sent for by Uncle Peter, 237
    settlement by, of dressmaker's account, 237
    wedding of, 238

POTTE *v.* KETTLE,
    action of, 45

POTTLE, MR.,
    accident of, on escalator, 331
    experiences of, 331
        in Court of Appeal, 332
            High Court of Justice, 331
            House of Lords, 332
    sagacious Cook consulted by, 331
    spectacles left at home by, 331

POUNDS,
    three, lent to Stout Stranger, 84

PRACTICE,
    large and lucrative, 214

PRACTITIONER, DISGRUNTLED,
    views of, as to Court of Appeal, 245
                     Judges, 245

442

PRACTITIONER, DISGRUNTLED (*continued*)
    views of (*continued*)
        as to Juniors, 245
          Leaders, 245
"PRAYER, JESSICA'S FIRST." *See* "JESSICA'S FIRST PRAYER"
PRESENCE OF MIND,
    of Adolphus Brown, 52
      Experienced Judge, 23
      Tactful Magistrate, 13
PREVIOUS CONVICTIONS,
    nine, of Prisoner, 88
PRINCE, BLACK, 309
PRINT DRESS,
    lilac, worn by Young Person, 167
PRISON,
    Plaintiff in, more than once, 198
PRIVY COUNCIL,
    Enthusiastic Beginner's brief in, 31
PROCEDURE,
    invented by Old Stager, 109
PROCEEDINGS,
    protracted and costly, 374
PROGNOSTICATIONS,
    gloomy, 225
PROMISE,
    Distinguished Bencher, by, 375
PROOF,
    given by Profound Lawyer, 297
PROPOSITION,
    startling, in head note, 213
PROUD PARENT,
    advertisements answered by, 155
    advice to, 155
PRUDENT COUNSEL,
    briefs lost by, 113
    determination of, to sit tight, 113

PRUDENT COUNSEL (*continued*)
    insulted, 113
    opposed by Strident Person, 113
    rebuked, 113
    risks not taken by, 113

PSYCHOLOGICAL MOMENT,
    arrival of, for joke, 36

PUBLIC,
    interest, execution stayed in case of, 24
    servant, of unblemished reputation, 13
    terrified by Mildew, J., 163

PUBLICITY,
    loss of, 349

PUFFENDORF,
    cited by Emeritus Professor, 148

PUFFINGTON'S SETTLEMENT, IN RE,
    referred to by Judge, 66

PUMP COURT,
    photograph of, 168
    visited by Enthusiastic Tourists, 181

PUMPKIN, K.C.,
    fear of, 359
    personal appearance of, 359
    plucking up of courage by, 359
    portrait of, 359

PUN,
    made by Snorter, 19

PUNT, J.,
    decision of, 213

PUPIL,
    Diligent. *See* DILIGENT PUPIL
    Lady, Elderly Junior, and, 27
    opinion of, in ejectment action, 19

PURITY,
    of language, of Sarah Stout, 288

PURSE,
    of Old Bailey Practitioner, 140

PUSHLEIGH OF RUNNYMEDE, LORD,
 arms of, 309
 career of, 309
 selection of title by, 309

PUSHLEIGH, SIR SAMUEL. *See* PUSHLEIGH OF RUNNY-
MEDE, LORD

PUTNEY. *See* JENKINSON, MRS.

Q

QUALIFICATIONS,
 of Profound Lawyer, 298

QUARRIES,
 Plaintiff employed in, 280

QUEEN ELIZABETH,
 visit of, to Inner Temple Hall, 181

QUESTION,
 admissibility of, 341, 342
 leading, put by Careful Junior, 183
 rash, put by Mr. Whitewig, 88

QUICK ONE,
 clerk fond of, 288

QUINTILIAN,
 Works of, studied by Blushing Beginner, 57

R

RABBIT-LIKE BEHAVIOUR,
 of Footle, K.C., 55

RABELAIS,
 quoted by Sound Lawyer, 98

RAILWAY ACCIDENT,
 claim arising out of, 49
 shock caused by, 49
 Traveller in, 49

RAILWAY COMPANY,
 physician of, Traveller visited by, 49

RAJATARANGINI,
 summarised by Abu'l Fazl, 193

445

RASH ATTENDANT, *and see* DEFEATED LITIGANT
approach of, to Defeated Litigant, 43
horrid oaths addressed to, 43

REAL NAME,
and address, given by Much-Respected Colleague, 13

REAL PROPERTY LAWYER,
a courageous trespasser, 80
alarmed by dog, 80
displeasure of housekeeper with, 81
knowledge of, as to reversions, etc., 79
left whisker of, seized by Surly Gamekeeper, 80
pride of Lincoln's Inn in, 79
regarded as hot stuff, 79
short cut taken by, 79
train missed by, 81

REBUKE,
of Client to Prudent Counsel, 113

RECORD,
black, of Plaintiff, 189, 280
of prisoner, enquired as to, 88
produced, 88

RECRUITING SPEECHES,
manly and eloquent, of Beefy Thomas, 131

RED HERRING,
alluded to by Tearful Performer, 115

RED NOSE,
of Holder in Due Course, 3

RE-EXAMINATION,
by Junior, 267
Leader, 267

REFEREES, OFFICIAL, *and see* OFFICIAL REFEREES
attendance of, at wedding, 328

REFRESHER,
agreement as to, 361

REGISTRATION,
of title, 79

REJOICING, UNIVERSAL,
    at burning of Palace of Justice, 217, 218

REMORSE,
    not exhibited by Foozle, J., 120

RENT,
    owing by Experienced Advocate, 105

RENVOI,
    doctrine of, 147

REPORTER, DEAF,
    death of, 213
    decision of Punt, J., reported by, 213
    quoted by Diligent Counsel, 213
    volume produced by, 213

RES GESTÆ,
    facts to be regarded as, 342

RESERVATIONS,
    of Profound Lawyer, 298

RESPECT,
    for judicial office, 301

REST,
    retirement to, of Grump, J., 52

RETAINER,
    by Stout Stranger, 83
    of Howler, K.C., and Squeaker, K.C., 345

REVENUE,
    large sums due to, 242

REVERSIONS. *See* REAL PROPERTY LAWYER

RHINE,
    visited by Enthusiastic Tourists, 181

RICHARD THE THIRD,
    referred to by Capable Guide, 181

RICH WIFE,
    of Stuffin, J., 9

RIDER,
    to jury's verdict, 40

RIGHT OF WAY,
    case concerning, 31
ROBERT, UNCLE,
    attendance of, at consultation, 347
    instructing of Learned Youth by, 347
    opinion of Learned Youth held by, 347
    symptoms of cerebral hæmorrhage exhibited by, 347
ROBES,
    of Lord Pushleigh of Runnymede, 309
ROMAN,
    Catholic, marriage in Amsterdam between, and Irish
        Protestant, 52
    Law, failure of Alfred in, 155
ROME,
    run of film in, 328
ROSENBAUMSKI. *See* FITZCHOLMONDELY, ALGERNON
ROW,
    unnecessary, got up with Judge, 113
ROYALTY,
    ten per cent, 328
RUN,
    phenomenal, of film, 328
RUNNING-DOWN CASE,
    conducted by Leader, 264
    tried by experienced Judge, 231, 264
RUSSELL,
    oratorical effort of, 295

S

SAFE SEAT,
    of Stuffin, J., 9
SAGACIOUS OLD BUFFER,
    advice of, 160
    authorities referred to by, 159
    clients of, 159
    dignified appearance of, 159
    palatial offices of, 159
    purchase by, of "Law for the Million," 160
    rebinding of volumes by, 160

448

SAGACIOUS OLD BUFFER (*continued*)
      reception by, of Young Solicitor, 160
      retirement of, 160
      solutions of legal problems by, 159
      sympathetic manner of, 159

ST. JOHN, FLORENCE,
      charms of, 193

ST. JUDE'S,
      marriage of Mabel Gudgeon at, 238

ST. POLYCARP'S,
      Beefy of, 363

SALMON,
      landed by Templar, 171
      lost by Templar, 171

SARCASTIC COUNSEL,
      grim smile of, 69
      surprise of, 69

SATURDAY,
      relaxation of Judicial Personage on, 313

SAUCERS,
      procured by Cautious Solicitor, 173

SAVOY,
      lunch at, 202

SCIENTIST,
      action of tort brought by, 205
      admitted to workhouse, 206
      case of, stopped by jury, 206
      explosive invented by, 205
      lunch of, 205
      petition of right of, 205

SCHOLARSHIP,
      of sermon, 301

SCOTCHMEN,
      thrifty habits of, 98

SCOTLAND YARD,
      visit to, of Elderly Trustee, 75

449

SCOUNDREL,
    cunning. *See* PLAINTIFF
    swindling, 317
SCOUTS, BOY, 301
SCREAM,
    shrill, of Voluble Plaintiff, 353
SEAT,
    for Counsel, 217
        Judge, 217
SECOND THOUGHTS,
    of Enthusiastic Beginner, 32
SEEDS,
    sown by Diligent Counsel, 214
SEEDY INDIVIDUAL,
    handing of cheque to, 169
    hurrying of, to bank, 169
    Mr. Buffle visited by, 168
    sale of photograph by, 169
SELF-SACRIFICE,
    of Mr. Titmouse, 210
SENIOR CLASSIC,
    of Sixties, a Promising Equity Junior, 1
SERVITUDE, PENAL,
    handed out by Snappy, J., 367
SHAFTESBURY AVENUE,
    dancing lessons given by Madame Frou-Frou in, 91
SHAKESPEARE, WILLIAM,
    alluded to by Witty Judge, 35
    charged with fraud, 35
SHARP, MR.,
    and Special Case, 241
SHERIFF, HIGH. *See* CHAPLAIN, HIGH SHERIFF'S
SHIELD,
    quartering of, 309, 310
"SHIRLEY'S LEADING CASES,"
    studied by Adolphus Brown, 51

SHOCK,
    to Traveller, 49
SHRIMPTON-ON-SEA,
    visited, 337
SHROPSHIRE,
    clergyman in, 242
                marriage of, 242
SILK, *and see* LEADER
    absence of, in other Court, 1
    application for, by Utter Barrister, 62
    brief lost by, 21
    cheered by arrival of client, 21
    confidential communication of, to Zealous Clerk, 21
    consultation with, 222, 279
    masterly performance of, 222
    various appointments of, 21
    wink of, 21
    world-wide fame of, 279
SIMPLE, YOUNG MR.,
    conference between, and Venerable Solicitor, 369
    hearty voice of, 369
SIMPLICITY,
    of Sagacious Cook, 331
SIR JOHN, 21
SIR NATHANIEL, 45
SIR PEREGRINE, 45
SIX,
    Beefy best, of his time, 363
SIX CLERKS' OFFICE,
    history of, 373
SIXPENCE,
    tendered by Real Property Lawyer, 80
SLANDER,
    claim and counterclaim for, 45
SLASHER, MR.,
    beautiful iron shot of, 119
    down in nine at eighteenth, 120

SLASHER, MR. (*continued*)
    loss of twenty pounds by, 120
    opponent of Foozle, J., 119
    ordered to pay costs, 120
    tact of, 119
    taken aback, 120

SLEEPLESS NIGHTS,
    of Mr. Fledgling, 151

SMART YOUNG PERSON,
    acquittal of, 7
    calm of, 7
    "Chubby" carried by, 7
    fur-trimmed coat of, 7
    powdered nose of, 7
    sun-burn stockings of, 7

SMILE,
    of Bobby Chump, 295
        Mr. Pottle, 331
    sweet, of Mabel Gudgeon, 237

SMYTHE-BILKINGTON-SMYTHE, MISS.   *See* BARONY OF
    MONTAZURE AND FRONT-DE-BŒUF

SNAFFLETON, MISS (INFANT),
    engagement of, to Tommy, 284
    interview of, with Old-Fashioned Judge, 283

SNAPPY, J.,
    forgetfulness of, 367
    Jane's opinion of, 367
    meditations of, 367
    severity of, 367

SNORTER,
    pun made by, 19

SNOW,
    at wedding, 328
    dying woman covered with, 328
    infant discovered in, 327
    untrodden, 185

SOAP,
    used to induce epileptic symptoms, 35

SOB,
    of Young Person, 167

SOB-STUFF,
    indulged in by Tearful Performer, 115

SOBS,
    muffled, of Bert Baumstein, 328

SOCIETY FOR ABOLITION OF GAMING, WAGERING
    AND CHURCH ESTABLISHMENTS, 242

SOCIETY SUIT,
    for slander, 45
    settlement of, 46

SOLICITOR,
    Blushing Beginner instructed by, 57
    careful note by, 288
    delight of, with Inexperienced Advocate, 4
    eminence of, 365
    instructing Old Hand, 15
    intelligent, offer of, to Man of Affairs, 235
    manners of, 365
    venerable, conference between Mr. Simple and, 369
                disappearance for ever of, 369
                horrid maledictions of, 369
    visit of, to Silk, 21
    want of intelligence of, 365
    watery smile of Defeated Litigant's, 43

SON,
    promising, of Man of Affairs, 235

SOUND LAWYER,
    appointment of, as County Court Judge, 97
    opinions of, on artists, 97
                Latin races, 97
                legislators, 97
                literary men, 97
                married women, 97
                Mothers-in-law, 98
                Scotchmen, 98
    quotations of, 98
    resolution of, not to joke, 97

453

SPECTACLES,
    left at home, 331, 332
SPEECH,
    opening, telling passages for, 361
SPINSTER EXECUTRIX,
    humorous story concerning, 19
SPLASHER, K.C.,
    conservative views of, 361
    conversation between Clerk and, 361
    sad story read by, 361
SQUEAKER, K.C.,
    engagement in Court of Appeal of, 345
    legal knowledge of, 345
SQUEAKY VOICE,
    of Fragile Creature, 101
STAIRS,
    found troublesome, 373
STAMPS,
    sums due to Revenue for, 242
STATEMENT OF CLAIM,
    particulars of, 151
STATUTE OF USES, 335, *and see* USES, STATUTE OF
STAY OF EXECUTION,
    successful application for, 16
    unsuccessful application for, 70
STENOGRAPHER,
    salary of, raised, 248
    signs of exhaustion shewn by, 342
STEPS,
    concealed, 217
STEVENSON, ROBERT LOUIS,
    style of, 241
STICKIT, J., *and see* DIEHARD, J.
    best interests of country served by, 325
    holding on to job by, 325
    merit of, rewarded, 325
    regrets of, 325

STOCKBROKER,
profession of, adopted by Circuiteer, 10

STORY, *and see* GOOD STORY,
clear and vivid, 369

STOUT,
Sarah, affidavit of, 288
stranger, loan of three pounds to, 84
smell of cloves left by, 84
visit of, to Industrious Youth, 83

STRAIN,
tremendous, on nervous system, 295

STRANGE OATHS,
of Surly Gamekeeper, 80

STRANGER. *See* STOUT

STRATFORD-ON-AVON,
visited by Enthusiastic Tourists, 181

STRIDENT PERSON,
offensive speech of, 113
row of, with Judge, 113
transfer of briefs to, 113

STROKE,
brilliance of Brawn as, 363

STRUCTURE, SOCIAL,
menace to, 361

STUFF-GOWNSMAN
read with by Alfred, 155

STUFFIN, J.,
Judgeship of, 9
reception on platform of, 10
rich wife of, 9
safe seat of, 9

STUMER,
cheque negotiated, 148

"STUMPY." *See* "CHUBBY"

SUBPŒNA,
received by Profound Lawyer, 297

SUBROGATION, DOCTRINE OF,
Drop, J., on, 371

SUFFOLK,
Chicken-Farm at Eye in, 155

SUN-BURN STOCKINGS,
worn by Smart Young Person, 7

SUPPER,
Real Property Lawyer late for, 81

SURLY GAMEKEEPER,
not pacified by Real Property Lawyer, 80
progress of Real Property Lawyer barred by, 80
seizure of Real Property Lawyer's left whisker by, 80
strange oaths of, 80

SWEARING, *and see* OATH
horrible, of Junior, 128

SWITZERLAND,
visited by Enthusiastic Tourists, 181

SYSTEM,
expensive legal, 355
nervous, strain on, 295

T

TACTFUL MAGISTRATE,
address of, to Much-Respected Colleague, 13
comfortable dinner of, 13
fine imposed by, 13
presence of mind of, 13
recognition of Much-Respected Colleague by, 13

TACTICS,
of Foozle, J., 120

TALK,
slangy, 283

TAXICAB,
collision between Bus and, 297
negligence of, 231, 232

456

TEA,
    brought by Chambermaid, 337
    comfortable, of Real Property Lawyer, 79
    consumed by Miss Jones, 27
    cup of, 225

TEARFUL PERFORMER,
    advice to plaintiff of, 116
    conviction of plaintiff prayed in aid by, 116
    emotion of, 116
    engagement in another Court of, 116
    final speech of, 115
    methods of, 115
    tricks of trade known to, 115

TEARS, *and see* EMOTION
    of Aged Judge, 202
        Mabel Gudgeon, 237
        Mrs. Titmouse, 209
    shed by Dearlove, J., 95

TEETH,
    front, loss of First Offender's, 178

TEETOTALLER,
    tenant not a, 73

TEMPLARS, ATHLETIC,
    "Cuisine du Cardinal" passed by, 185
    "Dent du Chien" climbed by, 185
    failure of, to discuss beauty of peaks, 185
    forensic giants of past recalled by, 185
    judgment of Court of Appeal debated by, 185
    Long Vacation of, 185
    speculations as to judicial changes by, 186
    visit to Alps of, 185

TEMPLE,
    residence of Old Buffer in, 373

TEN-FORTY,
    caught by Emily, 225

TENNYSON,
    quoted by Sound Lawyer, 98

457

TERM REPORTS,
    referred to by Sagacious Old Buffer, 159
TERROR,
    inspired by Mildew, J., 163
TETANUS,
    anticipated by Old Hand, 16
THIEVES,
    indulgence extended to, 355
THOUGHTS,
    deep, of Mildew, J., 163
THREE-MILE LIMIT, 147
THRIFTY HABITS,
    of Scotchmen, 98
THUMB,
    moistened by Inspector, 88
THUNDER, VOICE OF,
    County Court Judge's, 267
TIBET,
    marriage laws of, 242
TIBIA,
    matrimonial prospects impaired by injury to, 16
TICHBORNE CASE,
    stories of, 373
TICKET,
    for concert refused by Defeated Litigant, 43
        Continent obtained by White-haired Trustee, 75
TICKETS,
    lost by Incompetent Clerk, 251
"TIDDLYWINKS." *See* K.C., M.P.
TITLE,
    choice of, 309
TITMOUSE, MR.,
    brief handed to, 209
    extreme course taken by, 209
    happy marriage of, 209

458

TITMOUSE, MR. (*continued*)
    judgment signed against, 210
    substituted as defendant, 210

TITMOUSE, MRS.,
    conversation of, with Judge, 209
    incapable housekeeping of, 209
    sued in County Court, 209
    tact of, 210
    threat to, 209

TITTLEBAT, MR.,
    acceptance of one guinea fee by, 135
    baldness and prosperity of, 135
    entertainment of, at luncheon, 135
    unexpected victory obtained by, 135
    visit of Leading Solicitor to, 135, 136

TOMBSTONES,
    inscriptions on, 342

TOMMY. *See* SNAFFLETON, MISS (INFANT)

TOMPKYNS, MR.,
    careful notes made by, 349
    close-up explained to, 349, 350
    offer to, 350
    order of chaperon to, 350
    repetition of close-up by, 350
    visit of Corinne Bozieu to, 349

TOMPKYNS, MRS.,
    action against, 39
    answer of, to Mrs. Jenkinson, 39
    cross-examination of, 40
    loss of necklace by, 39
    opinion of jury concerning, 40

TONES,
    confidential, of Profound Lawyer, 298

TOOTING,
    Plaintiff resident in, 279

TOPNOT, K.C.,
    retainer of, 221

459

TOURS,
  visited by Alfred, 155

TRAFFIC,
  obstruction of, 149

TRAIN,
  caught by County Court Judge, 214
  missed by Heavyside, J., 251
          Real Property Lawyer, 81

TRAMP STEAMER,
  voyage taken by Alfred on, 155

TRAMWAY,
  negligence of conductor of, 15

TRANSFER,
  of Briefs to Strident Person, 113

TRAP,
  escalator a, 331

TRAVELLER,
  interview between physician and, 49
  paralysed condition of, 49
  settlement of claim by, 49
  shock to, 49

TREATISE,
  contemplated by Utter Barrister, 61
  contents of, 61
  destruction of, 62
  in nine volumes, 61
  price of, 62

TRIAL, NEW,
  ordered, 332

TRUMPETERS,
  reception of Stuffin, J., by, 10

TRUSTEE,
  confidence reposed in White-haired, 75

TRUSTEES,
  for sale, 335

460

TRUTH,
    distinguishing of, from fiction, 190
    emblematical figure of, 310
    wormed out of Cunning Scoundrel, 280

TUNNEL,
    engine entering, 353

TWO TEMPLARS,
    meeting of, after Long Vacation, 171

TWO-THIRDS,
    junior's, 361

U

UKULELE,
    professional player of, 92

UNBLEMISHED REPUTATION,
    public servant of, 13

UNCLE THOMAS,
    Circuiteer's conversation about, 9

UNDERWRITERS,
    fraudulent claim upon, 353

UNIFORM,
    of Beefy Thomas, 131

UNION OF SOCIALIST SOVIET REPUBLICS,
    enforcing judgment in, 347

UNIVERSITY CAREER,
    of Adolphus Brown, 51
        Circuiteer, 9

UNNECESSARY ROW,
    got up by Blowhard, K.C., 55

UNWOMANLY,
    conduct of Mrs. Tompkyns, 40

UPSIDE DOWN,
    plan held, 298

USES, STATUTE OF, 335, *and see* STATUTE OF USES

USHER. *See* BRONCHIAL USHER

461

UTTER BARRISTER,
> advertisement drafted by, 61
> application for silk by, 62
> attachment of, to Charming Young Person, 61
> bright idea of, 61
> destruction by fire of treatise of, 62
> good appearance of, 61

V

VA.,
> tourists from, 181

VACATION, LONG. *See* TEMPLARS, ATHLETIC

"VACCINATION, LAW RELATING TO,"
> by Mr. Buffle, 167

VANITY BAG,
> carried by Smart Young Person, 7

VENERABLE PAPERS,
> contemplated by Silk, 21

VERDICT,
> obtained by Blushing Beginner, 57
> Irene, 40
> Old Hand, 16

VERSAILLES,
> Treaty of, 353

VEUVE MONTE CRISTO,
> consumed by Lady Member of "Pongo's," 91

VICTORY. *See* TITTLEBAT, MR.; FLEDGLING, MR.

VIENNA,
> run of film in, 328

VIOLET ROBES,
> reason for wearing, 123

W

WAGGA-WAGGA,
> wealthy piano manufacturer from, 139

WAGES,
> artificial raising of, 361

WAISTCOAT,
  direction of, 350
WALLACE, EDGAR,
  last work of, 314
  robust style of, 241
WALLET,
  of Millionaire's nephew, 139
WARNING,
  addressed to Much-Respected Colleague, 13
  insufficient, 331
WARSAW,
  Mr. Algernon FitzCholmondely born in, 70
WATERY SMILE,
  of Defeated Litigant's solicitor, 43
WEAK VOICE,
  of Enthusiastic Beginner, 32
WESTMINSTER ABBEY,
  wedding in, 328
WHISKIES AND SODA,
  several, required by Adolphus Brown, 52
WHISKY, DOUBLE,
  ordered by Lunatic, 205
WHITECHAPEL,
  County Court, case skilfully conducted in, 83
WHITE-HAIRED TRUSTEE,
  advice, followed by, 76
        offered to, 76
  confidence reposed in, 75
  financial mess of, 75
  visit of, to Scotland Yard, 75
WHITEWIG, MR.,
  admission of prosecutor to, 87
  confidence of, 87
  consultation of, with prisoner, 87
  cross-examination of inspector by, 87, 88
  disagreeable things said by prisoner of, 88
  fatal question of, 88
  invited by Judge to defend prisoner, 87
463

WIFE,
    ill-tempered and plain, 337
    of prisoner, expectations of, 88
    petition presented by, 337
    Profound Lawyer's statement to, 298

"WILFRED,"
    considered by Mildew, J., 164

WIG,
    head hidden by, 359
    tried on by Little Effie, 291

WILL,
    lost, of Mr. Buffin, 287

WITNESS ACTION,
    successfully conducted by Promising Equity Junior, 1

WITTY JUDGE,
    experiences of, with Bronchial Usher, 35
    forestalling of, 36
    intended joke of, 35
    rebuke to Counsel by, 36
    transference of Bronchial Usher to Commercial Court by,
      36

WOBBLING,
    signs of, shewn by County Court Judge, 213

WORK,
    importance of, 227
    splendid bit of, 341

WORKERS. *See* AMALGAMATED UNION OF FRIENDLESS
    FEMALE WORKERS

WORKHOUSE,
    Scientist taken to, 206

Y

YACHT, UNSEAWORTHY,
    charter of, 242

YEAR-BOOKS,
    production of, 248
    referred to by Erudite Judge, 341, 342

YORK-ANTWERP RULES,
Drop, J., on, 371

YOUNG MAN, *and see* IRENE
visit of, to Irene, 39

YOUNG PERSON,
accompanied by Seedy Individual, 169
assisted by Mr. Buffle, 168
coy look of, 168
pain suffered by, 168
sobs of, 167

YOUNG SOLICITOR,
advice to, of Sagacious Old Buffer, 160
cars of, 160
fears of, 159
gratitude of, 160
inability of, to learn law, 159
knighthood of, 160
Parliamentary honours of, 160
residence of, 160

YOUTH, AMBITIOUS,
chamber companions of, 73
Coloured Gentleman's offer to, 73
requirements of, 73
search of, for chambers, 73

YOUTH, CALLOW,
brief in Divorce Court of, 271
discovery of Weeping Lady by, 271
injured nose of, 272
retirement to rest of, 272
tactful sympathy of, 271

YOUTH, INDUSTRIOUS,
enquiries as to Stout Stranger made by, 84
loan of, to Stout Stranger, 83
meeting of, with Stout Stranger, 83
opinion of, as to fate of Stout Stranger, 84
skilful conduct of case by, 83

YOUTH, LEARNED,
consultation attended by, 347
dissertation from, 347

YOUTH, LEARNED (*continued*)
    instructed by Uncle Robert, 347
    Statement of Claim prepared by, 347
    Uncle Robert's opinion of, 347

YOUTH, NERVOUS,
    aphasia of, 197
    brief read to jury by, 197, 198
    County Court brief delivered to, 197
    late arrival of, 197

YOUTHFUL BARRISTER,
    anxiety of, 7
    briefed in Exceedingly Painful Case, 7
    long and incoherent speech of, 7
    pleasant surprise experienced by, 7

YOUTHFUL COUNSEL,
    complimented by Aged Judge, 201
    failure to speak up by, 325
    incoherence of, 201
    purchase of coal-scuttle by, 202

Z

ZANZIBAR,
    Law of Succession in, 193

THE
DOG LOVER'S
PUZZLE BOOK

THE DOG LOVER'S PUZZLE BOOK

Compiled by Lucy York

An Hachette UK Company
www.hachette.co.uk

Summersdale Publishers Ltd
Part of Octopus Publishing Group Limited
Carmelite House
50 Victoria Embankment
LONDON
EC4Y 0DZ
UK

www.summersdale.com

Printed and bound in Poland

ISBN: 978-1-80007-933-5

THE
DOG LOVER'S
PUZZLE BOOK

BRAIN-TEASING PUZZLES, GAMES AND TRIVIA

KATE MAY

summersdale

INTRODUCTION

If you've picked up this book, it's fair to say you're a fan of our furry four-legged friends. Whether you're stopping to chat to dog-walkers at the local park or curling up with your own pooch at your feet after your morning stroll, there's nothing like having dogs around to melt away the stress of modern life and keep you amused with their quirky antics.

If you think you know your Abruzzenhund from your Xoloitzcuintli, or your Scooby Doo from your Snoopy, *The Dog Lover's Puzzle Book* will keep you entertained for hours. It features an eclectic mix of conundrums, including crosswords, word searches, sudokus, anagrams and plenty of trivia questions to nourish and challenge dog-obsessed brains.

What could be better than sitting at home, with a snoring doggo flopped out in front of the fire (or while your pup paws at you for cuddles every five minutes), and opening up this carefully curated collection of canine-friendly puzzles? May *The Dog Lover's Puzzle Book* prove a welcome addition to every dog addict's bookshelf. Enjoy!

WORD SEARCH:
POPULAR NAMES FOR FEMALE DOGS

Find these popular names for female dogs in the grid.

```
R  J  G  Y  C  F  T  U  H  B  C  S  L  P  J
B  E  L  L  A  D  X  S  F  C  B  J  N  B  V
H  U  O  L  M  B  C  D  E  O  D  J  H  Y  F
J  I  N  O  C  R  F  J  I  C  G  C  Z  S  W
A  I  K  M  N  B  H  G  S  O  P  H  I  E  V
F  R  T  G  C  X  S  W  Y  H  N  B  G  Y  D
G  U  B  V  C  G  T  F  F  R  F  N  K  M  N
V  C  S  E  O  L  H  C  H  Y  J  G  E  J  I
K  J  R  J  U  H  G  F  G  H  J  I  G  F  M
S  D  S  H  J  N  V  X  Q  A  G  L  K  H  G
Y  H  I  A  F  C  X  D  R  G  B  N  Y  M  V
C  C  D  A  D  E  R  N  A  J  Y  S  F  C  O
U  D  S  X  V  I  X  M  N  Y  I  G  T  F  A
L  K  J  H  V  O  E  S  K  A  S  L  M  C  N
Y  E  S  G  H  V  C  J  D  I  K  H  G  L  P
```

BELLA	LUCY	MOLLY
DAISY	MAGGIE	SOPHIE
SADIE	CHLOE	COCO

CROSSWORD: TASTY TREATS

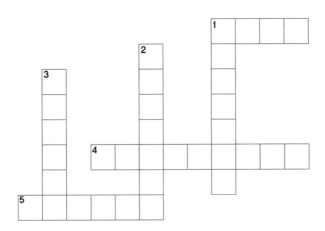

ACROSS

1. Masticate (4)

4. Violet Beauregarde turned into one of these (9)

5. Bugs Bunny's favourite snack (6)

DOWN

1. Fowl (7)

2. Goes well with a cup of tea (7)

3. Fruit with a slippery skin (6)

TRIVIA

Queen Elizabeth II's love of corgis was well documented – her very first corgi even went on the royal honeymoon! What was the dog's name?

a) Susan
b) Victoria
c) Sharon

PAIRS GAME

Match up the 20 puppies in 20 seconds. The first one has been done for you.

MAZE

Can you help the dog find the bone?

ANAGRAMS: CANINE CHARACTERS

Rearrange these letters to reveal well-known dog characters.

HERB LUCK RYE

SEAL IS

REAL MY

NO POSY

WORD LADDER

In this word ladder, change one letter at a time to turn the word "woof" into "tail".

WOOF

TAIL

CROSSWORD: HEFTY HOUNDS

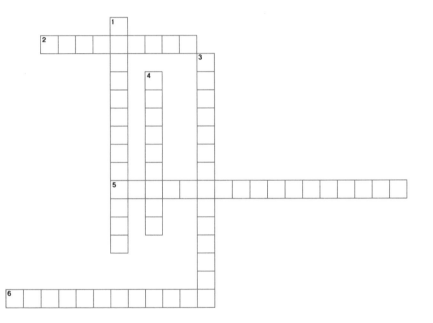

ACROSS

2. Will come to your rescue in the Swiss Alps (2,7)

5. Massive Italian (10,7)

6. Shares its name with the easternmost province of Canada (12)

DOWN

1. French dog from the mountains on the French-Spanish border (5,8)

3. Celtic dog famed for protection against wolves (5,9)

4. Canine sleuth Scooby Doo was this breed (5,4)

COUNTING CONUNDRUM

$$\text{bone} + \text{bone} + \text{bone} = 60$$

$$\text{bone} + \text{ball} + \text{ball} = 30$$

$$\text{ball} - \text{bowl} = 3$$

$$\text{bone} + \text{ball} + \text{bowl} = \text{?}$$

RIDDLE

The following clues will reveal a dog-friendly activity.

My first is in woof and also in wag
My second is in paw, but not in print
My third is in Labrador, but not in pug
My fourth is in kibble and also in pack
My fifth is in nail, but not in claw
My sixth is in nose, but not in boop
My seventh is in sleepy, but not in lively

What am I?

WORD SEARCH:
POPULAR NAMES FOR MALE DOGS

Find these popular names for male dogs in the grid.

U	H	V	X	D	G	A	I	K	N	B	G	R	D	B
X	S	I	P	K	H	B	F	C	D	E	C	Y	B	U
J	Y	D	O	C	N	H	W	T	G	C	H	E	R	D
X	G	T	Y	H	B	N	J	I	M	K	A	G	T	D
F	D	X	D	E	L	K	P	J	P	V	R	N	R	Y
O	Y	S	W	E	R	T	H	V	G	Y	L	B	N	J
U	F	B	S	R	N	J	M	K	H	G	I	F	T	Y
V	C	D	O	K	I	U	Y	J	A	K	E	Z	M	W
L	K	N	B	T	G	F	T	Y	R	D	X	S	K	X
Z	V	Y	G	H	V	B	H	U	K	H	M	N	V	B
H	Y	G	D	C	X	D	K	G	F	C	V	H	U	I
K	J	R	O	I	O	C	M	N	B	V	M	A	X	S
F	H	D	G	N	A	S	W	Q	P	K	H	G	C	M
B	I	R	S	J	G	N	H	B	V	C	F	T	D	Z
F	I	H	S	L	N	B	V	G	R	O	C	K	Y	S

FIDO	MAX	CHARLIE
BUDDY	ROCKY	JAKE
JACK	TOBY	CODY

ACROSTICS

Solve the clues correctly and the shaded squares will reveal a muscular German dog breed. What is it?

1. Bean, pea or lentil
2. Not as difficult
3. Unequal rectangle
4. Mother _____
5. Nocturnal burrowing mammal

1.					
2.					
3.					
4.					
5.					

TRIVIA

Which dog featured in the classic J. M. Barrie story *Peter Pan?*

  a) Bullseye
  b) Nana
  c) Pilot

QUIZ: PUPPY PARENTING

Here are three questions about dog motherhood. Do you have the knowledge to pick the correct answers?

1. **At which age do female dogs become fertile?**
   a) 4 weeks
   b) 6 months, but it can vary depending on the breed
   c) 1 year

2. **How long does a dog's pregnancy last?**
   a) 57–65 days
   b) Around 7 weeks
   c) 9 months

3. **Until what age should puppies stay with their mother?**
   a) 4 weeks
   b) 3 months
   c) 8–10 weeks

SPOT THE DIFFERENCE

Can you spot the ten differences between these two pictures?

WORD BUILDER

The letters of a seven-letter word have been numbered 1 to 7. Solve the clues to reveal a very British dog breed.

Letters 4, 6 and 7 give us fuel for the fire.

Letters 1, 2 and 7 give us creepy-crawly.

Letters 5, 2, 3 and 4 give us boring.

Letters 7, 2, 3 and 4 give us common coastal bird.

1	2	3	4	5	6	7

MYSTERY SUDOKU

Complete the grid so that every row, column and 3 x 3 box contains the letters SMYDZKEOA in any order. One row or column contains a seven-letter word that is a Siberian dog breed that was used for herding reindeer.

			Z		Y	K		S
	O		E				D	
K							Y	
Y		A			M		E	O
		O				A		
D	S		A			Y		Z
	Y							E
	D				Z		A	
S		M	O		E			

MISSING WORD

Fill in the blank space with a dog-related word to make two compound words or phrases.

Shirt		Spin
Snow		Park
Cake		About

19

WORD SEARCH:

THE LADY AND THE TRAMP (AND FRIENDS)

Find these characters from *The Lady and the Tramp* in the grid.

```
L  B  C  G  Y  H  E  P  X  T  R  A  M  P  W
B  H  G  C  V  I  F  R  K  X  K  H  B  U  I
O  T  D  S  S  H  B  N  C  F  R  E  S  D  F
G  Y  H  H  L  J  Y  U  F  C  X  S  G  A  W
U  H  C  J  K  H  J  D  V  Y  F  H  K  O  U
H  A  F  D  G  K  N  B  A  Y  T  F  X  D  S
D  J  N  U  G  H  K  M  L  L  P  L  G  I  R
D  C  O  Y  A  H  V  D  S  E  T  C  R  H  U
J  T  F  J  L  P  L  P  U  G  V  O  H  Y  R
S  X  B  H  J  E  I  J  B  G  B  E  A  P  K
M  N  V  H  Y  G  X  O  L  K  M  N  B  H  Y
U  F  D  P  L  K  D  C  I  J  U  H  R  V  G
H  U  F  C  V  Y  G  K  D  G  O  R  D  E  P
T  R  U  S  T  Y  L  J  N  B  Y  G  U  J  D
X  S  E  Q  A  H  B  M  P  L  G  J  P  C  I
```

LADY	TRAMP	JOCK
TRUSTY	BORIS	TOUGHY
PEDRO	DACHSIE	PEG

CROSSWORD: POISONOUS TO DOGS

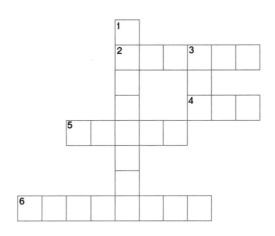

ACROSS

2. The genus that includes onion and garlic (6)

4. Ancient evergreen (3)

5. Baby oak (5)

6. Hand covering for red-coated vulpes (8)

DOWN

1. The bulb that gives us St David's favourite bloom (8)

3. Climbing plant (3)

21

TRIVIA

What was the name of the robotic dog released by Sony in 1999?

    a) Bobo
    b) Bert
    c) Aibo

PAIRS GAME

Match up the 20 dog toys in 20 seconds. The first one has been done for you.

WORD WHEEL

See how many words of four or more letters you can make from the letters below. All words must include the central letter, and proper nouns don't count! Can you find the name of a dog breed that possibly hails from modern-day Croatia and that uses all the letters?

MAZE

Can you help the hungry puppy find its dinner?

ANAGRAMS:
THE WAY OF THE WOLF

Rearrange these letters to reveal the names of films that featured wolves as primary characters.

BE KNOTHOLE JUG

WEAN FIGHT

HA LAP

GOLFER HUNT WHY

WORD LADDER

Change "walk" into "heel" by altering one letter at a time to make a new word on each step of the ladder:

WALK

HEEL

CROSSWORD: A BREED APART

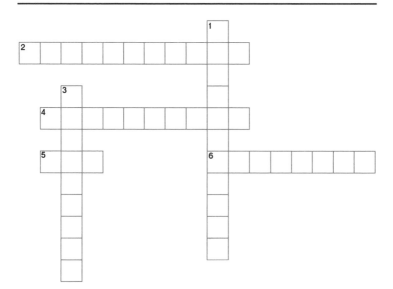

ACROSS

2. A dog bred to catch and hold poachers without hurting them (11)

4. The Coton de Tuléar is the official dog of this island nation (10)

5. This Japanese dog is famed for its ability to climb trees (3)

6. The national dog of Cuba (8)

DOWN

1. The first breed of dog ever to have been cloned (6,5)

3. A breed with a biblical name depicted in rock carvings from the first century (6,3)

COUNTING CONUNDRUM

🐾 + 🐾 = 14

🐾 + 🐾 = 18

🐾 + 🐾 = 13

🐾 = ?   🐾 = ?   🐾 = ?

WORD LINK

Each of the three words in the clues below have a word in common. For example, if the clues were "count", "faith" and "weight", the answer would be "lose" (lose count, lose faith and lose weight). Answer each of the following clues correctly to reveal a word in the shaded column, which is the leader of the pack.

1. over, top, rain
2. rag, baby, voodoo
3. tight, jump, tow
4. back, head, stomach
5. dream, life, sail

1.			
2.			
3.			
4.			
5.			

WORD SEARCH:
ANATOMY OF A DOG

Find the words in the grid that describe different parts of a dog.

```
A  J  G  H  V  U  K  N  V  F  R  E  S  D  G
H  D  M  N  V  G  H  A  C  K  L  E  S  Y  B
C  P  E  F  X  S  G  V  Y  H  G  E  J  N  Y
F  K  I  W  G  T  Y  G  A  S  X  S  W  V  L
J  N  B  H  C  T  T  D  L  G  A  K  I  B  H
Y  R  S  X  Z  L  G  I  K  B  T  F  T  I  J
G  O  L  M  N  G  A  R  E  W  A  S  H  C  M
G  H  N  U  I  T  M  W  O  P  L  P  E  H  U
A  C  D  E  V  G  Y  N  J  U  R  C  R  I  Z
N  E  A  R  S  G  H  D  S  W  E  T  S  L  Z
B  H  Y  U  P  B  K  O  B  H  V  C  R  T  L
V  C  X  E  D  F  R  T  C  V  N  Y  U  J  E
M  K  S  L  M  N  B  V  C  K  F  G  H  Y  T
R  O  O  K  J  U  Y  T  R  D  F  C  V  B  N
N  U  H  G  T  Y  B  P  A  L  W  E  D  T  G
```

EARS	NOSE	TAIL
DEWCLAW	HACKLES	MUZZLE
HOCK	WITHERS	DEWLAP

ACROSTICS

Solve the clues correctly and the shaded squares will reveal a swift Hungarian sighthound with great endurance. What is it?

1. One who would die rather than renounce their faith
2. Thorny tree common in Africa
3. Playing on a console
4. Japanese gangster
5. Mooring device

1.					
2.					
3.					
4.					
5.					

TRIVIA

The Basenji breed does what instead of bark?

        a) Gnashes its teeth

        b) Sneezes

        c) Yodels

QUIZ: A GRAND OLD AGE

Here are three questions about dog ages. Do you have the knowledge to pick the correct answers?

1. **Which lives longer, a feral or a domesticated dog?**
   a) A domesticated dog
   b) A feral dog
   c) Neither – they both live to around the same age

2. **What is the average life span of a dog?**
   a) 11–13 years
   b) 5–7 years
   c) 18–20 years

3. **How many human years are the first two years of a dog's life equivalent to?**
   a) 1
   b) 7
   c) 9–12.5

SPOT THE DIFFERENCE

Can you spot the ten differences between these two pictures?

WORD BUILDER

The letters of a seven-letter word have been numbered 1 to 7. Solve the clues to reveal a silky toy dog breed.

Letters 1, 2 and 4 give us what you do yoga on.

Letters 6, 5 and 4 give us a complete collection.

Letters 3, 2, 4 and 7 give us not on time.

Letters 6, 2, 3 and 4 give us a table-top seasoning.

1	2	3	4	5	6	7

BETWEEN THE LINES

A nine-letter dog breed can be inserted in the blank line so that, reading downwards, nine three-letter words are formed. What is the hidden French herding dog between the lines?

E	P	B	B	A	T	A	T	O
B	N	D	N	E	N	K	N	E

HIDDEN WORDS

In each of the sentences below, a dog-related word is hidden. For instance, in the sentence "I've been looking for my dog all afternoon, but he eludes me", the word "heel" is hidden in "he eludes".

1. Toby will eat anything bar ketchup.

2. Patch is behaving himself now, but he won't be the same at home.

3. Anoushka's dog was still sulking after the fiasco at the vet's.

4. When Tina met Tendai's new puppy, she was just a little bit envious.

5. Badaya was going to keep taking Bailey to the dog shows: they would win a ribbon eventually.

38

WORD SEARCH: A DOG GROOMER'S ARSENAL

Find the things a groomer would use in the grid.

```
H  Y  F  C  X  S  C  L  I  P  P  E  R  S  K
M  N  H  B  G  V  F  R  T  D  X  C  R  T  G
U  N  D  E  R  C  O  A  T  R  A  K  E  J  H
V  R  D  C  X  U  A  Z  S  E  F  R  V  G  T
Y  S  B  N  J  U  S  K  M  V  G  T  B  L  S
M  N  H  I  G  V  C  H  A  S  W  A  R  T  H
D  Y  H  A  U  I  J  N  B  H  T  F  D  S  E
R  C  V  M  M  K  I  O  P  H  N  B  Y  H  A
Y  C  F  R  D  P  X  Z  E  R  F  G  V  T  R
E  K  M  N  L  P  O  I  U  Y  T  R  F  G  S
R  N  B  H  Y  T  R  O  C  D  E  M  N  B  V
C  X  A  S  G  C  G  H  J  K  I  U  Y  T  R
E  D  S  H  L  O  I  J  N  O  T  E  L  U  G
C  G  R  O  O  M  I  N  G  T  A  B  L  E  C
A  Y  G  V  R  B  L  J  B  Y  T  F  H  K  L
```

BRUSH	CLIPPERS	SHEARS
DRYER	UNDERCOAT RAKE	GROOMING TABLE
COMB	BATH	SHAMPOO

CROSSWORD: CANINE COPS

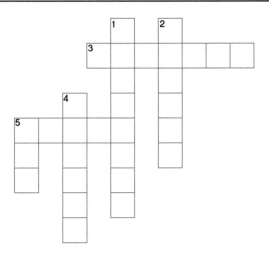

ACROSS

3. Police dog named after a Mexican spirit in the 1990s American TV show _____ and Bonetti (7)

5. *Police Dog* _____ , 1961 American crime film directed by Edward L. Cahn (5)

DOWN

1. Name of Belushi's partner pooch in 1989 film *K-9* (5,3)

2. Partner of German Shepherd Rex in Canadian police drama (6)

4. Police dog Reno and human partner Jake fight crime in this 1995 film starring Chuck Norris (3,3)

5. Canine character of 1978 TV series of the same name featuring a Labrador Retriever (3)

TRIVIA

In what year was London's famous Battersea Dogs & Cats Home founded?

a) 1820
b) 1860
c) 1890

PAIRS GAME

Match up the 20 paw prints in 20 seconds. The first one has been done for you.

WORD WHEEL

See how many words of four or more letters you can make from the letters below. All words must include the central letter, and proper nouns don't count! Can you find the name of a dog breed associated with Rhodesia, also known as an African Lion Hound, that uses all the letters?

MAZE

Can you help the dog find its way back to its owner?

ANAGRAMS: RARE POOCHES

Rearrange these letters to reveal the names of some of the world's rarest dog breeds.

GRANOLA GLOOM TOOT

BHUTAN SOY

ACTUAL BURN

EMAIL NOT

WORD LADDER

Change "good" into "girl" by altering one letter at a
time to make a new word on each step of the ladder:

GOOD

GIRL

CROSSWORD:
SHORT-HAIRED DOGGOS

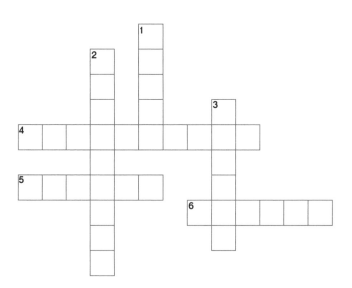

ACROSS

4. Grey ghost hunting dog (10)

5. Terrier from this East Coast city (6)

6. Hungarian pointer dog (6)

DOWN

1. Fighter (5)

2. 101 of these required for a fur coat (9)

3. Australian sheepdog, or perhaps a Scottish water horse (6)

47

COUNTING CONUNDRUM

$$\text{comb} + \text{bone} = 13$$

$$\text{comb} \times \text{bone} = 42$$

$$\text{bone} - \text{comb} = 1$$

$$\text{comb} = ? \qquad \text{bone} = ?$$

RIDDLE

The following clues will reveal a house built for a dog.

My first is in walk but not in hunt
My second is in pet and also in bed
My third is in nose, but not in tail
My fourth is in new, but not in trick
My fifth is in feed and also in sleep
My sixth is in play, but not in fetch

What am I?

WORD SEARCH: WILD DOGS

See if you can find all of these wild dogs in the grid.

```
J  Y  H  R  A  C  C  O  O  N  D  O  G  F  S
J  G  E  W  A  Q  S  C  X  D  H  Z  I  G  H
Y  T  X  G  I  K  N  J  K  P  L  K  O  B  O
E  T  F  O  X  E  R  W  D  X  C  D  Y  B  R
A  B  H  Y  F  P  L  G  O  R  D  S  X  C  T
E  A  Z  B  Y  G  J  G  V  L  E  W  Q  I  E
N  H  Y  L  N  M  N  U  I  B  F  F  R  E  A
D  L  X  E  R  I  G  W  V  G  T  Y  H  J  R
B  H  A  I  D  N  N  H  Y  U  D  H  O  L  E
V  S  C  K  R  A  G  H  R  D  X  C  E  W  D
D  Y  B  N  C  U  P  O  K  N  H  Y  R  D  D
X  C  R  I  V  A  Y  B  N  H  U  I  J  M  O
I  O  R  N  B  H  J  Y  U  J  V  C  D  E  G
F  F  C  G  Y  H  J  A  I  P  L  K  N  C  F
A  E  W  S  B  U  S  H  D  O  G  M  V  F  A
```

WOLF	DINGO	DHOLE
AFRICAN WILD DOG	JACKAL	FOX
RACCOON DOG	BUSH DOG	SHORT-EARED DOG

ACROSTICS

Solve the clues correctly and the shaded squares will reveal a hunting dog with an oily, weather-resistant coat and webbed feet. What is it?

1. Dull-witted and clumsy
2. Body art
3. A badger-like Indonesian creature
4. Emblem
5. Your money back

1.					
2.					
3.					
4.					
5.					

TRIVIA

Which of the following was a chart hit for
Florence and the Machine?

a) "Dog Days are Here"

b) "Dog Days are Over"

c) "Dog Days are Gone"

QUIZ:
A GUIDE TO DOG SPEAK

Here are three questions about the sounds dogs make. What does it mean when your dog makes these sounds? There might be more than one correct answer.

1. **Whining or crying**

    a) They want attention
    b) They are in emotional distress or pain
    c) They are apologizing after you scolded them

2. **Grunting**

    a) They need the toilet
    b) They are happy and content
    c) They have seen something they want to chase

3. **Growling**

    a) They want to play
    b) They are ready to mate
    c) They are angry or scared

SPOT THE DIFFERENCE

Can you spot the ten differences between these two pictures?

WORD BUILDER

The letters of a seven-letter word have been numbered 1 to 7. Solve the clues to reveal a powerful guard dog breed.

Letters 1, 2 and 4 give us what you step on when you walk in the door.

Letters 6, 5 and 4 give us healthy.

Letters 7, 2 and 4 give us not thin.

Letters 3, 2 and 4 give us rested on a chair.

1	2	3	4	5	6	7

MYSTERY SUDOKU

Complete the grid so that every row, column and 3 x 3 box contains the letters BDETINRGO in any order. One row or column contains a six-letter name of a canine character from *The Incredible Journey* by Sheila Burnford.

			O		B	D		I
	T		N				G	
D							B	
B		E			R		N	T
		T				E		
G	I		E			B		O
	B							N
	G				O		E	
I		R	T		N			

BETWEEN THE LINES

A nine-letter dog breed can be inserted in the blank line so that, reading downwards, nine three-letter words are formed. What is the hidden large, shaggy-coated Scottish dog between the lines?

O	D	Z	C	S	C	F	I	O
E	N	N	Y	E	X	N	K	D

MISSING WORD

Fill in the blank space to make two compound words or phrases.

Tail		Yard
Fore		Print
Over		Tails

WORD SEARCH: FAMOUS DOG LOVERS

Find these famous dog owners in the grid.

```
L  L  I  H  C  R  U  H  C  N  O  T  S  N  I  W
A  G  F  C  D  E  S  C  F  T  Y  H  B  J  U  N
U  H  A  U  D  R  E  Y  H  E  P  B  U  R  N  R
R  V  G  T  Y  H  N  J  H  G  F  R  E  S  Z  S
E  P  O  K  Y  D  E  N  N  E  K  F  N  H  O  J
N  D  R  T  A  B  A  J  U  K  N  K  I  H  V  E
B  R  D  Q  U  E  E  N  V  I  C  T  O  R  I  A
A  J  U  I  K  M  N  K  I  J  H  B  V  G  P  N
C  X  D  E  R  F  G  V  H  Y  U  P  U  K  M  S
A  H  G  V  G  C  F  R  E  D  X  S  E  D  R  I
L  H  B  Y  U  O  J  I  K  M  N  J  I  H  B  M
L  F  C  D  E  L  K  M  P  U  L  G  V  S  R  M
R  O  L  Y  A  T  H  T  E  B  A  Z  I  L  E  O
G  E  O  R  G  E  W  A  S  H  I  N  G  T  O  N
I  P  A  U  L  M  C  C  A  R  T  N  E  Y  A  S
```

QUEEN VICTORIA   LAUREN BACALL   WINSTON CHURCHILL

AUDREY HEPBURN   PAUL McCARTNEY   JOHN F. KENNEDY

ELIZABETH TAYLOR   JEAN SIMMONS   GEORGE WASHINGTON

CROSSWORD: CANINE KARAOKE

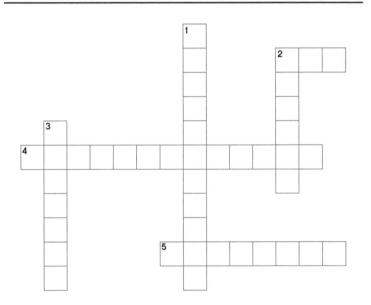

ACROSS

2. In his debut single, Lobo sang about "Me and You and a Dog Named _____" (3)

4. Rufus Thomas sang about doing this in his 1963 hit song (7,3,3)

5. Elvis sang about being nothing but one of these (5,3)

DOWN

1. George Michael's 2002 song with an animated video featuring a dog (5,3,3)

2. In the 1934 musical movie *Evergreen*, what wouldn't Daddy buy for singer Jessie Matthews? (3,3)

3. This group let the dogs out (4,3)

TRIVIA

What item did a dog named Pickles famously find in 1966?

a) The stolen Jules Rimet Trophy that would be awarded to the winning team of the football World Cup

b) A fur hat belonging to the Queen

c) An unexploded bomb

PAIRS GAME

Match up the 20 grooming tools in 20 seconds.
The first one has been done for you.

WORD WHEEL

See how many words of four or more letters you can make from the letters below. All words must include the central letter, and proper nouns don't count! Can you find the name of a short-legged dog breed with a big personality that uses all the letters?

63

MAZE

Can you help the dog find the ball?

ANAGRAMS: DOGGY DITTIES

Rearrange these letters to reveal the names of songs that feature dogs.

MAHATMA DRYER

DIVE GLOOMY

GOB IN

GOLD INK

CROSSWORD: ARTY DOGS

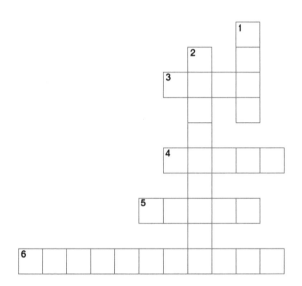

ACROSS

3. Spanish artist who painted *The Dog* (4)

4. Game played by the dogs in C. M. Coolidge's painting *A Friend in Need* (5)

5. A King Charles Spaniel was this artist's model (5)

6. The dog breed featured in Sir Edwin Landseer's *A Jack in Office* (4,7)

DOWN

1. Dog's body part famously painted by Edvard Munch (4)

2. George Stubbs painted *A Couple of _____* (9)

COUNTING CONUNDRUM

🐾 + 🐾 + 🐾 = 30

🐾 + 🐕 + 🐕 = 18

🐕 – 🐺 = 2

🐺 + (🐾 × 🐕) = ?

MINI SUDOKU: SALUKI

Salukis are elegent long-eared hounds, prized by nomadic people of the Middle East. Take a moment to celebrate these majestic dogs by completing the grid so that every row, column and 2 x 3 box contains the letters that make up the word "Saluki".

	A				
S				A	
L			K		
	S				
		U			
K		S		I	

WORD SEARCH: MYTHICAL DOGS

Find these dogs from myths and legends in the grid.

```
I  G  V  X  F  R  T  G  A  B  J  U  P  L  B
B  V  T  Q  I  Q  I  R  N  G  V  B  H  U  L
S  C  A  V  A  L  L  J  N  M  A  Y  G  B  A
T  F  D  F  R  L  K  M  B  H  R  T  G  V  C
F  R  T  S  X  E  R  F  C  G  G  Y  H  B  K
A  X  E  H  A  N  D  L  E  H  O  U  N  D  S
T  H  D  S  A  Y  G  V  R  H  S  P  L  M  H
N  H  Y  U  J  V  C  D  B  R  T  G  M  J  U
A  B  Y  U  S  L  K  M  E  B  V  X  Z  S  C
S  A  S  W  E  D  U  R  R  G  V  B  H  Y  K
E  K  N  L  O  P  Y  I  U  V  U  R  D  X  S
P  F  H  Y  N  J  U  I  S  M  N  I  P  O  H
V  C  R  D  F  T  G  S  W  O  A  N  B  H  U
B  A  R  G  H  E  S  T  U  Y  N  V  C  D  E
R  T  G  A  L  N  H  Y  U  I  J  V  C  F  R
```

BLACK SHUCK	BARGHEST	CERBERUS
QIQIRN	ARGOS	AXEHANDLE HOUND
LUISON	PESANTA	CAVALL

ACROSTICS

Solve the clues correctly and the shaded squares
will reveal a fluffy dog favoured by Queen Victoria.
What is it?

1. Temple
2. Without parents
3. Breakfast cereal
4. Itchy skin complaint
5. Shrivelled grape

1.					
2.					
3.					
4.					
5.					

TRIVIA

The Lhasa Apso was originally bred for
what purpose?

a) Herding mountain goats

b) Guarding palaces and monasteries

c) For its fur – used to produce a felt-like fabric

QUIZ:
DOG'S BODY LANGUAGE

Here are three questions about dog body language. Do you have the knowledge to pick the correct answers? There may be more than one correct answer.

1. **If a dog's tail is wagging, it...**

    a) ... is happy.
    b) ... is hungry.
    c) ... has seen another dog.

2. **If a dog's ears are back, it...**

    a) ... is being playful.
    b) ... is worried.
    c) ... is about to attack.

3. **If a dog shows its teeth, it...**

    a) ... is hungry.
    b) ... is angry or feels threatened.
    c) ... is laughing.

72

SPOT THE DIFFERENCE

Can you spot the ten differences between these two pictures?

WORD BUILDER

The letters of a seven-letter word have been numbered 1 to 7. Solve the clues to reveal a speedy little dog breed.

Letters 4, 3 and 7 give us a hole in the ground.

Letters 5, 6 and 7 give us a companion animal.

Letters 2, 3 and 7 give us a chart-topping pop song.

Letters 1, 6 and 7 give us not dry.

1	2	3	4	5	6	7

MYSTERY SUDOKU

Complete the grid so that every row, column and 3 x 3 box contains the letters HREBTIPAS in any order. One row or column contains a seven-letter word that is a wrinkly and loyal Chinese dog breed.

			T		E	R		S
	P		H				B	
R							E	
E		A			I		H	P
		P				A		
B	S		A			E		T
	E							H
	B				T		A	
S		I	P		H			

RIDDLE

The following clues will reveal a dog accessory.

My first is in catch, but not in give
My second is in growl, but not in snarl
My third is in leash and also in bowl
My fourth is in lap, but not in dog
My fifth is in bark, but not in whine
My sixth is in rub, but not in head

What am I?

WORD SEARCH: THE CAST OF *101 DALMATIANS*

Find these dogs that are all characters in
101 Dalmatians in the grid.

```
P T V C F T D X S W U J N O M
I P P U H G V C Y R E D E X Z
A O W E D C F L B T U I N P K
I N L P H B L G L F T D E E N
B G U K M O P O U T F C D N S
W O D E R T G V O F Y G B N J
M N K I O E P C Y T R E D Y G
B V A Y N J S K J U I O P Y T
L U C K Y V G W T Y H H N J U
I M F E N Q A H O K C U G H B
V C R E N F X E R T Y H N M U
I O H G A R F G A N D Y R E S
X W E D D F J P H B Y L K M N
P L K I Y F V C H B T Y O S A
W P E R D I T A J I K N J L P
```

PONGO	PERDITA	PATCH
ROLLY	LUCKY	PENNY
TOWSER	DANNY	SCOTTIE

CROSSWORD: WHAT BIG EARS YOU HAVE!

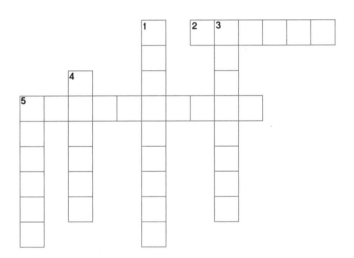

ACROSS

2. Central Asian hound (6)

5. Keen-scented dog (10)

DOWN

1. Floppy-eared little sausage (9)

3. Nickname for this popular type of bulldog (8)

4. Silky-eared spaniel (6)

5. Fred was a famous comic-strip version of this hound (6)

TRIVIA

What is the fastest recorded speed for a Greyhound?

a) 56 km/h (35 mph)
b) 68 km/h (42 mph)
c) 72 km/h (45 mph)

PAIRS GAME

Match up the 20 squirrels in 20 seconds. The first one has been done for you.

WORD WHEEL

See how many words of four or more letters you can make from the letters below. All words must include the central letter, and proper nouns don't count! Can you find the name of a German dog breed that comes in three sizes using all the letters?

MAZE

Can you help the momma dog collect her puppy?

ANAGRAMS:
DOG TALES

Rearrange these letters to reveal the titles of books that feature dogs.

SUGARED POOPS

ACHE SLIME MOOSE

SHADOWY OMEGA

LORDLY EEL

WORD LADDER

Change "wild" into "tame" by altering one letter at a time to make a new word on each step of the ladder:

WILD

TAME

CROSSWORD:
FICTIONAL DOGS AND THEIR OWNERS

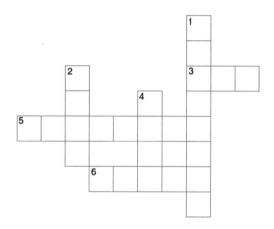

ACROSS

3. The Grinch's only friend (3)

5. Doc Brown named his dog after this scientist in *Back to the Future* (8)

6. Tom Hanks' slobbery companion in 1989 cop buddy film (5)

DOWN

1. Robert Neville's beloved German Shepherd in *I Am Legend* (8)

2. Inhabitant of Hagrid's Hut (4)

4. Pumpkin Jack's ghostly pet (4)

COUNTING CONUNDRUM

🐕 + 🐕 + 🐕 = 12

(🐕 × 🐕) + 🥏 = 26

🥏 + (🥏 × 🦴) = 100

🥏🥏 + (🦴 × 🐕) = ?

DOWN THE MIDDLE

Complete all the following words correctly to reveal, in the shaded squares, a small dog the perfect size for cuddles.

Y	E		P	S
C	H		S	E
P	U		P	Y
B	U		D	Y
P	O		C	H
D	O		G	Y

WORD SEARCH: PUP PARAPHERNALIA

Find all these items a dog needs in the grid.

```
U  G  E  J  N  U  I  M  N  B  F  R  T  P  L
K  N  J  T  Y  F  C  T  R  E  A  T  S  Q  Z
W  E  C  F  A  H  Y  B  N  J  U  L  O  K  M
N  J  U  P  K  R  B  V  G  L  E  A  S  H  F
B  A  L  L  Y  U  C  L  P  O  J  N  M  Y  G
V  B  F  R  D  X  S  Y  G  V  B  H  L  N  M
K  L  O  P  I  H  V  G  P  R  D  S  I  A  J
U  Y  H  L  M  C  I  O  Y  G  V  C  C  S  D
S  X  B  G  B  H  O  U  J  N  M  N  K  S  F
C  Z  S  A  E  C  F  L  G  G  S  A  M  E  E
D  F  M  N  S  H  Y  U  L  N  M  K  A  N  B
V  F  R  P  G  K  C  P  L  A  N  H  T  R  T
F  V  O  R  D  I  E  B  J  U  R  V  T  A  N
L  O  M  N  B  V  C  T  E  S  R  F  G  H  H
P  U  I  X  B  V  T  Y  O  K  M  N  U  P  L
```

BALL	COLLAR	LEASH
BASKET	CRATE	LICK MAT
POOP SCOOP	HARNESS	TREATS

ACROSTICS

Solve the clues correctly and the shaded squares
will reveal a dog breed that sounds fragile but isn't.
What is it?

1. Wrapped item arrives in the post
2. Fluid retention
3. Appetizer with chicken livers and water chestnuts
4. Ravine
5. Come out

1.					
2.					
3.					
4.					
5.					

89

TRIVIA

What is the name of Bill Sikes' dog in *Oliver Twist*?

a) Geoff
b) Cutie Pie
c) Bullseye

QUIZ:
WHAT MAKES A DOG?

Here are three questions about dog anatomy. Do you have the knowledge to pick the correct answers?

1. **How many taste buds does a dog have on the tip of its tongue?**
   a) 1,700
   b) 20,000
   c) None – they are all in its nose

2. **How many bones does a dog have?**
   a) 206
   b) 320
   c) 5,000

3. **Where are a dog's sweat glands?**
   a) In their armpits
   b) In their noses and paw pads
   c) They don't have any

SPOT THE DIFFERENCE

Can you spot the ten differences between these two pictures?

WORD BUILDER

The letters of a seven-letter word have been numbered 1 to 7. Solve the clues to reveal the family dogs belong to.

Letters 2, 3 and 5 give us a connecting word.

Letters 5, 4, 3 and 7 give us another word for eat.

Letters 4, 1 and 7 give us cold cubes.

Letters 6, 4 and 5 give us help.

1	2	3	4	5	6	7

MYSTERY SUDOKU

Complete the grid so that every row, column and 3 x 3 box contains the letters RBEPMNSIA in any order. One row or column contains a six-letter word that is a disease that all dogs must be vaccinated against.

		P		B	M			E
	A		I				N	
M							B	
B		S			R		I	A
		A			S			
N	E		S			B		P
	B							I
	N				P		S	
E		R	A		I			

BETWEEN THE LINES

A stocky little herding dog can be inserted in the blank line so that, reading downwards, ten three-letter words are formed. What is the hidden dog breed between the lines?

A	T	A	A	T	A	H	O	E	B
E	N	E	P	E	T	T	B	O	G

CROSS OUT

Cross out all the letters that appear more than once. The letters that are left, reading from left to right and top to bottom, will spell out the name of a famous animated dog. What is it?

Q	W	G	E	Y	U	P	A
A	S	D	F	R	H	J	O
D	F	M	K	J	S	K	H
Y	E	U	P	I	W	Q	T

WORD SEARCH: WORKING WOOFERS

See if you can find all of these working dogs in the grid.

```
M  Y  G  E  U  C  S  E  R  R  E  T  A  W  H
Y  G  G  C  F  R  E  D  X  A  T  R  V  G  T
H  B  U  U  H  I  L  K  J  N  B  U  M  Y  H
X  E  A  Q  A  S  Z  G  T  Y  H  F  I  J  E
J  N  R  A  O  P  H  B  V  T  Y  F  L  D  R
S  H  D  D  U  G  F  M  O  D  E  L  I  A  A
G  V  D  S  E  A  D  O  V  G  H  E  T  B  P
J  I  O  H  B  R  T  P  L  K  M  S  A  I  Y
B  V  G  T  R  E  S  A  Q  W  E  N  R  V  G
T  K  M  I  H  B  V  D  E  I  Y  I  Y  P  O
K  J  N  U  Y  T  X  S  V  A  W  F  D  C  G
T  Y  H  B  N  J  N  O  I  K  V  F  O  H  B
G  Y  G  C  A  Q  M  Y  G  H  D  I  G  R  U
J  H  N  M  L  P  O  N  H  Y  U  N  H  B  V
P  O  L  I  C  E  D  O  G  H  Y  G  M  B  P
```

GUARD DOG	MODEL	THERAPY
HERDER	MOVIE STAR	TRUFFLE SNIFFING
MILITARY DOG	WATER RESCUE	POLICE DOG

CROSSWORD: DOGS OF THE INTERNET

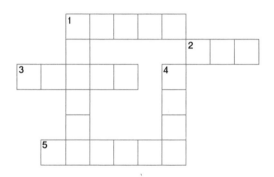

ACROSS

1. Billed as "the most famous French Bulldog in the world" (5)

2. Pomeranian with lots of Facebook likes (3)

3. Senior dog with friends around the world (5)

5. Coonhound famed for standing on things (6)

DOWN

1. A talking Husky (6)

4. Dachshund Harlow's beloved fellow pooch (4)

TRIVIA

How many teeth does the average adult dog have?

a) 24
b) 36
c) 42

PAIRS GAME

Match up the 20 kennels in 20 seconds. The first one has been done for you.

WORD WHEEL

See how many words of four or more letters you can make from the letters below. All words must include the central letter, and proper nouns don't count! Can you find the name of a compact, long-coated dog breed created for the ruling classes of ancient China using all the letters?

MAZE

Can you find your way to the paw print?

ANAGRAMS: CANINE CAREERS

Rearrange these letters to reveal the names of jobs that involve working with dogs.

GORGED MOOR

GENERAL MAN KEN

READING ROT

RETAINER VAIN

WORD LADDER

Change "food" into "bite" by altering one letter at a time to make a new word on each step of the ladder:

FOOD

BITE

CROSSWORD: FICTIONAL FURBALLS

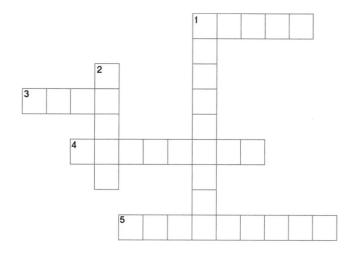

ACROSS

1. Canine member of the Griffin family (5)

3. Dorothy's faithful companion (4)

4. Big red dog (8)

5. Stretchy pooch in *Toy Story* (6,3)

DOWN

1. Family pet named after a German composer (9)

2. Piano playing muppet (5)

COUNTING CONUNDRUM

🐕 + 🐕 + 🐕 = 30

🐕 + 🐕 + 🐕 = 20

🐕 + 🐕 + 🐕 = 9

🐕 + (🐕 × 🐕) = ?

RIDDLE

The following clues will reveal a word for all things dog.

My first is in coat, but not in brush
My second is in sat, but not in sit
My third is in hound, but not in puppy
My fourth is in praise but not in pet
My fifth is in whine, but not in woof
My sixth is in cuddle and also in stroke

What am I?

107

WORD SEARCH: THEY WROTE ABOUT DOGS

Find these authors in the grid, who have all written about dogs.

V	F	Y	Y	M	F	T	B	N	B	H	S	O	P	J
B	Y	L	E	A	D	Z	S	D	C	B	P	N	J	V
T	B	W	B	R	U	C	E	C	A	M	E	R	O	N
J	I	N	W	K	R	B	J	I	K	G	F	P	H	W
A	G	K	H	T	B	H	G	K	O	J	H	I	N	V
G	R	T	I	W	X	S	M	Y	U	N	B	V	G	S
A	P	B	T	A	G	T	F	K	R	T	N	K	R	N
R	C	S	E	I	J	A	C	K	L	O	N	D	O	N
T	C	R	J	N	H	G	F	G	H	J	I	G	G	M
H	D	S	C	J	N	D	X	V	A	M	L	K	A	G
S	H	C	A	F	T	X	D	Y	G	B	N	Y	N	V
T	O	L	L	I	M	A	C	I	D	E	I	T	A	K
E	L	E	A	N	O	R	A	T	K	I	N	S	O	N
I	K	A	H	V	T	E	S	K	B	S	L	M	N	N
N	T	S	W	I	L	S	O	N	R	A	W	L	S	P

MARK TWAIN   ELEANOR ATKINSON   JACK LONDON

W. BRUCE CAMERON   KATIE DiCAMILLO   JOHN GROGAN

WILSON RAWLS   GARTH STEIN   E. B. WHITE

ACROSTICS

Solve the clues correctly and the shaded squares will reveal a large breed originally bred as cattle-driving dogs. What is it?

1. Chef's instructions
2. Eight-legged sea creature, more than one
3. Excite
4. Walk softly
5. The person who takes your dog out

1.					
2.					
3.					
4.					
5.					

QUIZ:
BIZARRE DOG BELIEFS

Here are three questions about dog superstitions. Do you have the knowledge to pick the correct answers?

1. **What does a dog howling outside your home mean?**

    a) You will soon die
    b) There is a ghost outside your door
    c) You will fall in love during the next full moon

2. **Why won't sailors bring a dog onboard a ship?**

    a) Because it will bring bad luck
    b) Because it will cause the sailors to get lost
    c) Because it will cause the ship to sink

3. **According to the French, if you step in dog poo with your left foot, what does it mean?**

    a) That you will meet your next lover around the corner
    b) That you will have good luck
    c) That someone didn't bother to clean up after their dog

SPOT THE DIFFERENCE

Can you spot the ten differences between these two pictures?

WORD BUILDER

The letters of a seven-letter word have been numbered 1 to 7. Solve the clues to reveal a working dog who is no stranger to the Arctic.

Letters 6, 4 and 5 give us strange.

Letters 7, 3 and 2 give us a hair product.

Letters 1, 6 and 4 give us a clump of turf.

Letters 2, 6 and 7 give us a yuletide cake.

1	2	3	4	5	6	7

MYSTERY SUDOKU

Complete the grid so that every row, column and 3 x 3 box contains the letters GSOEFLDPA in any order. One row or column contains a seven-letter word that is an intelligent dog who lives on Terry Pratchett's Discworld.

		O		G	A			E
	L		F				P	
A							G	
G		S			D		F	L
		L				S		
P	E		S			G		O
	G							F
	P				O		S	
E		D	L		F			

BETWEEN THE LINES

A German Spitz dog that makes an ideal companion can be inserted in the blank line so that, reading downwards, eight three-letter words are formed. What is the hidden dog breed between the lines?

F	B	W	F	A	S	F	P
D	T	Y	N	P	N	N	Y

HIDDEN WORDS

In each of the sentences below, a dog-related word is hidden. For instance, in the sentence "I've been looking for my dog all afternoon, but he eludes me", the word "heel" is hidden in "he eludes".

1. Chima had filled Bruce's bowl with healthy dry food, but he knew the dog would much prefer all the treats in the cupboard.

2. Chico was very pleased with his jumbo new dog toy.

3. Despite his owner's pleas Harley rolled in the mud.

4. Rocky's collar was covered in mud after she came in from a wet walk, but Gary had scrubbed it until it looked brand new again.

5. When Sarah brought her puppy over, Kate had to grab all the children's toys and put them out of reach.

115

WORD SEARCH: DINKY DOGGIES

See if you can find all these small dog breeds in the grid.

```
P  G  C  B  U  H  B  G  T  Y  H  V  T  R  I
O  H  P  E  K  I  N  G  E  S  E  R  O  R  O
M  G  T  Y  H  B  H  U  J  G  V  E  Y  R  E
E  S  A  W  E  D  X  C  H  A  B  I  P  J  J
R  O  H  R  V  G  T  M  U  C  X  R  O  F  A
A  T  Y  H  N  P  H  H  N  P  I  R  O  B  P
N  F  D  A  Q  W  A  X  P  O  K  E  D  G  A
I  V  B  F  T  U  C  P  D  S  E  T  L  G  N
A  B  J  U  H  K  M  N  I  C  F  Y  E  P  E
N  A  C  I  D  E  R  F  J  L  Y  K  H  I  S
N  M  H  I  G  V  T  G  P  L  L  L  B  H  E
F  C  X  E  R  F  C  V  G  Y  H  O  V  H  C
J  N  M  E  S  E  T  L  A  M  R  S  N  N  H
V  C  X  D  E  R  H  V  H  Y  U  P  L  T  I
B  R  U  S  S  E  L  S  G  R  I  F  F  O  N
```

BRUSSELS GRIFFON	CHIHUAHUA	TOY POODLE
JAPANESE CHIN	MALTESE	PAPILLON
PEKINGESE	SILKY TERRIER	POMERANIAN

CROSSWORD: SUCH A BRAVE DOG

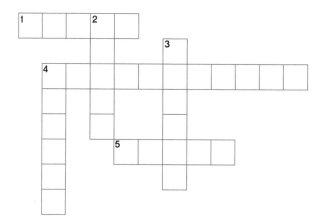

ACROSS

1. Siberian Husky who helped to deliver essential diphtheria serum in Alaska (5)

4. Saved numerous swimmers in the Welsh city he was named for (7,4)

5. St Bernard who saved more than 40 people in Switzerland (5)

DOWN

2. German Shepherd who found the last survivor of the 9/11 attacks (5)

3. Prince Llewellyn's dog, who killed a wolf to save the baby (6)

4. This dog sergeant killed an enemy soldier during the Second World War (6)

TRIVIA

What breed of dog was developed in Germany by a tax collector who needed a guard dog for protection?

a) German Shepherd

b) Dobermann (also known as Doberman Pinscher)

c) Bullmastiff

PAIRS GAME

Match up the 20 dog collar tags in 20 seconds.
The first one has been done for you.

WORD WHEEL

See how many words of four or more letters you can make from the letters below. All words must include the central letter, and proper nouns don't count! Can you find the name of a small Mexican dog breed that uses all the letters?

MAZE

This dog is sleepy. Can you help it find its bed?

ANAGRAMS: DOGS ON THE BRAIN

Rearrange these letters to reveal things that have dog in their names.

HOD TOG

REDO FIG

DO GUNS

HID FOGS

WORD LADDER

Change "pant" into "lick" by altering one letter at a time to make a new word on each step of the ladder:

PANT

LICK

CROSSWORD: NOT SUCH A GOOD BOY

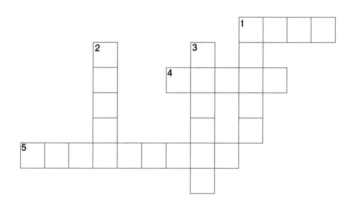

ACROSS

1. Rabid dog goes on the rampage in Stephen King's cult horror (4)

4. Dog who comes back with extra bite in *Pet Sematary* (5)

5. Napoleon's partner in crime in *The Aristocats* (9)

DOWN

1. Amos' pet in *The Fox and the Hound* (5)

2. Talking Dobermann in *Up* (5)

3. The Looney Tune who kept Road Runner in his sights was this type of animal (6)

COUNTING CONUNDRUM

$$\text{🦴} + \text{🦴}\text{🦴} + \text{🦴} = 80$$

$$\text{🦴} + (\text{🐾}\text{🐾} + \text{🐾}\text{🐾}) = 84$$

$$\text{🐾} - \bigstar = 3$$

$$\text{🦴} + (\bigstar \times \text{🐾}) = \text{?}$$

WORD LINK

Each of the three words in the clues below have a word in common. For example, if the clues were "count", "faith" and "weight", the answer would be "lose" (lose count, lose faith and lose weight). Answer each of the following clues correctly to reveal a word in the shaded column, which is a dog with no home.

1. lamp, goal, sign
2. robe, room, tub
3. foot, back, thread
4. heart, dead, drum
5. school, page, play

1.			
2.			
3.			
4.			
5.			

ACROSTICS

Solve the clues correctly and the shaded squares will reveal a black fox-like dog breed. What is it?

1. Tasty crustacean
2. Waxy light source
3. Cyber criminal
4. At your place of employment
5. Canoeing stick

1.					
2.					
3.					
4.					
5.					

127

TRIVIA

Which breed's sense of smell can be used as evidence in court?

- a) Poodle
- b) Basset Hound
- c) Bloodhound

QUIZ:
BREED BRAIN TEASERS

Here are three questions about dog breeds. Do you have the knowledge to pick the correct answers?

1. **Which dog breed has a black tongue?**
   a) Husky
   b) Poodle
   c) Chow Chow

2. **Which is the smallest of all dog breeds?**
   a) Dachshund
   b) Shih Tzu
   c) Chihuahua

3. **Which breed was once known as St John's Newfoundland?**
   a) Newfoundland
   b) Labrador Retriever
   c) Puli

SPOT THE DIFFERENCE

Can you spot the ten differences between these two pictures?

WORD BUILDER

The letters of a seven-letter word have been numbered 1 to 7. Solve the clues to reveal an extra digit on the forepaws of dogs.

Letters 3, 2 and 1 give us married.

Letters 7, 6 and 1 give us a stack of cash.

Letters 5, 6, 4 and 2 give us what you use to tie your shoe.

Letters 6, 5 and 2 give us beer.

1	2	3	4	5	6	7

BETWEEN THE LINES

A German breed, the name meaning "guard dog" can be inserted in the blank line so that, reading downwards, eight three-letter words are formed. What is the hidden dog breed between the lines?

S	F	E	V	E	T	A	S
E	G	E	N	E	N	T	Y

MISSING WORD

Fill in the blank space to make two compound words or phrases.

House		Down
Out		Home
Snow		Kick

WORD SEARCH: CANINE COMMANDS

Find these dog commands in the grid.

```
U  B  C  R  H  K  N  B  H  Y  T  D  C  X  L
W  E  D  X  G  T  F  C  V  H  Y  B  H  U  E
J  L  M  N  D  G  T  R  D  C  X  S  L  E  A
Z  I  F  R  T  R  V  B  H  U  J  N  E  L  V
P  E  J  N  C  H  O  G  V  C  D  S  E  Z  E
R  D  G  P  O  O  M  P  B  H  G  F  H  Y  I
C  O  E  R  F  H  M  U  I  N  J  I  K  B  T
G  W  F  C  X  D  E  E  G  T  O  K  N  J  U
H  N  V  F  R  W  A  Z  X  S  E  F  C  O  T
G  B  H  Y  S  N  J  M  K  L  T  L  H  V  P
C  X  D  S  I  E  A  T  F  I  B  H  K  N  J
I  D  N  A  T  S  R  T  A  M  K  I  O  P  N
H  B  V  G  T  D  X  W  U  U  Y  H  I  G  T
Y  F  C  D  E  R  P  K  M  N  J  U  I  P  L
H  V  C  F  E  J  D  H  J  U  S  T  A  Y  J
```

SIT	STAY	COME
LEAVE IT	LIE DOWN	DROP IT
STAND	WAIT	HEEL

134

CROSSWORD: STARRING JACK RUSSELL

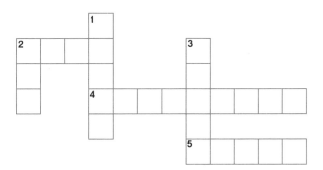

ACROSS

2. Jim Carrey's sidekick in *The Mask* (4)

4. A boy receives a pet dog for his birthday in this 2000 film (2,3,4)

5. Dr Frasier Crane's canine housemate (5)

DOWN

1. Ewan McGregor's co-star in *Beginners* (5)

2. Katie's envious pet with a secret life (3)

3. Canine actor who played Jack in *The Artist* (5)

TRIVIA

Which toy dog breed is also known as the
"Chrysanthemum Dog"?

    a) Shih Tzu
    b) West Highland Terrier
    c) Bichon Frisé

PAIRS GAME

Match up the 20 bones in 20 seconds. The first one has been done for you.

WORD WHEEL

See how many words of four or more letters you can make from the letters below. All words must include the central letter, and proper nouns don't count! Can you find the name of a gentle giant of a dog with long eyebrows and a beard that uses all the letters?

138

MAZE

Can you help the dog find its toy?

ANAGRAMS: CELEBRITY POOCHES

Rearrange these letters to reveal the names of famous dog actors.

DETACH GREENWOOD

BITE GRIT

REVERSALS KIT

MAINS DO

WORD LADDER

Change "cat" into "dog" by altering one letter at a time to make a new word on each step of the ladder:

CAT

DOG

CROSSWORD: GUARDIANS OF THE FLOCK

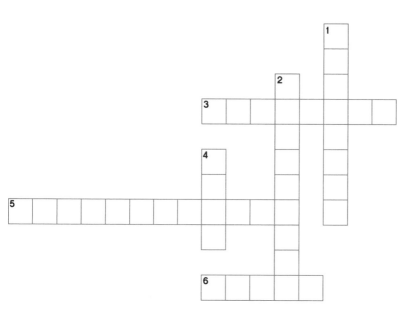

ACROSS

3. An alternative name for this German sheep-herding breed (8)

5. Sheepdog trial champion (6,6)

6. Favoured pet of Queen Elizabeth II (5)

DOWN

1. This Belgian herding dog also has a strong military background (8)

2. A sturdy pooch that keeps livestock in line, Australian _____ (6,3)

4. Mop-coated Hungarian herding dog (4)

COUNTING CONUNDRUM

🐕 × 🐕 = 72

🐕 × 🐕 = 36

🐕 × 🐕 = 32

🐕 = ?   🐕 = ?   🐕 = ?

MINI SUDOKU: KUVASZ

The Kuvasz is a powerful dog originating in Hungary, historically used to guard livestock but now increasingly popular as pets. Take a moment to celebrate these noble canines by completing the grid so that every row, column and 2 x 3 box contains the letters that make up the word Kuvasz.

		U			
	K				U
	V			S	
		K			
			A		
	S		K		Z

144

WORD SEARCH:
FROM THE LAND OF THE RISING SUN

L	H	V	G	T	Y	C	X	S	J	A	S	T	F	G
V	T	Y	U	J	N	B	J	U	A	M	S	O	P	H
G	C	O	D	W	E	R	G	J	P	P	H	N	C	K
A	R	Y	S	I	O	Y	V	C	A	W	I	E	Y	H
E	K	J	I	A	B	H	O	T	N	O	B	M	K	B
H	Y	I	C	X	D	D	R	P	E	H	A	B	A	Y
F	C	D	T	R	I	G	V	B	S	Y	I	F	I	A
W	U	H	J	A	M	K	I	G	E	F	N	T	K	P
L	N	V	K	T	B	C	X	W	S	Y	U	B	E	Y
U	N	K	F	U	D	S	J	K	P	U	P	L	N	N
J	O	Y	G	F	C	U	H	S	I	K	B	C	G	Y
H	F	C	C	H	U	I	K	U	T	L	K	M	B	V
G	T	R	D	A	X	C	G	Y	Z	B	H	U	J	N
A	M	J	U	R	Y	U	K	Y	U	I	N	U	R	E
D	S	H	I	K	O	K	U	C	F	R	U	L	O	P

HOKKAIDO	SHIBA INU	SHIKOKU
AKITA	TOSA	KISHU
KAI KEN	JAPANESE SPITZ	RYUKYU INU

ACROSTICS

Solve the clues correctly and the shaded squares will reveal an important member of airport and police personnel. What is it?

1. Seat for horse-racing
2. Not as far away
3. Home of castaways
4. Give it a miss
5. Travelling by air

1.					
2.					
3.					
4.					
5.					

146

TRIVIA

Which dog breed, the largest of its kind, is known as the "King of Terriers"?

a) Staffordshire Bull Terrier

b) Airedale Terrier

c) Yorkshire Terrier

QUIZ: TRUE OR FALSE

Here are three essential questions about dogs. Do you have the knowledge to pick the correct answers?

1. **The dog was the first animal to be domesticated.**

    a) True
    b) False

2. **Dogs are omnivores.**

    a) True
    b) False

3. **Dogs can only see in black and white.**

    a) True
    b) False

148

SPOT THE DIFFERENCE

Can you spot the ten differences between these two pictures?

WORD BUILDER

The letters of a seven-letter word have been numbered 1 to 7. Solve the clues to reveal a cowardly cartoon dog.

Letters 7, 5 and 4 give us a hearing appendage.

Letters 1, 5, 6 and 7 give us a wire prison.

Letters 1, 2 and 6 give us an integral machine part.

Letters 4, 3 and 6 give us a carpet.

1	2	3	4	5	6	7

MYSTERY SUDOKU

Complete the grid so that every row, column and 3 x 3 box contains the letters OGEVWLRNM in any order. One row or column contains a seven-letter word that is a dog of mixed heritage.

			L		N	E		R
	O		G				V	
E							N	
N		M			W		G	O
		O				M		
V	R		M			N		L
	N							G
	V				L		M	
R		W	O		G			

BETWEEN THE LINES

A dog with distinctive ears can be inserted in the blank line so that, reading downwards, eight three-letter words are formed. What is the hidden dog breed between the lines?

A	D	A	F	O	S	F	A
E	D	T	T	D	Y	E	Y

152

RIDDLE

The following clues will reveal a dog's relationship to its owner.

My first is in fed, but not in pet
My second is in roll and also in over
My third is in sit, but not in stay
My fourth is in eat and also in beg
My fifth is in tongue, but not in lick
My sixth is in dog, but not in walk

What am I?

153

WORD SEARCH: WHAT DID DOGGY SAY?

These are all sounds that dogs make.
Find them in the grid.

```
N  G  C  Y  H  C  D  P  L  M  N  J  H  A  C
X  D  E  R  H  B  A  R  K  B  V  F  R  T  Y
L  K  M  I  P  O  U  H  V  G  F  R  Y  H  E
D  E  R  Y  G  T  F  W  H  I  N  E  N  H  L
I  A  R  L  K  M  I  J  N  B  H  Y  L  C  P
R  C  S  X  E  R  T  G  B  H  Y  W  J  N  J
I  K  M  N  H  Y  U  P  L  K  O  B  V  G  T
Y  J  N  C  V  G  Y  T  F  H  S  Z  X  E  R
T  G  V  B  H  H  R  L  M  N  J  U  H  G  V
C  S  R  T  D  X  C  U  U  J  O  K  M  N  B
U  N  G  V  S  D  E  R  N  L  Y  G  C  F  D
B  O  P  E  A  I  J  O  L  T  B  C  F  R  S
W  R  G  A  H  Y  G  V  H  U  J  K  M  N  J
I  E  L  B  V  C  F  H  T  G  R  O  W  L  C
F  R  E  D  X  S  R  Y  G  O  K  J  C  K  L
```

BARK	WHINE	HOWL
GROWL	SIGH	CRY
YELP	GRUNT	SNORE

CROSSWORD: CARTOON CANINES

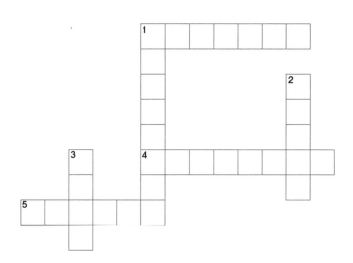

ACROSS

1. Loyal friend of Fry in *Futurama* (7)

4. Family pet named after a bug in *King of the Hill* (4,4)

5. _____ Little Helper, Simpsons pet (6)

DOWN

1. Rick and Morty's adversary (8)

2. George's self-appointed best friend in *The Jetsons* (5)

3. Pet pooch in *The Flintstones* (4)

155

TRIVIA

What breed of dog is comic strip hound Snoopy?

      a) Bloodhound

      b) King Charles Spaniel

      c) Beagle

PAIRS GAME

Match up the 20 sticks in 20 seconds. The first one has been done for you.

157

WORD WHEEL

See how many words of four or more letters you can make from the letters below. All words must include the central letter, and proper nouns don't count! Can you find the name of a popular type of dog that includes six separate breeds using all the letters?

MAZE

It's vet check-up day. Can you guide this dog into its carrier?

ANAGRAMS: PAWS FOR LUCK

Rearrange these letters to reveal the names of dog mascots.

HYDRAE UNGODLY

DRAG HELP HOT

ENCASED ZIP MUSK

LATERAL NINJA REST

WORD LADDER

Change "paw" into "pug" by altering one letter at a time to make a new word on each step of the ladder:

PAW

PUG

CROSSWORD: THE VOICE OF DOG

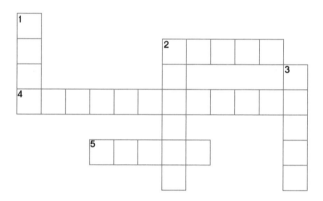

ACROSS

2. *Beverly Hills Chihuahua* starred Drew Barrymore as this character (5)

4. *Spiderman* star spoke Lou's words in *Cats and Dogs* (5,7)

5. First name of the voice of Bella in *A Dog's Way Home* (5)

DOWN

1. This Russell was the voice of Copper in *The Fox and the Hound* (4)

2. Michael J. Fox went on an incredible journey as this canine character (6)

3. This Thompson was Lady in the 2019 remake of *Lady and the Tramp* (5)

COUNTING CONUNDRUM

🦴 + 🦴 + 🦴 = 27

🦴 − 🪢 − 🪢 = 3

🪢 × 🪵 = 6

🦴 − (🪢 + 🪵) + 1 = ?

163

WORD SEARCH: GIVE ME SOME ATTENTION!

These are all ways to show your dog some love.
Find the words in the grid.

U	F	P	Y	K	M	T	N	G	V	B	Q	U	G	J
B	F	G	A	Y	D	X	S	U	C	I	J	O	B	P
S	L	M	N	T	B	C	G	F	Y	Y	J	E	G	F
C	D	X	C	R	R	F	T	Y	C	G	L	Z	S	L
R	T	F	G	C	B	R	U	B	T	D	H	F	T	L
A	C	V	G	C	H	S	W	F	D	N	B	I	Y	P
T	V	C	F	B	J	K	F	U	R	F	C	H	B	N
C	D	F	W	R	K	H	C	H	L	K	G	N	J	M
H	C	V	J	U	H	F	F	G	L	J	T	G	S	L
S	R	M	A	S	S	A	G	E	T	G	H	K	T	G
C	H	V	F	H	C	G	H	I	O	P	L	V	R	X
C	A	G	H	F	T	Y	H	J	C	G	J	M	O	B
S	N	U	G	G	L	E	M	N	Y	F	G	G	K	P
L	F	C	V	G	T	Y	H	X	K	L	I	O	E	N
G	C	V	H	Y	U	I	A	B	M	K	B	N	L	P

STROKE   SCRATCH   RUB

CUDDLE   MASSAGE   SNUGGLE

TICKLE   BRUSH   PAT

ACROSTICS

Solve the clues correctly and the shaded squares will reveal a Warner Bros pal of Pussyfoot. Who is it?

1. Page edge
2. Missing
3. Bridge over the Grand Canal in Venice
4. Enclosed space for transformation
5. An organization that provides services for a business or individual

1.					
2.					
3.					
4.					
5.					

TRIVIA

How many muscles control a dog's ear movements?

a) 8
b) 18
c) 22

QUIZ: COUNTING CANINES

Here are three number-related questions about dogs. Do you have the knowledge to pick the correct answers?

1. **How many degrees is a dog's field of vision?**
   a) 360
   b) 180
   c) 250

2. **What is the average heartrate of a dog?**
   a) 70–100 bpm
   b) 40–60 bpm
   c) 100–140 bpm

3. **How many eyelids does a dog have?**
   a) 2
   b) 3
   c) 4

SPOT THE DIFFERENCE

Can you spot the ten differences between these two pictures?

WORD BUILDER

The letters of a seven-letter word have been numbered 1 to 7. Solve the clues to reveal a dastardly cartoon sidekick.

Letters 1 and 7 give us belonging to me.

Letters 5, 2, 3 and 6 give us a plucked string instrument.

Letters 1, 6, 5 and 4 give us what snow will do in the sun.

Letters 1, 2, 3 and 6 give us the silent button on the remote control.

1	2	3	4	5	6	7

MYSTERY SUDOKU

Complete the grid so that every row, column and 3 x 3 box contains the letters DBROTSPEG in any order. One row or column contains the seven-letter name of a canine character in the comic strip *Dilbert*.

			G		E	R		P
	T		D				O	
R							E	
E		B			S		D	T
		T				B		
O	P		B			E		G
	E							D
	O				G		B	
P		S	T		D			

BETWEEN THE LINES

A high-energy French pack hound, dating from the late seventeenth century, can be inserted in the blank line so that, reading downwards, eight three-letter words are formed. What is the hidden dog breed between the lines?

O	C	H	A	L	I	H	A
T	P	P	E	G	Y	T	Y

CROSS OUT

Cross out all the letters that appear more than once. The letters that are left, reading from left to right and top to bottom, will spell out the name of a superhero dog of DC fame. What is it?

Z	K	X	C	V	B	N	M
R	B	L	M	Y	J	H	X
H	G	P	F	G	F	T	D
C	V	Z	O	D	L	J	N

WORD SEARCH: DISNEY DOGS

Find all these dogs from Disney in the grid.

```
L  H  V  C  G  Y  H  F  C  A  D  U  O  N  M
K  I  G  V  C  F  R  P  L  U  T  O  N  K  O
M  B  G  T  R  Y  F  H  Y  V  C  J  U  I  J
N  B  C  X  F  E  F  P  L  D  N  H  R  j  B
G  T  F  O  P  L  N  V  G  E  E  D  B  Z  D
R  T  O  V  P  U  J  N  T  I  K  M  B  H  O
U  G  V  G  F  P  L  T  N  J  U  Y  G  C  D
E  S  D  B  V  G  E  H  C  G  F  R  T  K  G
N  H  U  I  K  Y  C  R  R  y  G  V  G  Y  E
J  K  I  O  A  L  B  V  C  F  R  G  Y  o  R
W  R  N  F  D  E  R  S  H  Y  G  G  L  J  B
V  K  A  P  L  H  B  V  G  T  Y  C  U  R  T
F  L  V  H  D  A  N  T  E  J  I  O  J  D  C
G  T  D  X  Z  S  W  Q  B  O  L  T  K  O  P
L  J  B  G  Y  U  A  C  X  V  H  L  N  M  I
```

PLUTO	GOOFY	LAFAYETTE
BOLT	BRUNO	COPPER
DANTE	DODGER	DUG

CROSSWORD: DOGS IN CHILDREN'S BOOKS

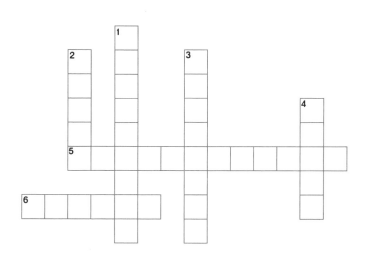

ACROSS

5. The dog in Lynley Dodd's iconic picture book series (5,7)

6. Eric Knight's famous sheepdog (6)

DOWN

1. Kate DiCamillo's classic was a hit all because of this dog (4-5)

2. The Labrador Retriever in Sheila Burnford's *The Incredible Journey* (5)

3. The star of *Born to Run* by Michael Morpurgo (4,4)

4. What was wrong with Harry in Gene Zion's *Harry the _____ Dog* (5)

TRIVIA

Bluey, an Australian cattle dog, holds the record as the oldest dog of all time. How old was he when he finally crossed the Rainbow Bridge?

a) 22
b) 26
c) 29

175

PAIRS GAME

Match up the 20 dog bowls in 20 seconds. The first one has been done for you.

WORD WHEEL

See how many words of four or more letters you can make from the letters below. All words must include the central letter, and proper nouns don't count! Can you find the name of a type of setter developed by a Welshman that uses all the letters?

MAZE

Can you help this dog find its friend?

ANAGRAMS: COMIC CANINES

Rearrange these letters to reveal the names of comic strips about dogs.

BEARD FESTS

RAMMED AUK

NEAT UPS

BLEED EVER

WORD LADDER

Change "find" into "ball" by altering one letter at a time to make a new word on each step of the ladder:

FIND

BALL

CROSSWORD: FASTER THAN A SPEEDING BULLET... ALMOST

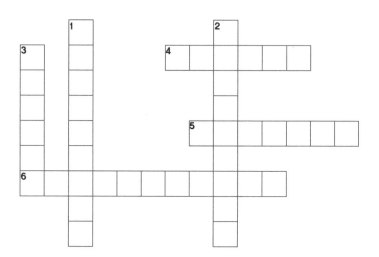

ACROSS

4. Wolf hunter of Russian descent (6)

5. Nicknamed the poor man's Greyhound (7)

6. This dog's name derives from a Mediterranean party island (6,5)

DOWN

1. You'd have to be quick to spot this breed that sounds like it should be Croatian (9)

2. Place your bets on this English breed (9)

3. Desert dog with a need for speed (6)

COUNTING CONUNDRUM

🏠🏠 + 🏠🏠 + 🏠🏠 = 36

(🎀🎀 × 🏠🏠) + 🏠🏠 = 228

🐰 + (🎀 × 🐰) = 50

🐰🐰 + (🏠 × 🎀🎀) = ?

DOWN THE MIDDLE

Complete all the following words correctly to reveal, in the shaded squares, a type of American wild dog.

L	I		K	S
W	O		F	S
L	O		A	L
G	R		W	L
F	E		C	H
S	M		L	L

ACROSTICS

Solve the clues correctly and the shaded squares will reveal a loyal Bobby. Who is it?

1. Bring together
2. Bitter green vegetable
3. Riddle
4. Over there
5. Fairy tales

1.					
2.					
3.					
4.					
5.					

TRIVIA

Which dog breed is named after the
French word for beard?

      a) Briard

      b) Beauceron

      c) Barbet

QUIZ:
DOGGY DID YOU KNOW?

Here are three random questions about dogs. Do you have the knowledge to pick the correct answers?

1. **What dog breed did Charles Darwin's ship, in which he explored most of the world, share its name with?**

    a) Chihuahua
    b) Beagle
    c) Labrador

2. **What sense are puppies born without?**

    a) Smell
    b) Hearing
    c) Taste

3. **What is a fear of dogs called?**

    a) Cynophobia
    b) Lycophobia
    c) Puppophobia

186

SPOT THE DIFFERENCE

Can you spot the ten differences between these two pictures?

WORD BUILDER

The letters of a seven-letter word have been numbered 1 to 7. Solve the clues to reveal Elle Woods' best friend at Harvard Law School in *Legally Blonde*.

Letters 1, 3 and 5 give us a mode of transport.

Letters 2, 4, 5 and 6 give us what people watch the sun doing in the morning.

Letters 7, 3 and 1 give us a massage.

Letters 5, 6, 2 and 1 give us a person from the country to the right of Bosnia.

1	2	3	4	5	6	7

MYSTERY SUDOKU

Complete the grid so that every row, column and 3 x 3 box contains the letters OKEZJBIRY in any order. One row or column contains a six-letter word that is the nickname for a popular type of terrier.

		K		Z	Y		E
	B		J				R	
Y							Z	
Z		O			I		J	B
		B				O		
R	E		O			Z		K
	Z							J
	R				K		O	
E		I	B		J			

BETWEEN THE LINES

A little lion dog can be inserted in the blank line so that, reading downwards, seven three-letter words are formed. What is the hidden dog breed, whose name means "little lion dog", between the lines?

E	F	O	I	S	J	A
F	X	L	E	Y	T	T

QUIZ: HAPPY FAMILIES

Here are three questions about dog families. Do you have the knowledge to pick the correct answers?

1. **What is a group of puppies called?**

    a) A litter
    b) A cluster
    c) A pouch

2. **What is the mother of a litter called?**

    a) A queen
    b) A lady
    c) A dam

3. **What is the father of a litter called?**

    a) A sire
    b) A stud
    c) A hound

ANSWERS

1. Word Search: Popular Names for Female Dogs

2. Crossword: Tasty Treats

Across: 1. chew, 4. blueberry, 5. carrot
Down: 1. chicken, 2. biscuit, 3. banana

3. Trivia

a)

4. Pairs Game

5. Maze

6. Anagrams: Canine Characters
Huckleberry, Lassie, Marley, Snoopy

7. Word Ladder
One possible solution: woof, wool, tool, toil, tail

8. Crossword: Hefty Hounds
Across: 2. St Bernard, 5. Neapolitan Mastiff, 6. Newfoundland
Down: 1. Great Pyrenees, 3. Irish Wolfhound, 4. Great Dane

9. Counting Conundrum
Bone = 20, ball = 5, bowl = 2, bone + ball + bowl = 27

10. Riddle
Walkies

11. Word Search: Popular Names for Male Dogs

12. Acrostics

1. legume, 2. easier, 3. oblong, 4. nature, 5. badger. The letters in the shaded squares spell "Leonberger".

13. Trivia

b)

14. Quiz: Puppy Parenting

1 b), 2 a), 3 c)

15. Spot the Difference

16. Word Builder
LOG, BUG, DULL, GULL
Bulldog

17. Mystery Sudoku
Mystery word: Samoyed

M	E	D	Z	A	Y	K	O	S
A	O	Y	E	S	K	Z	D	M
K	Z	S	M	O	D	E	Y	A
Y	K	A	D	Z	M	S	E	O
Z	M	O	Y	E	S	A	K	D
D	S	E	A	K	O	Y	M	Z
O	Y	Z	K	D	A	M	S	E
E	D	K	S	M	Z	O	A	Y
S	A	M	O	Y	E	D	Z	K

18. Missing Words
Tail, ball, walk

19. Word Search: The Lady and the Tramp (and Friends)

20. Crossword: Poisonous to Dogs

Across: 2. Allium, 4. yew, 5. acorn, 6. foxglove
Down: 1. daffodil, 3. ivy

21. Trivia

c)

22. Pairs Game

23. Word Wheel

Word that uses all letters = Dalmatian

24. Maze

25. Anagrams: The Way of the Wolf

The Jungle Book, White Fang, Alpha, The Hungry Wolf

26. Word Ladder
One possible solution: walk, wall, hall, hell, heel

27. Crossword: A Breed Apart
Across: 2. Bullmastiff, 4. Madagascar, 5. Kai, 6. Havanese
Down: 1. Afghan Hound, 3. Canaan Dog

28. Counting Conundrum
Dog face A = 7, dog face B = 6, dog face C = 12

29. Word Link
1 coat, 2 doll, 3 rope, 4 ache, 5 boat. The word in the shaded column is "alpha".

30. Word Search: Anatomy of a Dog

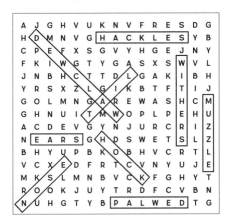

31. Acrostics
1. martyr, 2. acacia, 3. gaming, 4. yakuza, 5. anchor. The letters in the shaded squares spell "Magyar Agár".

32. Trivia
c)

33. Quiz: A Grand Old Age
1 a), 2 a), 3 c)

34. Spot the Difference

35. Word Builder
MAT, SET, LATE, SALT
Maltese

36. Between the Lines
Beauceron

37. Hidden Words
1 bark, 2 meat, 3 coat, 4 bite, 5 bone

38. Word Search: A Dog Groomer's Arsenal

39. Crossword: Canine Cops
Across: 3. Tequila, 5. *Story*
Down: 1. Jerry Lee, 2. Hudson (of *Hudson & Rex*), 4. *Top Dog*, 5. Sam

40. Trivia
b)

41. Pairs Game

42. Word Wheel
Word that uses all letters = ridgeback

43. Maze

44. Anagrams: Rare Pooches
Lagotto Romagnolo, Stabyhoun, Catalburun, Telomian

45. Word Ladder

One possible solution: good, gold, gild, gird, girl

46. Crossword: Short-haired Doggos

Across: 4. Weimaraner, 5. Boston, 6. Vizsla
Down: 1. Boxer, 2. Dalmatian, 3. Kelpie

47. Counting Conundrum

Dog brush = 6, dog toy = 7

48. Riddle

Kennel

49. Word Search: Wild Dogs

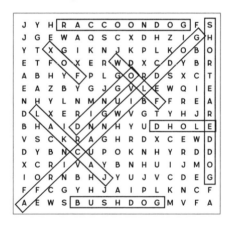

50: Acrostics

1. oafish, 2. tattoo, 3. teledu, 4. ensign, 5. refund. The letters in the shaded squares spell "Otterhound".

51. Trivia

b)

52. Quiz: A Guide to Dog Speak

1 all three answers are correct, 2 b), 3 c)

53. Spot the Difference

54. Word Builder
MAT, FIT, FAT, SAT
Mastiff

55. Mystery Sudoku
Mystery word: Bodger

R	N	G	O	E	B	D	T	I
E	T	B	N	I	D	O	G	R
D	O	I	R	T	G	N	B	E
B	D	E	G	O	R	I	N	T
O	R	T	B	N	I	E	D	G
G	I	N	E	D	T	B	R	O
T	B	O	D	G	E	R	I	N
N	G	D	I	R	O	T	E	B
I	E	R	T	B	N	G	O	D

56. Between the Lines
Deerhound

57. Missing Word
Bone, paw, coat

58. Word Search: Famous Dog Lovers

L	L	I	H	C	R	U	H	C	N	O	T	S	N	I	W
A	G	F	C	D	E	S	C	F	T	Y	H	B	J	U	N
U	H	A	U	D	R	E	Y	H	E	P	B	U	R	N	R
R	V	G	T	Y	H	N	J	H	G	F	R	E	S	Z	S
E	P	O	K	Y	D	E	N	N	E	K	F	N	H	O	J
N	D	R	T	A	B	A	J	U	K	N	K	I	H	V	E
B	R	D	Q	U	E	E	N	V	I	C	T	O	R	I	A
A	J	U	I	K	M	N	K	I	J	H	B	V	G	P	N
C	X	D	E	R	F	G	V	H	Y	U	P	U	K	M	S
A	H	G	V	G	C	F	R	E	D	X	S	E	D	R	I
L	H	B	Y	U	O	J	I	K	M	N	J	I	H	B	M
L	F	C	D	E	L	K	M	P	U	L	G	V	S	R	M
R	O	L	Y	A	T	H	T	E	B	A	Z	I	L	E	O
G	E	O	R	G	E	W	A	S	H	I	N	G	T	O	N
I	P	A	U	L	M	C	C	A	R	T	N	E	Y	A	S

59. Crossword: Canine Karaoke

Across: 2. Boo, 4. "Walking the Dog", 5. Hound Dog
Down: 1. "Shoot the Dog", 2. Bow Wow, 3. Baha Men

60. Trivia

a)

61. Pairs Game

62. Word Wheel

Word that uses all letters = Dachshund

63. Maze

64. Anagrams: Doggy Ditties
"Martha My Dear", "I Love My Dog", "Bingo", "Old King"

65. Crossword: Arty Dogs
Across: 3. Goya, 4. poker, 5. Manet, 6. Jack Russell
Down: 1. head, 2. Foxhounds

66. Counting Conundrum
Dog face D = 10, dog face E = 4, dog face F = 2, dog face F + (dog face D × dog face E) = 42

67. Mini Sudoku: Saluki

I	U	A	K	S	L
L	S	K	I	U	A
U	L	I	A	K	S
K	A	S	L	I	U
S	I	L	U	A	K
A	K	U	S	L	I

68. Word Search: Mythical Dogs

I	G	V	X	F	R	T	G	A	B	J	U	P	L	B
B	V	T	Q	I	Q	I	R	N	G	V	B	H	U	L
S	C	A	V	A	L	L	J	N	M	A	Y	G	B	A
T	F	D	F	R	L	K	M	B	H	R	T	G	V	C
F	R	T	S	X	E	R	F	C	G	G	Y	H	B	K
A	X	E	H	A	N	D	L	E	H	O	U	N	D	S
T	H	D	S	A	Y	G	V	R	H	S	P	L	M	H
N	H	Y	U	J	V	C	D	B	R	T	G	M	J	U
A	B	Y	U	S	L	K	M	E	B	V	X	Z	S	C
S	A	S	W	E	D	U	R	R	G	V	B	H	Y	K
E	K	N	L	O	P	Y	I	U	V	U	R	D	X	S
P	F	H	Y	N	J	U	I	S	M	N	I	P	O	H
V	C	R	D	F	T	G	S	W	O	A	N	B	H	U
B	A	R	G	H	E	S	T	U	Y	N	V	C	D	E
R	T	G	A	L	N	H	Y	U	I	J	V	C	F	R

69. Acrostics

1. pagoda, 2. orphan, 3. muesli, 4. eczema, 5. raisin. The letters in the shaded squares spell "Pomeranian".

70. Trivia

b)

71. Quiz: Dog's Body Language

1 a), 2 b), 3 b)

72. Spot the Difference

73. Word Builder

PIT, PET, HIT, WET

Whippet

74. Mystery Sudoku

Mystery word: Shar-Pei

I	H	B	T	A	E	R	P	S
A	P	E	H	S	R	T	B	I
R	T	S	I	P	B	H	E	A
E	R	A	B	T	I	S	H	P
T	I	P	E	H	S	A	R	B
B	S	H	A	R	P	E	I	T
P	E	T	R	B	A	I	S	H
H	B	R	S	I	T	P	A	E
S	A	I	P	E	H	B	T	R

75. Riddle

Collar

76. Word Search: The Cast of *101 Dalmatians*

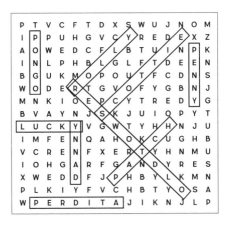

77. Crossword: What Big Ears You Have!

Across: 2. Afghan, 5. Bloodhound
Down: 1. Dachshund, 3. Frenchie, 4. Cocker, 5. Basset

78. Trivia

b)

79. Pairs Game

80. Word Wheel

Word that uses all letters = Schnauzer

81. Maze

82. Anagrams: Dog Tales

A Dog's Purpose, Lassie Come Home, A Dog's Way Home, Old Yeller

83. Word Ladder
One possible solution: wild, wile, tile, tale, tame

84. Crossword: Fictional Dogs and Their Owners
Across: 3. Max, 5. Einstein, 6. Hooch
Down: 1. Samantha, 2. Fang, 4. Zero

85. Counting Conundrum
Puppy = 4, frisbee = 10, double frisbee = 20, bone = 9, double frisbee +
(bone × puppy) = 56

86. Down the Middle
LAPDOG

87. Word Search: Pup Paraphernalia

88. Acrostics
1. parcel, 2. oedema, 3. rumaki, 4. canyon, 5. emerge. The letters in the
shaded squares spell "Porcelaine".

89. Trivia
c)

90. Quiz: What Makes a Dog?
1 a), 2 b), 3 b)

91. Spot the Difference

92. Word builder
AND, DINE, ICE, AID
Canidae

93. Mystery Sudoku
Mystery word: rabies

R	I	N	P	S	B	M	A	E
S	A	B	I	E	M	P	N	R
M	P	E	R	A	N	I	B	S
B	M	S	N	P	R	E	I	A
P	R	A	B	I	E	S	M	N
N	E	I	S	M	A	B	R	P
A	B	P	M	N	S	R	E	I
I	N	M	E	R	P	A	S	B
E	S	R	A	B	I	N	P	M

94. Between the Lines
Welsh Corgi

95. Cross Out
GROMIT

96. Word Search: Working Woofers

97. Crossword: Dogs of the Internet
Across: 1. Manny, 2. Boo, 3. Susie, 5. Maddie
Down: 1. Mishka, 4. Sage

98. Trivia
c)

99. Pairs Game

100. Word Wheel
Word that uses all letters = Pekingese

101. Maze

102. Anagrams: Canine Careers
Dog groomer, kennel manager, dog trainer, veterinarian

103. Word Ladder
One possible solution: food, fold, bold, bole, bile, bite

104. Crossword: Fictional Furballs
Across: 1. Brian, 3. Toto, 4. Clifford, 5. Slinky Dog
Down: 1. Beethoven, 2. Rowlf

105. Counting Conundrum
Dog face G = 10, dog face H = 5, dog face I = 2, dog face H + (dog face I × dog face H) = 15

106. Riddle
Canine

107. Word Search: They Wrote About Dogs

```
V  F  Y  Y  M  F  T  B  N  B  H  S  O  P  J
B  Y  L  E  A  D  Z  S  D  C  B  P  N  J  V
T  B  W  B  R  U  C  E  C  A  M  E  R  O  N
J  I  N  W  K  R  B  J  I  K  G  F  P  H  W
A  G  K  H  T  B  H  G  K  O  J  H  I  N  V
G  R  T  I  W  X  S  M  Y  U  N  B  V  G  S
A  P  B  T  A  G  T  F  K  R  T  N  K  R  N
R  C  S  E  I  J  A  C  K  L  O  N  D  O  N
T  C  R  J  N  H  G  F  G  H  J  I  G  G  M
H  D  S  C  J  N  D  X  V  A  M  L  K  A  G
S  H  C  A  F  T  X  D  Y  G  B  N  Y  N  V
T  O  L  L  I  M  A  C  I  D  E  I  T  A  K
E  L  E  A  N  O  R  A  T  K  I  N  S  O  N
I  K  A  H  V  T  E  S  K  B  S  L  M  N  N
N  T  S  W  I  L  S  O  N  R  A  W  L  S  P
```

108. Acrostics

1. recipe, 2. octopi, 3. thrill, 4. tiptoe, 5. walker. The letters in the shaded squares spell "Rottweiler".

109. Quiz: Bizarre Dog Beliefs

1 a), 2 a), 3 b)

110. Spot the Difference

111. Word Builder
ODD, GEL, SOD, LOG
Sled dog

112. Mystery Sudoku
Mystery word: Gaspode

D	F	P	O	S	G	A	L	E
S	L	G	F	E	A	O	P	D
A	O	E	D	L	P	F	G	S
G	A	S	P	O	D	E	F	L
O	D	L	G	F	E	S	A	P
P	E	F	S	A	L	G	D	O
L	G	O	A	P	S	D	E	F
F	P	A	E	D	O	L	S	G
E	S	D	L	G	F	P	O	A

113. Between the Lines
Eurasier

114. Hidden Words
1 feral, 2 bone, 3 leash, 4 wag, 5 ball

115. Word Search: Dinky Doggies

116. Crossword: Such a Brave Dog

Across: 1. Balto, 4. Swansea Jack, 5. Barry
Down: Trakr, 3. Gelert, 4. Stubby

117. Trivia

b)

118. Pairs Game

119. Word Wheel

Word that uses all letters = Chihuahua

120. Maze

121. Anagrams: Dogs All Day

Hot dog, fire dog, sun dog, dogfish

122. Word Ladder
One possible solution: pant, pint, lint, link, lick

123. Crossword: Not Such a Good Boy
Across: 1. Cujo, 4. Zowie, 5. Lafayette
Down: 1. Chief, 2. Alpha, 3. Coyote

124. Counting Conundrum
Dog collar = 20, paw print = 16, star = 13, dog collar + (star × paw print) = 228

125. Word Link
1 post, 2 bath, 3 bare, 4 beat, 5 boys. The word in the shaded column is "stray".

126. Acrostics
1. shrimp, 2. candle, 3. hacker, 4. in work, 5. paddle. The letters in the shaded squares spell "Schipperke".

127. Trivia
c)

128. Quiz: Breed Brain Teasers
1 c), 2 c), 3 a)

129. Spot the Difference

130. Word Builder
WED, WAD, LACE, ALE
Dewclaw

131. Between the Lines
Hovawart

132. Missing Word
Sit, stay, drop

133. Word Search: Canine Commands

134. Crossword: Starring Jack Russell
Across: 2. Milo, 4. My Dog Skip, 5. Eddie
Down: 1. Cosmo, 2. Max, 3. Uggie

135. Trivia
a)

136. Pairs Game

137. Word Wheel
Word that uses all letters = Wolfhound

138. Maze

139. Anagrams: Celebrity Pooches
Ace the Wonder Dog, Brigitte, Silver Streak, Madison

140. Word Ladder
One possible solution: cat, cot, dot, dog

141. Crossword: Guardians of the Flock

Across: 3. Alsatian, 5. Border Collie, 6. Corgi
Down: 1. Malinois, 2. Cattle Dog, 4. Puli

142. Counting Conundrum

Dog face J = 8, dog face K = 9, dog face L = 4

143. Mini Sudoku: Kuvasz

Z	A	U	S	K	V
V	K	S	Z	A	U
A	V	Z	U	S	K
S	U	K	V	Z	A
K	Z	V	A	U	S
U	S	A	K	V	Z

144. Word Search: From the Land of the Rising Sun

145. Acrostics

1. saddle, 2. nearer, 3. island, 4. forego, 5. flying. The letters in the shaded squares spell "sniffer dog".

146. Trivia

b)

147. Quiz: True or False
1 a), 2 a), 3 b)

148. Spot the Difference

149. Word Builder
EAR, CAGE, COG, RUG
Courage

150. Mystery Sudoku
Mystery word: mongrel

W	G	V	L	M	N	E	O	R
M	O	N	G	R	E	L	V	W
E	L	R	W	O	V	G	N	M
N	E	M	V	L	W	R	G	O
L	W	O	N	G	R	M	E	V
V	R	G	M	E	O	N	W	L
O	N	L	E	V	M	W	R	G
G	V	E	R	W	L	O	M	N
R	M	W	O	N	G	V	L	E

151. Between the Lines
Papillon

152. Riddle

Friend

153. Word Search: What Did Doggy Say?

154. Crossword: Cartoon Canines

Across: 1. Seymour, 4. Lady Bird, 5. Santa's
Down: 1. Snuffles, 2. Astro, 3. Dino

155. Trivia

c)

156. Pairs Game

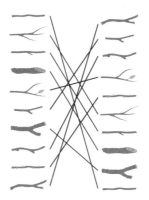

157. Word Wheel
Word that uses all letters = retriever

158. Maze

159. Anagrams: Paws for Luck
Lady Greyhound, Ralph the Dog, Spuds MacKenzie, Sallie Ann Jarrett

160. Word Ladder
One possible solution: paw, pew, peg, pug

161. Crossword: The Voice of Dog
Across: 2. Chloe, 4. Tobey Maguire, 5. Bryce
Down: 1. Kurt, 2. Chance, 3. Tessa

162. Counting Conundrum
Chew toy = 9, dog rope toy = 3, stick = 2, chew toy – (dog rope toy + stick) + 1 = 5

163. Word Search: Give Me Some Attention!

```
U  F  P  Y  K  M  T  N  G  V  B  Q  U  G  J
B  F  G  A  Y  D  X  S  U  C  I  J  O  B  P
S  L  M  N  T  B  C  G  F  Y  Y  J  E  G  F
C  D  X  C  R  R  F  T  Y  C  G  L  Z  S  L
R  T  F  G  C  B  R  U  B  T  D  H  F  T  L
A  C  V  G  C  H  S  W  F  D  N  B  I  Y  P
T  V  C  F  B  J  K  F  U  R  F  C  H  B  N
C  D  F  W  R  K  H  C  H  L  K  G  N  J  M
H  C  V  J  U  H  F  F  F  G  L  J  T  G  S  L
S  R  M  A  S  S  A  G  E  T  G  H  K  T  G
C  H  V  F  H  C  G  H  I  O  P  L  V  R  X
C  A  G  H  F  T  Y  H  J  C  G  J  M  O  B
S  N  U  G  G  L  E  M  N  Y  F  G  G  K  P
L  F  C  V  G  T  Y  H  X  K  L  I  O  E  N
G  C  V  H  Y  U  I  A  B  M  K  B  N  L  P
```

164. Acrostics

1. margin, 2. absent, 3. rialto, 4. cocoon, 5. agency. The letters in the shaded squares spell "Marc Antony".

165. Trivia

b)

166. Quiz: Counting Canines

1 c), 2 a), 3 b)

167. Spot the Difference

168. Word Builder

MY, LUTE, MELT, MUTE

Muttley

169. Mystery Sudoku

Mystery word: Dogbert

S	D	O	G	B	E	R	T	P
B	T	E	D	P	R	G	O	S
R	G	P	S	T	O	D	E	B
E	R	B	O	G	S	P	D	T
G	S	T	E	D	P	B	R	O
O	P	D	B	R	T	E	S	G
T	E	G	R	O	B	S	P	D
D	O	R	P	S	G	T	B	E
P	B	S	T	E	D	O	G	R

170. Between the Lines

Poitevin

171. Cross Out

KRYPTO

172. Word Search: Disney Dogs

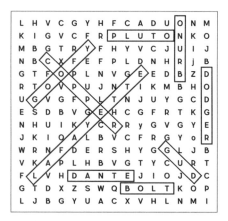

173. Crossword: Dogs in Children's Books
Across: 5. Hairy Maclary, 6. Lassie
Down: 1. Winn-Dixie, 2. Luath, 3. Best Mate, 4. Dirty

174. Trivia
c)

175. Pairs Game

176. Word Wheel
Word that uses all letters = Llewellin

177. Maze

178. Anagrams: Comic Canines
Fred Basset, Marmaduke, Peanuts, Belvedere

179. Word Ladder
One possible solution: find, bind, band, bald, ball

180. Crossword: Faster than a Speeding Bullet... Almost
Across: 4. Borzoi, 5. Whippet, 6. Ibizan Hound
Down: 1. Dalmatian, 2. Greyhound, 3. Saluki

181. Counting Conundrum
Kennel = 6, bow = 9, cuddly animal toy = 5, double cuddly animal toy + (kennel × double bow) = 118

182. Down the Middle
COYOTE

183. Acrostics
1. gather, 2. rapini, 3. enigma, 4. yonder, 5. fables. The letters in the shaded squares spell "Greyfriars".

184. Trivia
c)

185. Quiz: Doggy Did You Know?
1 b), 2 b), 3 a)

186. Spot the Difference

187. Word Builder

BUS, RISE, RUB, SERB

Bruiser

188. Mystery Sudoku

Mystery word: Yorkie

I	J	R	K	O	Z	Y	B	E
O	B	Z	J	E	Y	K	R	I
Y	K	E	I	B	R	J	Z	O
Z	Y	O	R	K	I	E	J	B
K	I	B	Z	J	E	O	Y	R
R	E	J	O	Y	B	Z	I	K
B	Z	K	Y	R	O	I	E	J
J	R	Y	E	I	K	B	O	Z
E	O	I	B	Z	J	R	K	Y

189. Between the Lines

Lowchen

190. Quiz: Happy Families

1 a), 2 c), 3 a)

Have you enjoyed this book?
If so, find us on Facebook at **Summersdale Publishers**, on Twitter at **@Summersdale** and on Instagram and TikTok at **@summersdalebooks** and get in touch. We'd love to hear from you!

www.summersdale.com